THAMES TUNNEL TO CHANNEL TUNNEL

Conference of Engineers at Britannia Bridge' by John Lucas depicting Robert Stephenson, Joseph Locke, I. K. Brunel, G. P. Bidder, Charles H. Wild, Latimer Clark, Edwin Clark, Frank Foster and Alexander Ross, civil engineers, Admiral Moorson and Captain Claxton, nautical specialists, and Hemmingway, master mason

THAMES TUNNEL TO CHANNEL TUNNEL

150 years of civil engineering

Selected papers from the journal of the
Institution of Civil Engineers published to
celebrate its 150th anniversary

Edited by Will Howie and Mike Chrimes

Thomas Telford, London

Published by Thomas Telford Ltd, Thomas Telford House, 1 Heron Quays, London E14 9XF

British Library Cataloguing in Publication Data
    Thames tunnel to Channel tunnel: 150 years of civil engineering: selected papers from the journal of the Institution of Civil Engineers published to celebrate its 150th anniversary
    1. Civil engineering — History — Sources
    I. Institution of Civil Engineers
    624'.09'034   TA19

ISBN: 0 7277 0396 X

First published 1987

New material typeset by Transcript Limited, 31-35 Kirby Street, London EC1N 8TE
Printed and bound in Great Britain by William Clowes Ltd, Beccles and London

FOREWORD

The Institution of Civil Engineers dates from January 1818, when it was founded in London by a handful of young civil engineers, none of whom had then reached 30 years of age. Two years later, Thomas Telford, the leading engineer of the day, became its first President, and in 1828 the Institution received its Royal Charter. It is thus the oldest and the most distinguished engineering learned society in the world.

Since the Institution was founded to promote the science and art of engineering, its function as a learned society was the main reason for its existence, and its meetings were intended to spread information and knowledge on engineering developments. It was not surprising, therefore, that it soon became proper for the Institution to publish the proceedings of these meetings. That began in 1837, and the *Proceedings* have been published continuously ever since — making the longest uninterrupted publishing run of its kind in the world.

This commemorative book has been compiled to celebrate the 150th anniversary of the publication of the first volume of *Proceedings*. Its title, *From Thames Tunnel to Channel Tunnel*, is intended to symbolize the length of time over which *Proceedings* have been published by identifying an important project at each end of the 150 years.

Although there is a paper on the Thames Tunnel by Sir Marc Brunel, papers on the construction of the Channel Tunnel will not appear for some years yet. Civil engineers everywhere, however, look forward to the completion of this long-awaited enterprise with enthusiasm.

The papers which are reprinted here have been chosen partly for their intrinsic interest and partly to illustrate the wide range of projects which have been described and subjects discussed at the Institution's meetings during the past century and a half. For the most part the papers are reproduced in facsimile, but some pages — those of the Lary Bridge paper and a few of the drawings — have had to be reduced. They are no more than a few of the many hundreds of papers which have been presented in that time, and many papers of equal interest have had to be omitted.

In addition to the papers a number of illustrations have been inserted. Where these are related to the subject of a paper they are with that paper. But as well as these a selection of illustrations has been added to indicate a further part, and only a small one, of the work which civil engineers were doing during this time. All of these extra illustrations, except for those of the Barentin Viaduct and Crystal Palace, are from the Institution's collection. Thanks are expressed to J. G. James for the loan of the illustration of Barentin Viaduct, and to the Institution of Mechanical Engineers for the original of the Crystal Palace photograph.

At the inaugural meeting of the Institution, Henry Robinson Palmer, one of the original eight founder members, described its object as 'facilitating the acquirement of knowledge necessary in the civil engineering profession and for promoting mechanical philosophy'. These papers show how the Institution's members have contrived to achieve that objective and how well they have succeeded.

CONTENTS

MINUTES OF PROCEEDINGS

OF THE

INSTITUTION

OF

CIVIL ENGINEERS;

CONTAINING

ABSTRACTS OF THE PAPERS

AND OF THE

CONVERSATIONS,

FOR THE SESSION OF 1837.

LONDON:
PRINTED FOR THE INSTITUTION.
1837.

Title page from volume 1 of Minutes of Proceedings

O F F I C E R S.—1837.

COUNCIL.

President.
JAMES WALKER, F.R.S., L. & E., &c.

Vice-Presidents.
WILLIAM CUBITT, F.R.S.
BRYAN DONKIN, F.R.S.
JOSHUA FIELD, F.R.S.
HENRY R. PALMER, F.R.S.

Members.
FRANCIS BRAMAH.
I. K. BRUNEL, F.R.S.
GEORGE LOWE, F.R.S.
JOHN MACNEILL.
W. A. PROVIS.
JAMES SIMPSON.
ROBERT STEPHENSON.

Treasurer.
W. A. HANKEY.

Auditors.
NATHANIEL NICHOLLS.
JAMES HOWELL.

Secretary.
THOMAS WEBSTER, M.A.

Foreign Secretary.
SAMUEL WHITWELL.

Collector.
GEORGE. C. GIBBON.

List of officers reprinted from volume 1 of Minutes of Proceedings

Particulars of the construction of the Lary Bridge, near Plymouth

J. M. RENDEL, CorrMInstCE

*Reprinted from Trans. Instn Civ. Engrs, 1836,
vol. 1, 99-108, × 82%*

The paper describing the construction of the Lary Bridge was presented by James Meadows Rendel and was published in the first volume of the *Proceedings*. Rendel was born in Devonshire in 1799 and had a promising pedigree for a civil engineer, his father being a county surveyor and his grandfather a well-known architect, while an uncle was a millwright. Rendel acquired the rudiments of engineering knowledge from his father and uncle before moving to London as a surveyor under Thomas Telford.

In about 1822, while still a very young man, Rendel set up in practice in Plymouth and began a successful career covering bridges, roads, canals, docks, water supply and railways, although he did relatively little of the last. At the early age of 25, he was entrusted with the work on the Lary Bridge near Plymouth. Work began in August 1824 and the bridge was opened in July 1827. The bridge comprised five cast iron elliptical arches supported on masonry piers and abutments. With the exception of Southwark Bridge, it was the largest iron bridge to be built up to that time.

Rendel had a clear idea of the nature of engineering and of engineers. In a discussion at the Institution he remarked, 'Instead of accusing engineers of knowing so little, it was rather a subject of surprise that they knew so much when it was considered how much they were required to mix in the active business of life; and he considered that no other profession demanded such varied acquirements, or the exercise of such general common sense and judgement'.

Rendel was an early member of the Institution and was its President in 1852 and 1853. In 1838 he moved to London and founded there the firm of consulting engineers which still exists under the name of Rendel Palmer and Tritton. He died in 1856.

As this bridge is founded on a shifting sand, in a rapid tideway, and presents some novelties in the design, it is hoped that an account of the methods successfully adopted for laying and securing the foundations, and some particulars of the superstructure, will be acceptable to the members of the Institution.

The Lary, over which this bridge is built, and from which it derives its name, is the estuary of the river Plym, and connected with Plymouth Sound by Catwater. The general width of the estuary is half a mile, but at the site of the bridge the shores abruptly approach each other, and form a strait between 500 and 600 feet wide. The tide rushes through this strait with a velocity of 3 feet 6 inches a second, and flows on an average 16 feet perpendicular.—The depth at low water is from 5 to 6 feet.

By borings it appeared that the bed of the river was sand to a depth of 60 feet—the lofty lime rock on each shore dipping abruptly from high water, and forming a substratum nearly horizontal across the strait. The sand in the wide parts of the estuary above and below the bridge is fine; at the site of the bridge the current leaves only the coarser kind; but this is not sufficient to resist the heavy land floods, to which the Plym is liable, and it frequently happens that the bed of the river is scoured away several feet in depth in winter and refilled in the summer.

When called on by the Earl of Morley, who built this bridge at his sole expense, to prepare a design, I furnished one on the principle of suspension, spanning the whole width of the strait, and having the towers on its rocky shores. Our president * was consulted by his lordship, and the plan being approved of by him, an act was obtained in the session of 1823 authorizing its erection; but on the commencement of the works, difficulties arose which led to the abandonment of the suspension bridge and the ultimate adoption of the present one of cast iron.

The drawings (see Plates XIV. and XV.) which accompany this paper, will, I trust, give a general idea of the finished structure. The arrangement of the design differs materially from other works of a similar nature : first, in the masonry of the piers finishing at the springing course of the arches; secondly, in the curvilinear form of the piers and abutments; and thirdly, in the employment of elliptical arches. The adoption of these forms for the piers and arches in unison with the plan of finishing the piers above the springing course with cast iron instead of masonry, has, as I had hoped, given a degree of uniform lightness, combined with strength, to the general effect, unobtainable by the usual form of straight sided piers carried to the height of the roadway, with flat segments of a circle for the arches.

Having given these particulars of the situation and design of the work, I will now add some information as to the proportions of the several parts of the structure.

The centre arch is 100 feet span, and rises 14 feet 6 inches; the thickness of the piers, where smallest, being 10 feet. The arches adjoining the centre are 95 feet span each, with a rise of 13 feet 3 inches. The piers taken, as before, are each 9 feet 6 inches thick. The extreme arches are each 8 feet span, and rise 10 feet 6 inches. The abutments are in their smallest dimensions 13 feet thick, forming at the back a strong arch abutting against the return walls to resist the horizontal thrust. The northern abutment forms a considerable projection, which was deemed advisable in consequence of the obliquity of the adjoining wharf below the bridge; as well as to afford the noble proprietor an opportunity of building a toll-house on extra-parochial ground. The ends of the piers are semi-circular, having a curvilinear batter on the sides and ends formed with a radius of 35 feet, and extending upwards from the level of high water to the springing course, and downwards to the level of the water at the lowest ebb. The front of the abutments have a corresponding batter.

* The late Mr. Telford.

4

[Plate XIV, × 48%]

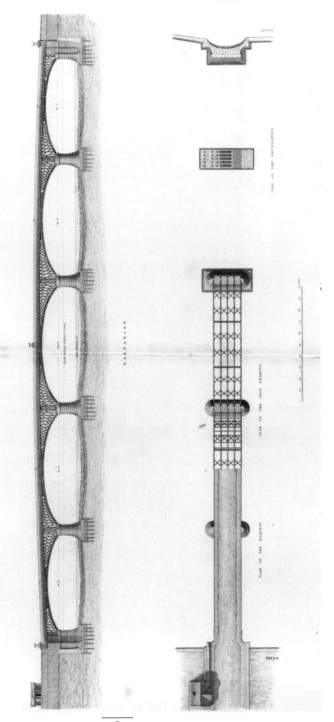

CAST IRON BRIDGE OVER THE LARY, NEAR PLYMOUTH.

BY JAMES M. RENDEL, CIVIL ENGINEER.

ELEVATION

PLAN OF THE FOUNDATION

PLAN OF THE IRON FRAMING

PLAN OF THE ROADWAY

[Plate XV, × 44%]

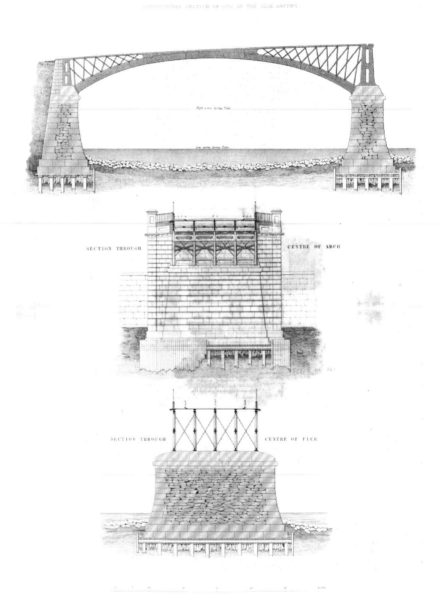

The parts of the piers and abutments which lie under water at the lowest ebbs, are composed of 2 feet courses of masonry with offsets, as will be better understood by reference to the drawing. (See plates.)

The roadway between the abutments is 24 feet wide, supported by 5 cast iron equidistant ribs. Each rib is 2 feet 6 inches in depth at the springing, and 2 feet at the apex by 2 inches thick, with a top and bottom flange of 6 inches wide by 2 inches thick, and is cast in 5 pieces ; their joints, (which are flanged for the purpose,) are connected by screw pins with tie plates equal in length to the width of the roadway, and in depth and thickness to the ribs ; between these meeting plates the ribs are connected by strong feathered crosses, or diagonal braces with screw pins passing through their flanges and the main ribs. The springing plates are 3 inches thick, with raised grooves to receive the ends of the ribs, which have double shoulders, thus : These plates are sunk flush into the springing course of the piers and abutments, which, with the cordon and springing course, are of granite. The pier standards and spandril fillings are feathered castings, connected transversely by diagonal braces and wrought iron bars passing through cast iron pipes, with bearing shoulders for the several parts to abut against. The roadway bearers are 7 inches in depth by $1\frac{1}{2}$ thick, with a proportional top and bottom flange ; they are fastened to the pier standards by screw pins through sliding mortices, whereby a due provision is made for either expansion or contraction of the metal—the roadway plates are $\frac{7}{8}$ of an inch thick by 3 feet wide, connected by flanges and screw pins, and project 1 foot over the outer roadway bearers, thus forming a cornice the whole length of the bridge.

After what has been stated of the character of the river and nature of its bed, it is unnecessary to remark that extreme caution was indispensable in preparing and securing the foundations.

We commenced by driving sheeting piles to a depth of 15 feet around the whole area of the base of the piers and abutments. These piles are of beech plank, 4 inches thick, having their edge grooved to fit thus, and were driven in double leading frames fixed to temporary guide piles :— great attention was paid to have them perfectly close. When pitched they were from 16 to 18 feet long, properly hooped and shod with plate iron shoes, weighing on an average 2 lbs. each. These piles were driven with a cast iron weight of 450 lbs. worked by seven or eight men in what is termed a ringing engine. They were driven several feet below low water by means of punches.

As these pilings were carried on, the sand was excavated from the space they enclosed to a depth of 5 or 6 feet below the general level of the river, and from 9 to 10 feet below the level of low water of ordinary tides. These excavations were effected by means of sand spoons of the following construction. Strong canvas bags, capable of containing about 2 cubic feet of sand, were firmly secured to elliptical rings of wrought iron, each ring having a socket to receive a long wooden handle in the direction of its transverse axis, and a swivel handle through its conjugate axis. Stages were fixed on the leading frames in which the sheeting piles were driven, at about 3 feet above low water, and each spoon was worked by three men in the following manner :—a rope was fastened to the loop in the swivel handle of the spoon frame, one end of which was passed over a single block fixed a few feet above the level of the stage, and the other end was held by one of the workmen, whose business it was to pull the spoon when at the bottom towards him, while a second pressed it downwards and guided it, by means of the long wooden handle, till it was thought to be filled; the third man, who was stationed at the rope which worked through the single block, then hoisted the spoon to the stage and discharged its contents into a shoot, which drained into the river. After the labourers had become used to the work, these operations were carried on with considerable despatch, favourable tides generally affording from 3 to 4 hours' work per day.

As these excavations proceeded, the ground was piled with whole timbers of large Norway and small sized Memel, and as many of beech as could be procured of the desired length; these piles, being properly shod and hooped, were driven from temporary stages, fixed above high-water level, by weights varying, according to the size of the pile, from 10 to 15 hundred weight; they were disposed in five rows, in the width of the foundations, from 4 feet to 4 feet 6 inches from centre to centre, and were driven till they did not sink more than one inch with eight blows of the 15 hundred weight driver falling from a height of 25 feet, and then received twenty additional strokes with the same weight and fall.

These piles, none of which were less than 35 feet long, were driven to the level of the stage, and then punched to their proper depth. The punches used for this purpose were made of sound and well seasoned elm, hooped throughout their length, and having at their lower ends a strong cast iron ring, about 18 inches wide; this ring had a thick partition plate, cast in the middle of its width, which separated the head of the pile from the end of the punch; the lower end of the ring was cast a little conical, and the pile heads were made to fit it accurately thus . By this means the pile heads were but little injured, and the loss of momentum occasioned by the intervention of a punch was reduced to a mere trifle.

The next operation was to cut off the bearing piles to their proper depth, and to pave and grout the spaces between them. The usual mode of cofferdams was manifestly inapplicable to such a bed of sand; I therefore, in an early stage of the works, proposed to the contractors that the pile heads should be levelled, and the spaces between them paved by means of a diving bell. To save expense, this bell was made of wood, and with the necessary machinery was finished and put to work within six weeks from the time it was determined on. With its assistance the works were carried on with expedition and success. When in operation it contained two men, who, being provided with the necessary instruments for cutting off the piles, paving the spaces between them, &c., continued at work for four hours, when they were relieved by two others.

As much depended on the regularity with which the pile heads were levelled, great care was bestowed on this part of the work. It was accomplished in the following manner:—the four angular piles of each foundation being cut as low as the water would permit, were accurately levelled from a plug on the shore, to ascertain how much each had to be reduced to bring it to its proper level; on each of these piles was marked the portion remaining to be cut by the bell men, which being done, all the remaining piles were levelled from them, by means of a spirit-level, accurately adjusted in a piece of wood, sufficiently long to be applied to three piles at a time. The paving between the pile heads was performed in an equally simple and satisfactory manner.

As this economical bell answered every required purpose, a general description of the whole apparatus may prove acceptable.

The internal dimensions of the bell were 5 feet 6 inches in length, 4 feet 6 inches in width, and 5 feet in height; the sides, ends, and top were made of two thicknesses of $1\frac{1}{2}$ inch well seasoned elm board; the inner case was constructed with its joints parallel to the top and bottom or mouth of the bell, whilst those of the outer one were vertical, or at right angles to the inner joints; the top joints were crossed in the same manner as the sides; all the joints had a slip of flannel, saturated in a composition of bees' wax, laid between them, and were dowelled together and set as close as possible by means of screw clamps, &c., the sides were rabbeted to the end, and the internal angles were strengthened with brackets. The whole surface between the inner and outer case was covered with double flannel, saturated as just described, and was then connected together by a number of wooden pins, dipped in tar and tightly driven; the top was perforated with six holes of 6 inches diameter each, in which was firmly fixed a corresponding number of strong lenses set in white lead; a hole of 3 inches diameter was made in the centre, in which was fixed a brass pipe with a screw to attach the air tube; four hoops of wrought iron, two internal and two external, were screw-bolted together through the sides and ends of the bell: internal and external cross-lacings were also screw-bolted to those hoops, and to the sides and top of the bell. In these lacings, the chains by which the bell was suspended, were fixed in strong iron eyes, which passed through the top of the bell, and were riveted to the inner lacings. All the screw-bolts were driven with tarred oakum, and every precaution was taken to render the whole air-tight. The bell thus finished weighed about 1 ton 10 hundred weight, but it required from 5 to 6½ tons to sink it, and overhaul the ropes by which it was suspended; cast iron plates, from 1¾ to 2 inches in the thickness, were therefore hung externally round its sides and ends, till it was sufficiently loaded to sink with steadiness in about 25 feet of water.

The bell was provided with two movable seats and a foot-board for the divers, and at top long boxes were fixed, in which their tools were kept; it was supplied with air by a double acting force-pump, the cylinders of which were 7 inches diameter in the clear, the pistons making a 14 inch stroke. This pump was generally worked by four men, and made, on an average, according to the depth of water and run of the tide, about eight double strokes per minute.

Around the foundations on which the bell was to be employed, temporary piles were driven, and cut off level about 15 feet above high water, and cross braced; on the top of these piles whole Memel timbers were firmly fixed, care being taken to have the side beams parallel to each other. A strong frame, equal in length to the distance between the parallel beams of the above stage, and about 4 feet wide, mounted on four small cast iron flanged wheels, traversed on an iron railway laid on the beams; this frame was moved on the railway by means of a rope connected to the sides, and worked by two common winches, one fixed at each end of the stage; on the beams of this traverse frame a railway was also laid, on which worked a carriage, mounted in a similar manner, and sufficiently large and strong to carry a purchase machine capable of raising the bell by the labour of four men; the bell was suspended to this carriage by two treble blocks, the upper block being lashed to one of the cross beams of the frame, and the lower connected to the sling chains of the bell by a strong shackle. This traverse frame was easily moved by winches affixed to the ends of the long frame, over which ropes worked, having their ends made fast to the purchase machine frame.

By these traverse frames the bell was moved with great celerity to any part of the foundations. The machinery required the attendance of six active men, viz. one to each of the four winches, and two to the purchase machine. It was the sole business of a careful man to attend to the signals of the divers, and to direct the men at the machinery and air-pumps accordingly. The signals were communicated by a line, one end of which was fixed in the bell, and the other held by the signal-man, whose place was on the stage. To avoid confusion in the signals, any thing requiring great precision was communicated to either the divers or signal-man by means of a board attached to the line on which either party wrote with chalk, and by these means a regular correspondence could be carried on.

By means of the bell and apparatus, the works proceeded with safety and expedition, and I feel confident that diving-bells may be employed by the bridge builder in a variety of cases with much greater advantage and economy than coffer-dams.

10

The foundations being prepared, and guides fixed to the plank piles, caissons were floated off from the shore with one, and in some instances two courses of masonry, and sunk. The greatest success attended these operations from the care that was taken to get the foundations perfectly level : of course, the heads of the plank piles were not cut off until the caissons were sunk.

The bottoms of the caissons were made of beech plank and beams ; the bottom plank was 4 inches thick and laid in the transverse direction of the pier, across which the beams 12 inches by 8 inches were placed so as to correspond with the rows of piles in the foundation. The spaces between the beams were filled with masonry set in Pozzuolana mortar, and grouted ; and a flooring of 3 inch plank, closely jointed and well caulked, so as to be perfectly water-tight, covered the masonry and beams. The top and bottom planks were trenailed to the beams, and the whole strengthened by a strong frame of beech, a foot square, surrounding the bottom and fastened to it by strong screw bolts and trenails.

The upper surfaces of the beams of this frame were grooved to receive a strong tongue, fitting a corresponding groove in the bottom beams of the sides and ends of the caissons, which were made in the usual way, and connected to the bottom by strong lewes irons fitted to cast iron boxes, firmly fixed in the bottom planking. The lewes irons were fixed about 8 feet apart, and were easily removed when the masonry was brought up to the height of the caisson. The introduction of the tongue in the bottom beams of the caisson proved of the greatest utility, as it prevented leaks from the slight sinkage of the bottom between the lewes irons, which it is impossible to prevent when the caisson grounds.

The caissons were furnished with sluices, and made 15 feet high, which gave the masons an opportunity of working about five hours each tide on an average of neaps and springs.

The masonry of the piers and abutments is composed of solid compact limestone, raised in the quarries of the noble proprietor of the bridge* in the adjoining cliffs, and Dartmoor granite, the latter used only, however, in the springing courses and cornices. The limestone is quarried in masses, varying from two to six tons weight, and these were taken to the work on a railroad, continued from the quarries across the river on a stage or temporary bridge, passing close to the piers and abutments, and under the stages on which the diving bell was worked as before described, and the machinery used in working the bell was applied to taking the stone from the waggons, and in setting it. This machinery was found of incalculable advantage in building with such heavy blocks of stone, moving them with ease and the minutest accuracy from over head, and, consequently, without obstructing or incommoding the builders in the caissons.

---

* From these quarries the large blocks of stone used in paving the breakwater are taken.

Experience having taught me that the mortar used in the construction of
these works is of an excellent quality, I shall, I hope, be excused if I add to
this already long paper a few words on this subject.

The blue lyas stone got from the coast of Dorsetshire was burnt at the bridge
as the works proceeded, and, whilst hot from the kiln, was ground in a mill to
a fine powder. It was then taken to another mill, and in its powdered state
mixed with prepared Pozzuolana and sand, and ground until it formed a tough
paste, no more water being used than was absolutely necessary. The best
mortar, or that used in the bottom courses of the piers and abutments, and for
the front work, was composed of one measure of powdered lime, one measure
of Pozzuolana, and two measures of sand. The backing mortar was prepared
with one measure of lime, half a measure of Pozzuolana, and two measures and
a half of sand : the sand was of an excellent quality, got from the site of the
bridge.

The following circumstance will sufficiently prove the goodness of this
mortar. Some masonry, which had been done in one of the foundations about
twelve months, had to be removed, when the stones were found so firmly united,
that gunpowder was necessary to separate them.

I have before described the bed of the river to be a loose sand moved by
the slightest increase of current, and that this circumstance, together with the
difficulty of founding piers and abutments, induced me to propose a suspension
bridge spanning the whole width of the river. It was however hoped, when
a change of plan became necessary, that the plank piles, with the aid of some
stone thrown round them, would be sufficient to meet the increased current
occasioned by the bridge ; but as the erection of the piers and abutments proceeded, the necessity of a more extended security for the foundations became
manifest, as the bed of the river, for its whole width, and to an extent of from
50 to 60 feet above and below the bridge, was gradually scouring away. I
therefore proposed to form an artificial bed, to the full extent to which the
natural one was removed, with clay from 18 inches to 2 feet thick, and
to cover the clay with rubble stone of all sizes from 200 lbs. each downwards. This plan of operation was suggested by observing these materials
in vast abundance in the adjoining limestone quarry spoil hills, and after I
had submitted the clay to experiment, and found it capable of resisting a
current acting immediately upon it at a velocity of 7 feet per second. The
clay and stone were deposited with great regularity, giving to the channels
under each arch a slight concavity in the middle : the combined thickness of
the clay and stone is from 2 feet to 2 feet 6 inches, and just replaces the
loss of the natural bed.

By this union of materials an indestructible bed has been produced. The
clay shields the natural bed from the current, whilst at the same time it forms a
tenacious cement in which the stone buries itself, and which is hardened by the
volume of water constantly pressing on it. In six months after this work was

finished, I ascertained that sea weeds were growing over its surface, and that it was sufficiently firm to resist an oyster dredge*.

Messrs. Johnson of Grosvenor Wharf, London, were contractors for the masonry, &c., and Mr. William Hazledine, of Shrewsbury, for the iron work.

The contract amount for the masonry, &c., was . . £13,365 0

Ditto   ditto   for the iron 13,761 0

Making the total cost £27,126 0

The work commenced in August 1824, and the Bridge was opened in July 1827.

* At the present time (1836) the surface is so hard, that heavily laden waggons would not sink in it.

On cements

C. W. PASLEY, KCB, FRS

Reprinted from Min. Proc. Instn Civ. Engrs, 1837,
vol. 1, 17-18

General Sir Charles Pasley was born in the year 1780 near Dumfries and not far from the birthplace of Thomas Telford. He was educated at the Royal Military Academy at Woolwich and was commissioned in the artillery not long after his 17th birthday. Within a year, he transferred to the Royal Engineers where he spent the remainder of his military career.

Pasley saw a good deal of active service, much of it in Spain during the Peninsular War, and he served with Sir John Moore in the retreat to Corunna. Pasley was of a somewhat pugnacious character, and he believed that instead of falling back on Corunna Moore should have turned on his pursuers and driven them back.

Pasley was interested in education and laid down principles for teaching artificers in the Royal Engineers their various trades. These principles were adopted and Pasley was appointed director of field instruction. He wrote a considerable number of treatises for the army including a code of rules for the duties of all ranks.

In addition to his military interests, Pasley was concerned with a wide range of issues. Among these was the question of decimalisation and he published a scheme for 'simplifying and improving the measures, weights and money used in this country without materially altering the present standard'. This scheme came to nothing and decimalisation had to wait for more than a century before being adopted in Britain.

The nature of Pasley's military duties directed his attention to civil construction affairs, and he joined the Institution as early as 1820. Perhaps because of his Eskdale birthplace, Pasley was proposed for membership by Telford himself and supported by no less than four of the founder members — Palmer, Field, Maudsley and Jones. Pasley was active in the Institution and contributed to many of its debates including, surprisingly, a speech on the Irish question, which was as inflammatory then as it is now.

The best known of Pasley's publications was his 'Observations on limes, calcareous cements, mortars, stuccos, and concrete, and on puzzolanas natural and artificial'. This work was widely used in its day and ran through several editions and was translated into several languages.

As the railways developed, the Government became concerned over such matters as safety and standards of construction, and in 1840 it set up a railway inspectorate in the Board of Trade. Unfortunately, the Act which established the inspectorate laid down that nobody who 'shall within one year of his appointment have been a director of or have held any office of trust or profit under any railway company' could become an inspector. That more or less excluded most railway experts in Britain and the inspectors had to be recruited mainly from the Royal Engineers. They were not well versed in railway work, however, but they were said to be cheaper to engage than civil engineers.

The first head of the inspectorate — General Sir Frederick Smith — lasted only one year, and Pasley was appointed to succeed him in 1841. Pasley remained in the post for five years.

After leaving the inspectorate, Pasley was occupied mainly in revising many of his publications and in the East India Company's Military College at Addiscombe. Pasley died in 1861.

Colonel Pasley said, that his attention had been directed to the subject of Cements, from reading in Smeaton's works, that all water limes were composed of carbonic acid and clay ; since, on dissolving these limes in carbonic acid, clay, of which brick could be made, was left. From this remark he had been led to make experiments similar to the following : he took two parts of chalk and one of clay. The chalk being pounded and mixed with the clay, balls were formed, which being burnt in a crucible, were ground and mixed as cements usually are. Some of these experiments failed, but he attributed their failure to his having used clay which was coarse and sandy ; whence it appeared, that substances would unite, when in the form of a fine powder, which would not unite when in a coarser form. These experiments were made in the years 1829, 30, 31, and 32. Subsequently, in 1836, he repeated his more successful experiments, but without the same success ; and he attributed their failure to the fact of the clay (the blue clay of the Medway,) containing a greater proportion of carbonate of lime, than it had contained five, or six years before. Continuing his experiments, he found, that 4 lbs. of dry chalk and 5 lbs. of the moist blue clay, fresh from the Medway, made the strongest cement ; but he had determined many other proportions which set immediately under water. With cement made according to the above proportions, thirty-one bricks had been set out from a wall, one brick being added every day, omitting the Sundays.

He had cemented bricks together, and he found in every case, that the bricks gave way and not the cement. He estimated the breaking force at the joints, at about 5000 lbs. on the 36 square inches, the surface of the brick. On comparing the strength of this cement with the chalk mortar, which had united some bricks, more than thirty years, he was led to consider the adhesive power of his artificial cement, forty days' old, as at least twenty times greater than that of the mortar.

An account of the actual state of the works at the Thames Tunnel

M. I. BRUNEL, MInstCE

Reprinted from Min. Proc. Instn Civ. Engrs, 1840, vol. 1, 85-86

Sir Marc Brunel's brief paper describes progress on the world's first underwater tunnel. Work on the tunnel began in 1824, but was suspended for a time, and the tunnel was not completed until 1843. The tunnel was originally intended for horse-drawn traffic and pedestrians, but is now part of the London Underground system.

Brunel, father of the more famous Isambard Kingdom Brunel the railway engineer, was born in France in the year 1769. As a boy, he served in the French navy and made a number of voyages to the West Indies. His mechanical talents developed early, and on one of these voyages he made a sextant which he used for his observations.

On returning to France in 1792, Brunel found the Revolution at its height and, since his royalist sympathies were out of key with the prevailing opinion, he was obliged to flee the country and seek safety in the United States of America. There he followed his mechanical bent and became a civil engineer and architect.

Although Brunel was engaged on numerous civil engineering projects in America and later on in Britain, he was probably more notable for his mechanical inventiveness. For instance, wanting to replace manual labour in making ships' blocks, he devised machinery for that purpose and — to all intents and purposes — invented mass production. According to an obituarist, 'the beautiful simplicity of these machines, their perfect adaptation to their various purposes, and notwithstanding the recent advances in mechanics, their continuing for nearly half a century in active work, without any improvements having ever been suggested, must rank them as among the most complete and ingenious pieces of mechanism ever invented'.

Among Brunel's other inventions were a machine for winding cotton thread into balls, an ingenious instrument combining several pens for copying manuscripts, a nail-making machine, a method of cutting veneers and a system for manufacturing shoes by machinery.

Marc Brunel was knighted in 1841, one of the first engineers to be honoured in that way, and he died in his 81st year in 1849. He was an early member of the Institution of Civil Engineers which he joined in 1823.

In consequence of local opposition, the works have not advanced much since the month of March, 1840; but, as that has been overcome, and facilities granted by the City, the works will be speedily resumed, and the shaft on the north bank commenced.

The progress of the Tunnel in the last year has been, within one foot, equal to that made in the three preceding years. During those periods collectively, the extent of the Tunnel excavated was 250 ft. 6 in., and during the last year the excavation has been 249 ft. 6 in. This progress has been made in spite of the difficulties caused by the frequent depressions of the bed of the river. These have been so extensive, that in the course of 28 lineal feet of Tunnel,

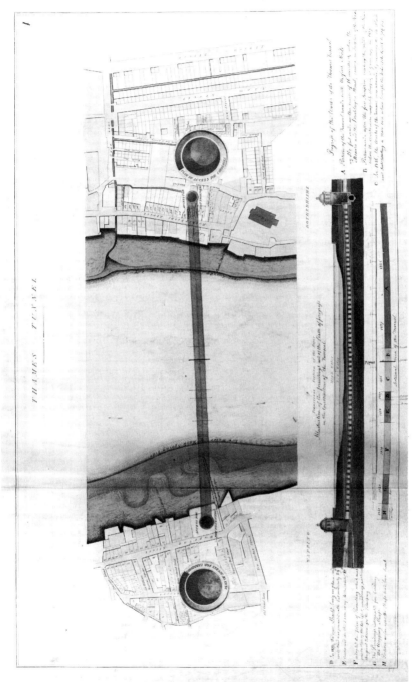

Thames Tunnel: plan and section by Sir Marc Brunel (c. 1841) showing progress of the works, 1824-41 (×28%)

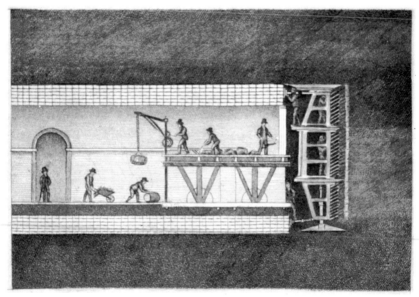

Thames Tunnel: excavation, c. 1827 (from a contemporary print, × 95.5%)

Sketch of works in the Thames Tunnel from Sir Marc Brunel's diary for Friday 1 January 1841 (× 92%)

the quantity of ground thrown upon the bed of the river, to make up for the displacement, in the deepest part of the stream, has been *ten times* that of the excavation, although the space of the excavation itself is completely replaced by the brick structure. On one occasion the ground subsided, in the course of a few minutes, to the extent of 13 feet in depth over an area of 30 feet in diameter, without causing any increased influx of water to the works of the Tunnel. The results now recorded confirm Mr. Brunel in his opinion of the efficiency of his original plan, which is " to press equally against the ground all over the area of the face, whatever may be the nature of the ground through which the excavation is being carried." The sides and top are naturally protected ; but the face depends wholly for support upon the poling boards and screws. The displacement of one board by the pressure of the ground might be attended with disastrous consequences; no deviation therefore from the safe plan should be permitted.

Kilsby Tunnel, London and Birmingham Railway; engineer: Robert Stephenson (lithograph by J. C. Bourne, 1839, × 60%). This major tunnel, 1 mile 682 yards long, was completed in 1838 and presented major dewatering problems which defeated the first contractor, and it had to be completed by direct labour

Description of the Bann Reservoirs, County Down, Ireland

J. F. la TROBE BATEMAN, MInstCE

Reprinted from Min. Proc. Instn Civ. Engrs, 1841, vol. 1, 168-170

The Victorian era was rich in extremely capable water engineers, prominent among whom was John Frederick la Trobe Bateman. Born near Halifax in 1810, Bateman was apprenticed at the age of 15 to a surveying and mining engineer in Oldham. This man's practice was a wide one, and Bateman was soon well versed in the elements of road works and water works in addition to mining and surveying. In 1833 Bateman established his own practice in Manchester and quickly became involved in hydraulic affairs. These were to dominate his professional life.

Not only was he responsible for the water supply schemes of many of Britain's major cities, including Glasgow, Manchester and Newcastle, but he was also connected with harbour and dock works and river improvements in various parts of the country, notably those for the Clyde Navigation Trust to which he acted as consulting engineer for many years. It is notable, too, that he brought out a scheme in 1869 for carrying a railway across the Channel between England and France.

That proposal was 'to lay a tube of cast iron on the bottom of the sea, between coast and coast, to be commenced on one side of the channel, and to be built up within the inside of a horizontal cylinder, or bell, or chamber, which shall be constantly pushed forward as the building of the tube proceeds'. Bateman's scheme was considered to be less practicable than a tunnel, but neither turned out to be 'a thing of early accomplishment', and only now is a Channel tunnel or fixed link, as it is now called, in prospect.

Bateman was only 25 years of age when he became associated with the great mechanical engineer Sir William Fairbairn, whose daughter he later married, on the reservoirs on the River Bann in Ireland. While the report on these works, which were intended to supply water to the linen mills in County Down, was signed by both men, the detailed design and supervision of the construction were done by Bateman alone. This experience pointed the direction which his practice was to take.

When Bateman died in 1889 he was one of the Institution's oldest members, having been elected as long before as 1840, thus having nearly 50 years of continuous membership. He served as President in 1877-78 and 1878-79. Among his many other distinctions were Fellowships of the Royal Societies of both London and Edinburgh, and he represented the former at the opening of the Suez Canal.

The construction of the reservoirs described in this communication was undertaken with the view of regulating the quantity of water in the River Bann, and more effectually supplying water power to the flourishing and increasing establishments on its banks; this river is, from the bare and naked character of the Mourne Mountains, among which it rises, naturally liable to the greatest irregularity in its volume; devastating floods frequently pour down the channel, where a few hours previously there was not sufficient water for agricultural purposes: greatly injurious as this must have been to the agriculturist, it was infinitely more so to the mill-owners, who

The Bann reservoirs.

21

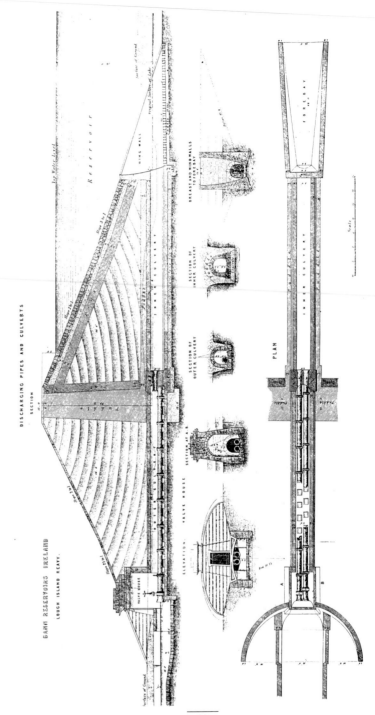

Bann Reservoirs: reservoirs' cross-section (from Min. Proc. Instn Civ. Engrs, 1851, volume 7, plate 10, × 47%)

depended entirely upon water power for their manufactories.

Mr. Fairbairn was consulted on the subject; he examined the locality, and advised the formation of reservoirs : the author was then appointed the engineer, and acting in some degree upon the suggestions of his predecessor, whom he continued to consult, the works. were undertaken which are described in the present paper.

The peculiarities in the act of parliament, granted in 1836, constituting the proprietors of the mills a Joint Stock Company, for the formation of the Bann reservoirs, are detailed. Act of parliamen'.

The works were originally intended to have been more extensive than have been really executed. The reservoir at Lough Island Reavy, is alone described : the ground in that spot was admirably adapted for the work, being the bottom of a basin, which was bounded on all sides by rugged hills of granite ; in the centre of the basin was a small lake, at the bottom of which was discovered a bed several feet in thickness, of fossil confervæ, similar to those discovered by Professor Silliman at Massachusetts, North America. This interesting geological fact was first noticed by Dr. Hunter of Bryansford; the confervæ appeared like an impalpable powder, but when viewed through a powerful microscope, they were found to be regular parallelograms, many of them covered with striæ. They are described by naturalists as the fossil skeletons of minute vegetables. Fossil confervæ.

The situation fixed upon for the reservoir, rendered necessary the construction of four embankments between the hills, so as to raise the water to a height of 35 feet above the summer level of the lake. Construction.

These embankments were all constructed in a similar manner, only varying in the slopes and thickness of the stone facing according to the extent and situation. Embankments.

The whole substratum of the valley was water-tight, either from the existence of the solid rock, dense clay, or of hard, compact, mountain gravel; so that there was no difficulty in securing the foot of the puddle. A trench was sunk into the water-tight stratum, whence the vertical puddle wall was carried up with the bank to the required height. It was 12 feet in width at 40 feet below the top, diminishing gradually to 8 feet wide at the summit, and was worked in regular layers of 8 inches in thickness. Puddle.

The embankments were formed in concave layers 3 feet thick, each layer being completed before another was commenced, steps being cut in the ground where necessary, to receive the layers.

In order further to secure the tightness of the bank, a lining of peat 15 inches in thickness was brought up on the inside of the puddle, and a layer of the same material was laid upon the face of the slope; it was cut small, placed in thin courses like the puddle, and merely trodden down without more moisture than it naturally contained. The author advocates the use of peat in such positions, as, from its light and fibrous nature, in case of a leak occurring, the draught would attract into it all the fibrous particles, which by Peat used.

degrees would stop the holes sufficiently for the silt to settle over and effectually close the aperture.

Above the peat a course of gravel 3 feet in thickness was laid, and upon that the stone pitching, forming the inner side of the bank.

Slopes. The inner slopes were for 20 feet below the top of the bank, 2½ horizontal to 1 vertical; the outer were 2 horizontal to 1 vertical; where they were deeper than 20 feet, the remainder of the backs sloped 3 to 1 on the inside, and 2½ to 1 on the outside.

All the embankments are 12 feet wide at the top, and 5 feet above the water level.

Discharge pipes. The centre of the deepest part of the embankment was traversed by a stone culvert, in which were placed two rows of cast-iron discharge pipes, 18 inches diameter, with suitable valves. A leak was discovered in the centre of the masonry of this culvert, occasioned by the engineer's instructions not being obeyed. The details of the methods employed for remedying this defect are given at length; as also those of the experiments upon cements made by the author

Cements. after the data given by Vicat. The materials which were most accessible for the work were tested very carefully, and from the results, it was determined to employ mortar composed of rich Manx or mountain lime carefully slaked, and clay burned with peat in the open air. The proportions were 2½ of clay to 1 of lime. They were ground together, and being mixed with as much water as was necessary, the mortar was used immediately. The mortar for the backing had one measure of sand added; the grout had two measures of sand in it, and was used thin.

The concrete was composed of one part of lime, two and a half of calcined clay, and about three parts of sharp gravel.

This cement appeared to set hard, and to be perfectly tight; but when the reservoir was partially filled, several leaks were discovered, which rendered an examination necessary, and some energetic measures were taken to stop them, all which are described.

Vicat's cement. The result of the author's experience seems to be, that mortar made from rich lime and calcined clay, as recommended by Vicat, may set and harden under water when there is little pressure, but that it is not able to resist the pressure of a considerable depth of water.

The details of the construction of the masonry of the valve house, the fore bay, the waste weir, the bridge of three arches, constructed over the feeder from the river Muddock, and the various feeders for supplying the reservoir, are given at length, with the particulars of the expenditure of the sum of £14,891, which was the cost of the work, exclusive of land compensation, or salaries and professional charges.

The particulars are also given of a series of observations with rain gauges continued for two years, for the purpose of furnishing data for computing the extent of reservoir which would be necessary to insure a supply of water throughout the year.

On an uniform system of screw threads

J. WHITWORTH, AssocInstCE

Reprinted from Min. Proc. Instn Civ. Engrs, 1841,
vol. 1, 157-160

Joseph Whitworth's paper illuminates one of the key features of modern engineering practice: the establishment of accepted standards. When Whitworth began his career as a manufacturer, about eight years before the paper was presented in 1841, there was no uniformity in the screw threads used in fitting up steam engines and other pieces of machinery. There were no general rules dealing with the relative strengths of the thread and the rest of a screw nor the pitch, depth or shape of the thread itself. Whitworth made a collection of screw bolts from the major workshops in England and ascertained the average dimensions of the screws most commonly used. His system was based on these observations, and it came into general use some 17 years after the paper was presented to the Institution.

Whitworth was born at Stockport in 1803, the son of a schoolmaster. At the age of 14 he went to work with an uncle to learn the business of cotton spinning, and in the next four years he mastered the construction and operation of every machine in his uncle's factory. Deciding to become a mechanic, he went to Manchester and later claimed that the happiest day he ever had was when he first earned a journeyman's wages. After a few years Whitworth moved to London to work in Maudsley's workshop where he discovered how to make a true plane — a problem which had teased mechanics for years. That must surely have been another remarkable day.

In 1833 Whitworth returned to Manchester and set up shop as 'Joseph Whitworth, tool maker, of London'. Whitworth was obsessed with accuracy in making machine parts, and the standard gauges by which fitters could work to accuracies of $\frac{1}{10000}$ of an inch — much closer than the eye could see — were due to him.

Like so many of his engineering contemporaries, Whitworth was an inventive man, and one of his most worthy innovations must have been his street-sweeping machine which is said to have transformed Manchester from one of the dirtiest of England's cities to one of the cleanest in no more than ten months.

While Whitworth was a distinguished member of the Institution for many years, he should probably more properly be thought of as a Mechanical, and he was President of that Institution in 1856. His most lasting social legacy is in the Whitworth Scholarships which have enabled generations of clever young men to enter the engineering profession. He founded the scholarships in 1869, and in a notable letter to Benjamin Disraeli said the following.

'Sir, — I desire to promote the engineering and mechanical industry of this country by founding 30 scholarships of the annual value of £100 each, to be applied for the further instruction of young men, natives of the United Kingdom, selected by open competition for their intelligence and proficiency in the theory and practice of mechanics and its cognate sciences.

'I propose that these scholarships should be tenable on conditions to be defined by a deed of trust regulating the administration of the endowment fund during my life, and thereafter the management of this fund, subject to the conditions specified therein, should vest in the Lord President of the Council or other Minister of public instruction for the time being.

'I venture to make this communication to you in the hope that means may be

found for bringing science and industry into closer relations with each other than at present obtains in this country'.
Whitworth became a baronet in 1869, and he died in 1887.

Uniform screw threads.

The subject considered in this paper, is the importance of having a constant thread for a given diameter in all screws used in fitting up steam engines and other machinery. It is argued, that uniformity of thread would be productive of economy, both in the use of screwing apparatus, and in the consumption of bolts and nuts. The refitting shop of a railway or steam packet company affords a striking instance of the advantage to be derived from the application of this principle. If the same system of screw threads were common to the different engines, a single set of screwing tackle would suffice for any repairs.

A common standard.

No attempt appears to have been hitherto made to attain this important object. Engineers have adopted their threads without reference to a common standard. Any such standard must be in a great measure arbitrary, and hence its absence may be accounted for.

Choice of thread.

The author enters at some length into the consideration of the circumstances affecting the choice of a thread, with a view to show

Characters and conditions.

that it cannot be determined by precise rules. The essential characters of the screw thread are—pitch, depth, and form. The required conditions are—power, strength, and durability. But the exact degree or proportion in which these conditions are required, cannot be ascertained, and consequently the characters on which they depend cannot be fixed by calculation. An approximation may be made, but within a certain limit the decision is arbitrary.

The mutual dependance of the several conditions, and the relation subsisting between the constituent characters, are noticed as having a tendency to perplex in the choice of a thread.

Want of uniformity.

From the vagueness of the principles involved in the subject, a corresponding latitude was naturally to be expected in the practical application of them, and accordingly, instead of that uniformity which is so desirable, there prevails a diversity so great as almost to discourage any hope of its removal. The only mode in which this could be effected, would be by a compromise ; all parties consenting to adopt a medium for the sake of common advantage. The average pitch and depth of the various threads used by the leading engineers, would thus become the common standard, which would not only have the advantage of conciliating general concurrence, but would in all probability approach very nearly to the true standard for practical purposes.

Selection of a standard.

The author then proceeds to describe the mode adopted by Messrs. Whitworth and Co., some years since, in selecting their threads upon this principle. An extensive collection was made of screw-bolts from the principal workshops throughout England, and the average thread was carefully observed for different diameters. The $\frac{1}{4}$ inch, $\frac{1}{2}$ inch, and $1\frac{1}{2}$ inch, were particularly selected, and taken as the fixed points of a scale by which the intermediate sizes were regulated, avoiding small fractional parts in the number of threads to the inch. The scale was afterwards extended to 6 inches. The pitches thus obtained for angular threads were the following:—

Diameter in inches	$\frac{1}{4}$	$\frac{5}{16}$	$\frac{3}{8}$	$\frac{7}{16}$	$\frac{1}{2}$	$\frac{5}{8}$	$\frac{3}{4}$	$\frac{7}{8}$	$1''$	$1\frac{1}{8}$	$1\frac{1}{4}$	$1\frac{3}{8}$	$1\frac{1}{2}$	$1\frac{5}{8}$	$1\frac{3}{4}$	$1\frac{7}{8}$	$2''$
No. of threads to the inch	20	18	16	14	12	11	10	9	8	7	7	6	6	5	5	$4\frac{1}{2}$	$4\frac{1}{2}$

Diameter in inches	$2\frac{1}{4}$	$2\frac{1}{2}$	$2\frac{3}{4}$	$3''$	$3\frac{1}{4}$	$3\frac{1}{2}$	$3\frac{3}{4}$	$4''$	$4\frac{1}{4}$	$4\frac{1}{2}$	$4\frac{3}{4}$	$5''$	$5\frac{1}{4}$	$5\frac{1}{2}$	$5\frac{3}{4}$	$6''$
No. of threads to the inch	4	4	$3\frac{1}{2}$	$3\frac{1}{2}$	$3\frac{1}{4}$	$3\frac{1}{4}$	3	3	$2\frac{7}{8}$	$2\frac{7}{8}$	$2\frac{3}{4}$	$2\frac{3}{4}$	$2\frac{5}{8}$	$2\frac{5}{8}$	$2\frac{1}{2}$	$2\frac{1}{2}$

Above the diameter of 1 inch the same pitch is used for two sizes, to avoid small fractional parts. The proportion between the pitch Pitch of and the diameter varies throughout the entire scale. thread.

Thus the pitch of the $\frac{1}{4}$ inch screw is $\frac{1}{5}$th of the diameter; that of the $\frac{1}{2}$ inch $\frac{1}{6}$th, of the 1 inch $\frac{1}{8}$th, of the 4 inches $\frac{1}{12}$th, and of the 6 inches $\frac{1}{15}$th.

The depth of the thread in the various specimens is then alluded Depth of to. In this respect the variation was greater than in the pitch. The thread. angle made by the sides of the thread being taken as an expression for the depth, the mean of the angle in 1 inch screws was found to be about 55°, which was also nearly the mean in screws of different diameters. Hence it was adopted throughout the scale, and a constant proportion was thus established between the depth and the pitch of the thread. In calculating the former a deduction must be made Calcufor the quantity rounded off, amounting to $\frac{1}{3}$rd of the whole depth, lating the i. e. $\frac{1}{6}$th from the top, and $\frac{1}{6}$th from the bottom of the thread. Making depth. this deduction, the angle of 55° gives for the actual depth rather more than $\frac{3}{5}$ths., and less than $\frac{2}{3}$rds of the pitch.

It is observed, that the system of threads thus selected has already been widely extended, demonstrating the practicability and advantage of the proposed plan. The author then notices the obstacles to general uniformity arising from the inconvenience which any change would occasion, in existing establishments, and also from the imperfect screwing tackle in general use. He anticipates as an important result of a combined effort to introduce uniformity, that screwing tackle generally would be much improved, and the efficiency and economy of bolts and nuts be thereby increased.

He recommends also standard gauges of the diameters and threads, as they would form a convenient adjunct to the screwing apparatus, and would be applicable to other useful purposes.

Account of the scaffolding used in erecting the 'Nelson Column', Trafalgar-square

T. GRISSELL, AssocInstCE

*Reprinted from Min. Proc. Instn Civ. Engrs, 1844,
vol. 3, 203-217*

In the history of civil engineering, the great names are usually those of the consulting engineers, although sometimes these were also partly promoters of schemes as well as their designers. Thomas Grissell, however, whose paper on some aspects of constructing the Nelson Column in Trafalgar Square was presented to the Institution in 1844, was a member of one of the biggest contracting concerns in Britain of its day.

Born in 1801, Grissell was articled to his uncle, Henry Peto, who was a well-established builder, and became his partner in 1825. On Peto's death five years later, Grissell was joined by his cousin, Samuel Morton Peto, and together they ran a hugely successful firm until Peto became Member of Parliament for Norwich in 1847.

The firm was well placed to take advantage of the first railway boom, and much of its work was in railway construction. Peto and Grissell's first railway contract was for the two Curzon Street stations in Birmingham, after which they took on contracts on the Great Western Railway and the South Eastern Railway. The company concentrated on the eastern counties of England and it built the line from Norwich to London and several of its branches. In conjunction with the great railway contractor Thomas Brassey, the company constructed several railway projects overseas.

Eventually Grissell tired of railway work, which he found arduous, and that part of the business was taken over by Morton Peto, while Grissell concentrated on the building side of the business. His best known project was the new Palace of Westminster on which he worked until he retired altogether in 1850, half way through the construction of that masterpiece.

Grissell joined the Institution in 1843 and he served briefly on its Council. He died in 1874.

Scaffolding of the Nelson Column.   In adopting the principle of timber scaffolding for buildings, in preference to poles and ropes, Messrs. Grissell and Peto, the contractors, were influenced by considerations of saving both time and expense. They had long been impressed with the want of scientific principle, exhibited in the ordinary scaffolding, and were more readily induced to turn their attention to that now referred to, which they believe to be an essential improvement, and calculated to be of considerable advantage to contractors on large works.

The author is well aware of the progress which has recently been made by the civil engineers and architects of this country, but he ventures to claim some share of merit for the practical builders, to whom is committed the execution of the works designed by the en-

---

* This plan is now adopted on many railways.

gineer and the architect; and when a review is taken of the stupendous public works which have been executed within the last few years, it is evident, that without the exercise of great skill and the introduction of new modes of reducing labour, the amount of work could not have been executed within the time.

The necessity for this reduction of labour on large works had been long felt in the north, and methods had been adopted in consequence, to emulate which, this timber scaffolding was introduced to London. The system had been employed, in rather a rude form, by Mr. Tomkinson of Liverpool, in his quarries and stone yards, for moving stones of large dimensions. Scaffolding of a somewhat similar kind was used in the erection of the Arc de Triomphe, Barrière de l'Etoile, and at the Eglise de la Madeleine, at Paris.*

The first time it was used by the author's firm, was for the erection of the Reform Club House (Pall Mall), under Mr. Barry, in 1838; then at the large graving-dock at Her Majesty's Dock-yard, Woolwich, under Mr. Walker (Pres. Inst. C.E.) in 1839, and it is now employed very extensively at the new houses of Parliament. In these constructions its general applicability was proved, and in the erection of the Nelson Column (commenced in 1840), where it was carried up to the height of 180 feet, its stability at a considerable elevation was fully tested. Its usefulness is manifested, by the facilities which it affords to the workmen, particularly in buildings of stone. By its aid, and with the travelling machine at its summit, one mason or 'setter,' can set as much work in one day, as was formerly done in three days; whilst at least six labourers are dispensed with, who, with the old mode of scaffolding, were always required to be in attendance. It is also well known, that scaffolding poles and cords are not only expensive, but are subject to rapid decay, and after a few years' wear become useless; in fact, the scaffolding of a moderately extensive building costs a large sum when first purchased, but it is almost valueless after a comparatively short period of time. Such is not the case with the timber scaffolding, which may be said to be of no greater cost to the contractor, than the expense of its erection, which will not exceed in any ordinary case three-pence per foot cube. It is not secured together by either bolts or spikes, so that the waste is trifling, and after having performed its duty as a scaffold, it may be removed piecemeal into the building, at the level of each floor and be used directly for constructing the roof and the internal carpentry of the structure. The

* The square timber scaffolding was employed by Domenic Fontana, in 1586, for the erection of the Egyptian Obelisk in front of St. Peter's at Rome. The means employed in that work are shown in detail in engravings, dated 1586, in the possession of Mr. Allen, at the New Houses of Parliament, and they are described with many other methods of using square timber scaffolding for external and internal constructions in the " Contignationes, ac pontes Nicolai Zabaglia una cum quibus dam ingeniosis praxibus, ac descriptione translationis obelisci Vaticani, aliorumque, per Equitem Dominicum Fontana susceptæ. Romæ, 1743."

timber having become seasoned by its exposure to the weather, is consequently better fitted for immediate use.

These advantages have been proved in the buildings which have been mentioned, and after an experience of more than five years, the author strongly recommends the adoption of the system. He also advises its use in moving and working large stones, either for permanent erections, or in masons' yards. If used on a wharf the rent would soon be saved in labour, and by allowing the stage to project 8 feet or 10

Fig. 1.

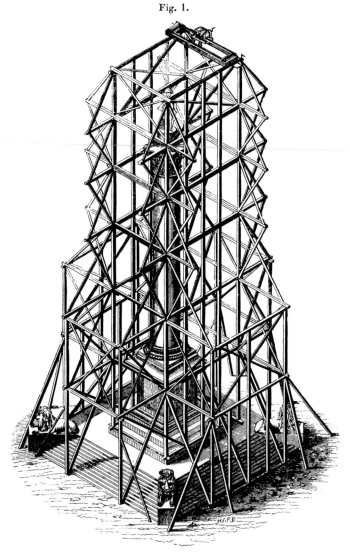

Scaffolding of the Nelson Column.

feet over the river, the scaffolding would be found to answer the purpose of a crane.

The scaffolding at the Nelson column, designed by Mr. Allen, under whose direction the work was executed, (Fig. 1,) was composed of sills, uprights, cross-heads, longitudinal-timbers, braces, and struts, which were used whole, without sawing; the upright timbers were slightly tenoned into the horizontal timbers, and the junctions were secured by iron dogs, driven into the timbers diagonally across the joints. This mode was preferred to bolts or spikes, on account of the ease with which they could be withdrawn, and because the timber was not injured. The base of the scaffold was 96 feet square, exclusive of the raking-braces; the height of each stage varied from 48 feet to 21 feet, upwards; and the total height was about 180 feet. The total amount of timber in the scaffold was 154 loads, or 7700 cubic feet, and the cost of its erection was £240.

Its stability was secured, at the height to which it was carried, by using flying wind-braces, supported upon cross transoms, running outwards about 6 feet beyond the perpendicular of the scaffold at each stage.

Mr. Nicholson remarked, that a scaffolding of a similar description was used in 1837 by Messrs. Cubitt, (Gray's-inn Road), for erecting the entrance gateway of the London and Birmingham Railway (Euston Square.)* It was composed of two parallel rows of whole timber uprights, 50 feet high and 17 feet apart, surrounding the building (Fig. 2); these were well stayed by diagonal braces, and a tram- *Mr. Nicholson.*

Fig. 2.

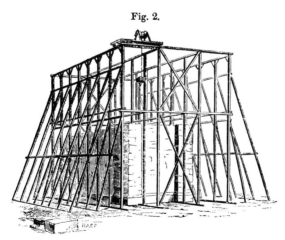

Scaffolding used for building the entrance of the Euston Square Station of the London and Birmingham Railway.

* In the "Drawings of the London and Birmingham Railway, by J. C. Bourne" (Ackermann and Co.) two views are given of this scaffolding.

way was formed on the top of each row, by horizontal sill pieces, bolted down and secured by plates. The building work was executed by the aid of travelling carriages upon the tram-ways, and when the masonry had reached the height of the first scaffold, a second series of uprights and sills was added, making the total height 90 feet, which enabled the work to be completed without an accident.

Mr. Harrison. Mr. Harrison believed, that a scaffolding of a somewhat similar construction was used by Messrs. Rennie, at the Victualling-yard at Plymouth, in 1826.

Mr. G. Rennie. Mr. Rennie said, that the scaffolding employed for raising the statue and other heavy parts of the work, at the Victualling-yard, was on the derrick principle, and was somewhat similar to that used for erecting the Commemoration Column at Devonport, (Fig. 3.)

Mr. T. Grissell. Mr. Grissell stated, that when writing the account of the scaffolding at the Nelson Column, that which had been used by Messrs. Cubitt, at the entrance of the London and Birmingham Railway, had entirely escaped his recollection; he now remembered it perfectly, and was happy to have the opportunity of acknowledging that fact. He could not speak too highly in praise of the system, and he thought its advantages had, as yet, been underrated. The waste of timber was comparatively nothing; while serving as scaffolding it was becoming seasoned, and like that at the Nelson Column, could be immediately worked up, in situations demanding dry timber. The cost was one-half, and sometimes one-third, of the ordinary kind of scaffold, if the loss by the rotting and destruction of poles and cords was taken into account. The saving of labour in raising the materials was very great, particularly where weights of from 8 tons to 14 tons required to be lifted. If steam power had been used at the Nelson Column, a still greater saving would have been effected.

Another considerable advantage was the freedom from danger to the workmen; during five years, in all the works where he had used this kind of scaffolding, only one man had been killed. That accident occurred at the Woolwich Graving Dock, when a man was thrown from the travelling carriage, by the handle of the winch striking him, from his having omitted to put on the break.

He believed, that this description of scaffolding, might be safely carried still higher than at the Nelson Column, for although before the statue was hoisted, he had felt somewhat anxious, and had thought of attaching guide chains, and using other precautions, the fabric had stood so well, that he should not now hesitate to go to a greater height, relying upon the scaffolding alone.

Mr. C. H. Smith. Mr. Smith had adopted the system of the travelling winch on a framing, with great advantage in his carving room, for moving the heavy blocks of stone, from which the capitals of the columns for the Royal Exchange were cut. Without such mechanical assistance, he could never have executed his task within the required time, nor could the capitals have been raised and placed on the carriages, to be conveyed away, without much danger of injury.

Mr. Giles said, that Corby Bridge, over the Eden, on the line of the Newcastle and Carlisle Railway, was built by Mr. Denton, the contractor, by means of whole timber scaffolding put together in three stages. The bridge consisted of five arches, of 80 feet span each, 100 feet in height, and contained 400,000 feet of stone-work, which was executed with the greatest facility, chiefly owing to the convenience afforded by the scaffolding, and without any accident, excepting to the foreman, who fell twice from a considerable height, but fortunately was not killed.

Mr. Fowler said, that the scaffolding at the Cathedral at Cologne, was of whole timber; there was little doubt, that the system was very similar to that which was employed, when the building was commenced in 1248. The crane which was used in raising the materials, still remained on the summit of one of the towers; it was once removed, but was speedily restored to its situation, as the superstitious fears of the inhabitants of Cologne were excited by the occurrence of a storm, immediately consequent upon the removal of the crane. It had subsequently been constantly repaired as it decayed, so that at present little of the original remained, but the form was still the same.

Mr. Fowler believed, that the materials for the York Column (Carlton Terrace) were raised by a kind of travelling carriage, on the top of the scaffolding.

Mr. Hawkins observed, that the scaffolds used at Vienna, for the erection of any building of importance, were always constructed of whole timbers, secured together by 'dogs.' In 1827 he superintended the erection of an extensive sugar-house at Vienna, where such scaffolding was used.

Mr. Colthurst stated, that at Devonport there was a column built of granite from Holman's Hill Quarry, near the Tamar. The shaft was 11 feet in diameter; its height, from the bottom of the shaft to the top of the capital was 65 feet 4 inches. The total height of the column, with its inferior and crowning pedestals, was 101 feet 4 inches. Its height above the street, including the rock on which it stood, was 124 feet. The abacus of the capital was composed of four stones, each weighing between 3 and 4 tons.*

The stones of the column were raised and set, entirely without the use of scaffolding, by means of a series of tall spars joined together (Fig. 3); the lowest being fixed into the ground and braced by diagonal pieces, was lashed and strutted to the lower part of the shaft. A gaff, with a jaw at the lower end, was then slung in the throat by a strong rope or chain, so as to work round the upright spar, in the jaw prepared for this movement; from the end of the gaff, blocks and a fall were suspended, in such a manner as to command every part of the work, by raising or depressing the point of the gaff, to increase or

---

* Vide 'The Public Buildings erected in the West of England;' by John Foulston. 4to. 1838, pp. 57 and 59.

Fig. 3.

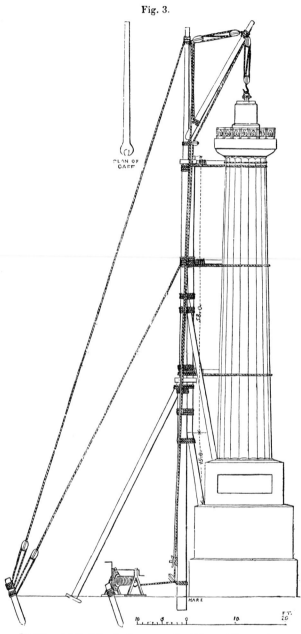

Derrick used for building the Commemoration Column at Devonport.

diminish its range. Crab winches sufficed to raise the stones; and it was stated that the work was executed in a very short time.†

Mr. Rendel had seen this column while in course of construction; the derrick appeared to act well, and it was certainly a cheap mode of raising the materials.
Mr. Ren-
del.

Mr. Smith said, that in a recent visit to Liverpool, he had observed an ingenious mode, adopted by Mr. Tomkinson, for raising building materials, which almost superseded the use of external scaffolding. It consisted of a very high double 'derrick,' placed upon wheels running on a tram-way, laid parallel with the walls of the building; the head of the derrick curved over towards the wall, and steam power was employed for raising the materials, which appeared to be accomplished with rapidity.
Mr. C. H.
Smith.

The President remarked, that the Institution always viewed with pleasure, papers descriptive of the methods adopted by contractors, in the execution of works designed by Civil Engineers or Architects. The profession was much indebted to the practical skill and intelligence of the contractors, and it would be extremely interesting, to find recorded in the Minutes of Proceedings of the Institution, the names of the inventors, and the dates of the introduction of such ingenious modes of accomplishing works of magnitude, as had been described by Messrs. Grissell and Peto. This could only be arrived at by, either the engineers or the contractors sending the necessary information, or by their giving it during the discussions at the meetings.
The Pre-
sident.

General Pasley described the method adopted by Mr. T. Slacks (Langholm), for building the obelisk which was erected on the Whitaw, Eskdale, to the memory of the late Major-General Sir John Malcolm, a native of that district.*
Maj.-Gen.
Pasley.

The obelisk, which was of white sand-stone, was carried up to the height of 100 feet above the foundation; it was built hollow, with thorough courses at intervals; through the centre of each of these courses was left a circular hole (Fig. 4.) In the lower of these holes, was placed the foot of a pole 40 feet long, and 10 inches diameter; the next hole above served as a stay, whilst the upper one supported the whole weight, as around the pole was firmly fixed a collar (D) of hard wood. Beneath this collar 17 metal balls, $3\frac{1}{2}$ inches in diameter, were introduced, which, running in corresponding circular grooves in the collar and the thorough course, enabled the pole to revolve easily. Across the top of the pole was mortised a beam 12 feet long and 12 inches square, in the form of the letter T, and it was strengthened by diagonal iron braces and straps. By means of a crab winch (B), with a rope passing over pulleys in each end of the transverse beam, the stones, as at (A), were raised to the requisite

† By the permission of the Council of the Royal Institute of British Architects, a model of the Devonport column, with the derrick, was exhibited.

* Vide Trans. Soc. Arts, 1836-7, vol. li., page 78.

Fig. 4.

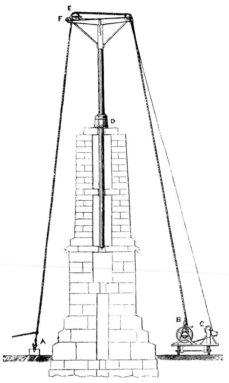

The Malcolm Column.

height, and by a traversing carriage (E) on the beam, a small crab (C), and the pulleys (F), the stone was enabled to run inwards to the spot for laying it. The crane was raised as each bond or thorough course was fixed, and the time consumed in the operation of moving it, did not exceed two hours.

This crane had been found very efficient, and had greatly reduced the cost of building the obelisk, which was completed in less than twelve months. For the ingenuity displayed in this simple modification of the balance crane used by Mr. Stevenson, at the Bell Rock Lighthouse, and for a clever hanging scaffolding used for completing the pyramidal top of the obelisk, the Gold Isis Medal was voted to Mr. Slack, by the Society of Arts, in 1836–7.

Mr. How-
kins.
A model was exhibited, of a moveable derrick crane (Fig. 5), which had been presented by Mr. Howkins. It was used by Mr. Wightman, at the works of the Granton Pier, Edinburgh, and was stated by him to be very superior to any other kind of crane. It consisted of a vertical post, supported by two timber back-stays, and a long moveable jib, or derrick, which was hinged against the post, below

Fig. 5.

Derrick crane used at Granton Pier (Edinburgh.)

the gearing; this jib was held by a chain, passing from a barrel over a pulley at the top of the post, in such a manner that the extreme end of the jib could be raised almost vertically, or be lowered nearly to a horizontal position.

The chief advantage it possessed over the old gibbet crane, was, that it commanded concentric circles of from 10 feet to 60 feet radius, which was of great use in large works, as it could extend its sweep over a circle of 120 feet diameter, without being moved from its position; whereas, the old gibbet crane commanded only one circle of comparatively limited extent, and in moving it, as the works proceeded, there was a considerable loss of time.

Mr. Bremner stated, that he had seen the crane at Granton Pier; it was a very useful machine, and the only fault he could find with it,

Mr. J. Bremner.

37

was, that in an exposed situation, there was a risk of the wheel-work being destroyed. He believed, that the contractors had found much advantage from its use.

Mr. Bremner had used, at the works of Lossiemouth Harbour, a crane of a somewhat similar description. The jib was composed of two spars, with the hoisting-chain working between them ; the radius of its sweep was 60 feet, so that any spot, within a circle of 120 feet in diameter, was fully commanded by it, and that extent of work could be completed without moving the crane.

Mr. Gale (Glasgow). Mr. Gale presented two drawings (Nos. 3665 and 3666,) of improved moveable jib cranes, the alterations in which, had been suggested by the serious accidents which had occurred from the failure of the ordinary cranes.

On investigating the circumstances connected with these accidents, he found, that in general they had arisen from the snapping of the jib-chain. After numerous experiments it occurred to him, that this defect might be obviated, by attaching the jib chain to the top of the post, instead of fixing it to the end of the jib; this alteration was productive of great advantage, the strain was found to be less than one-half that of the single jib crane, and it consequently required fewer men to work it.

He had also applied a rope instead of a chain for working the jib, as it was preferred by some builders, and he had also made some minor improvements in the other parts of the cranes.

These kind of cranes were, he believed, introduced by Mr. W. York, at Glasgow, in the year 1833, and Mr. Gale had used the improved sort in 1842, at the erection of the New Court Houses, Glasgow. Since that time many builders had adopted them, and their advantages were becoming daily so evident that he would send, early in the ensuing session, a paper descriptive of them.

Mr. J. Thomson. Mr. Thomson believed, that cranes of this description were first used at Glasgow, by builders. The contractor for the Grangemouth Docks, under Sir John Macneil, employed them in 1841 and 1842 with much advantage; he thought them the most useful kind of cranes for general work.

The President. The President agreed in the opinion of the general utility of the cranes ; he had been so pleased with them, that he requested Mr. Howkins to present to the Institution the model of that used at Granton Pier. With respect to the date of the introduction of the swinging-jib, or moveable derrick crane, it was used at Granton Pier by Messrs. Orrell of Liverpool, in 1838, and he believed, that it had been commonly used by them for some time previously.

Mr. Wicksteed. Mr. Wicksteed presented a drawing, (No. 3671,) of the tackle used in elevating the pipes of the ' stand-pipe ' of the East London Water-works (Fig. 6). A piece of timber (A), 9 inches square, was attached vertically to the upper flanch of the pipe, and held below by an iron girdle (B), which encircled the body of the pipe ; guy ropes

38

were attached to the top of the upright, which served as the points of suspension for the snatch blocks, through which were passed the fall ropes from the large and the small crab winches.   The iron girdle had at its opposite sides, two pivots, which traversed the lower end of two timber jibs (C), connected at their upper ends by a cross piece (D), from the centre of which were suspended, the blocks and tackle connected with the large crab, by which the pipes were raised. When each pipe had arrived at its height, the jib frame was drawn up vertically by the tackle from the small crab, and the pipe was lowered to its position; the pins were put into the flanches, and the whole apparatus was raised and attached to it, in order to use it for raising the next pipe.   This process was repeated, until the stand pipe was finished at a height of upwards of 130 feet.   It was stated to be a very simple and economical mode of proceeding.

Fig. 6.

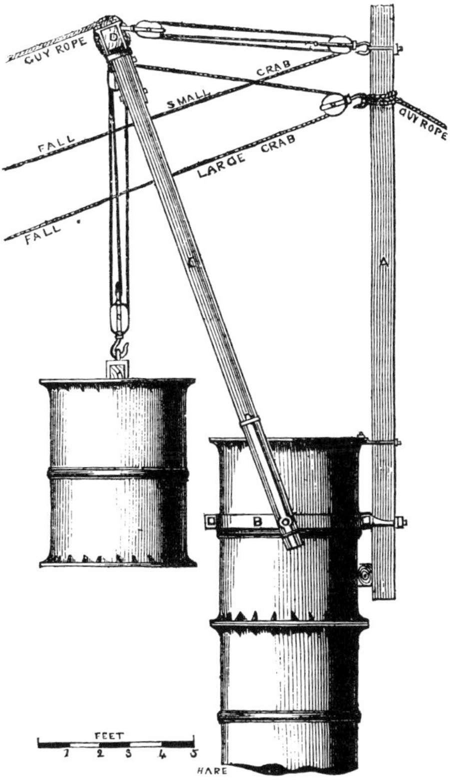

Tackle used in elevating the pipes of the ' Stand-pipe ' at the East London Water-works.

39

Fig. 7.

Sir M. I. Brunel.

Sir M. I. Brunel exhibited a model of the scaffolding used by Sir Christopher Wren in the erection of the Monument, on Fish Street Hill (Figs. 7 and 8). It was formerly the property of Sir William Chambers, and had been given by Mr. Heathcote Russell, C.E., to Sir M. I. Brunel, who presented it to the Institution.

At A A (Fig. 8.) the angles were left free from scaffold-boards, for the purpose of hoisting the stones, by the shear derricks at B B (Fig. 7). Scaffold - boards were placed across the angles at C C. The whole of the scaffold was constructed of the ordinary poles, attached by cords, and the ladders, which reached over three stories each, were formed of two uprights with treads nailed on the face.*

Mr. Allen.

Mr. Allen presented a sketch (Fig. 9) of the circular travelling crane, now in use for erecting the central or ventilating tower at the new Houses of Parliament. It consisted of a circular base curb, at the top of which was fixed a toothed rack. In the centre was fixed a vertical post, with diagonal braces, carrying a centre point, around which, the travelling

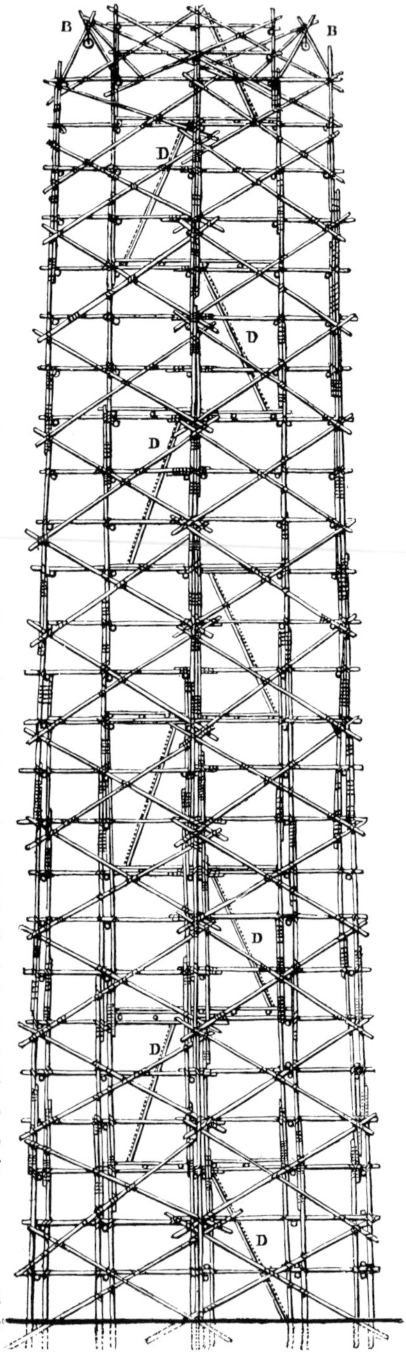

* Vide ' Civil Engineer and Architect's Journal,' 1838, page 267.

Fig. 8.

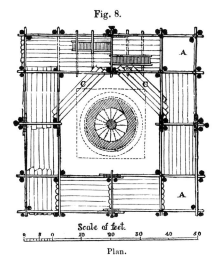

Scale of feet.

Plan.

crane worked, with its hoisting crab on the top. At the foot of each leg was inserted a toothed wheel, working into the rack, so that by means of winch handles the whole could be made to revolve. It was stated, that the saving in labour was very considerable, but that the saving as compared with the cost of constructing scaffolding would be very much greater.

Fig. 9.

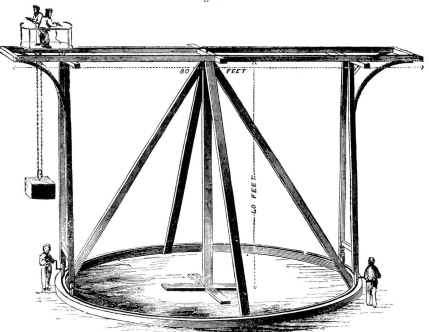

Revolving Scaffolding used at the new Houses of Parliament.

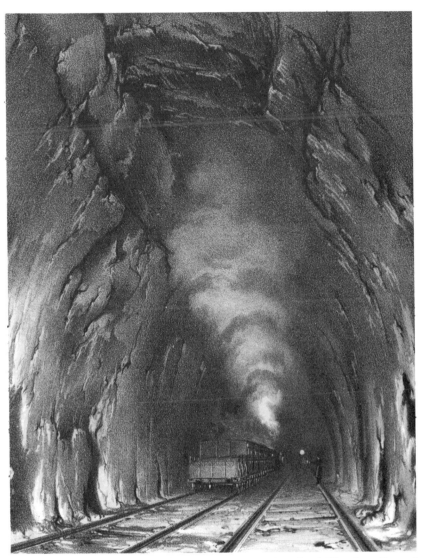

Box Tunnel, Great Western Railway; engineer: Isambard Kingdom Brunel (lithographs by J. C. Bourne, 1846, above × 39.5% and facing page × 78.5%). Completed in 1841, at the time of its completion the Box was the longest railway tunnel in the world (1 mile 1452 yards). As with Kilsby, there were major construction problems of driving through half a mile of Bath stone

Building for the Great Exhibition of Industry of all Nations in London, 1851 (Plate 2, × 45%)

On the construction of the building for the exhibition of the works of industry of all nations in 1851

M. D. WYATT, AssocInstCE

Reprinted from Min. Proc. Instn Civ. Engrs, 1851, vol. 10, 127-165

If it is at first sight odd to see a paper by a notable architect in this book, it has to be remembered that in the Institution's early days a considerable number of architects could be found among its members. What is more, not a few leading engineers, including both Thomas Telford and Robert Mylne, were prepared to describe themselves as both engineers and architects. It has to be said, however, that Digby Wyatt was a more substantial architect than most of those who were members of the Civils.

Wyatt was born near Devizes in 1820 and when he was 16 he entered the office of his architect elder brother as a pupil. His natural ability was displayed in the same year when he won the Architectural Society's essay prize. In the course of his career, Wyatt designed a number of important buildings including the India Office and Paddington Station on which he worked closely with Isambard Kingdom Brunel. He published a number of books and many papers, and was the first Slade Professor of Fine Arts at the University of Cambridge.

Perhaps the peak of Wyatt's career was when he was appointed secretary to the Executive Committee of the Great Exhibition of 1851. In his paper on the Great Exhibition building — the Crystal Palace — Wyatt points out that while the building was bigger than St Paul's Cathedral, its walls were only eight inches thick compared with the cathedral's 14 feet. He went on to note that 'St Paul's required 35 years to erect, the building will be finished in almost half that number of weeks'.

Almost everything about the Crystal Palace was revolutionary, and it foreshadowed many of the building techniques which were much later to become the hallmarks of the modern movement in architecture. Joseph Paxton drew up his plans in seven days and construction was marked by similar feats of speed. The contractors began to level the site on 30 July 1850, and the first column was erected on 28 September. The whole building was up in 22 weeks and fitting out and painting took only 16, ready for the royal opening on 1 May 1851.

The building was a triumphant masterpiece and has been rightly described as one of the most practical, graceful, magical buildings ever to appear in London'.

Wyatt joined the Institution in 1850, and he served on its Council for one year. He was knighted in the 1860s and died in 1877, only 57 years of age.

The first attempt to concentrate, within the compass of a few acres, material for forming a comprehensive idea of the industry of all nations, has been declared to be a great experiment, worthy of being tried, upon a scale commensurate with the industrial resources of this country. It will be admitted, that the immediate success of any such experiment must be directly proportioned to the perfection of the apparatus employed, and that, in attaining perfection in the construction of any great apparatus, three essential conditions are demanded : 1st. A just apprehension of the results to be produced ; 2ndly. A well-digested scheme for producing the results aimed at ; and 3rdly. Power and dexterity to arrange the whole, so as to insure the perfect accordance and working of all its parts, in the simplest and best manner.

The building must be regarded as the principal physical apparatus, by means of which this great experiment is to be tried, and in order to form some idea of its structural fitness, it is necessary to ascertain how far those connected with the work have understood and fulfilled their duty, in relation to these three essential conditions of success. It may be well, therefore, to consider, 1st. The results to be produced, or, in other words, the requisites of the building ; 2ndly. The scheme for producing the results aimed at, or, in other words, the design of the building ; 3rdly. The power and dexterity with which the scheme has been realized, or, in other words, the construction of the building.

Beginning, therefore, with

THE REQUISITES OF THE BUILDING,

it must be manifest, that as the first conditions of the Exhibition of 1851 differed, in many essential particulars, from those of all antecedent exhibitions, a recurrence to precedent was, to a great extent, precluded. Yet the study of previous arrangements, although not affording models for imitation, has proved serviceable, in enabling a knowledge to be obtained, of the difficulties which seemed most ikely to increase in proportion to the expansion of scale.

From the French Exhibition of 1849 many hints were obtained, and a reference to the published plan of the building for that exhibition* will suffice to demonstrate their nature.

The length of some of the stalls, which occasioned a difficulty in passing speedily from one point to another, and the shortness of others, which confused the spectator, by tempting him to diverge from a steady course, demonstrated the necessity for some arrangement by which it should be possible to examine the whole exhibition, by following a simple, and therefore easily remembered, system throughout ; and, at the same time, to find and reach with facility any particular object.

A square enclosed by long galleries was objectionable, as it lessened the apparent vastness of the building, since from no one point could the dimensions of more than one quarter of its extent be perceived.

The building erected by the King of Bavaria at Munich, expressly for periodical exhibitions of national works of industry, is a noble structure, but its academic plan, dividing it into regular halls

---

* *Vide* " A Report on the Eleventh French Exposition of the Products of Industry, prepared by the direction of, and submitted to the President and Council of the Society of Arts." By M. Digby Wyatt, Folio. Plates. Lond. 1849.

and chambers, while ministering to architectural proportion, diminishes the apparent extent, and increases the difficulty of arrangement, by assigning limited dimensions of space to certain groups of
objects, the amount of which, varying with every exhibition, necessarily requires compressing at one time, in order to bring the series
of objects within the limits of the apartment allotted to them, or
spreading out at another, in an attempt to cover space they may be
insufficient to fill. The massive character and great cost of the
" Industrie Gebäude," still further precluded the possibility of its
being adopted as a precedent.

The noble hall of the Kroll's Garten, at Berlin, in which the last
Prussian exhibition was held, was certainly well adapted for its
purpose, and bore testimony to the value of simplicity of plan, an
element of success found wanting in the plans of the Academy and
of the Arsenal at Berlin, in which accommodation had been provided for the previous exhibitions of the industry of the Zollverein.

The arrangements of the various displays of works of industry,
which had taken place in the apartments of the Royal Irish Society,
at Dublin ; in the rooms of the Society of Arts, and in Covent
Garden Theatre, in London ; at Edinburgh, Birmingham, Manchester, and in other places, were valuable, chiefly as having
practised exhibitors and others in the tasteful combination of objects
of beauty and utility.

A feeling that the complete novelty in the conditions of a cos-
mopolitan exhibition demanded an original method of treatment,
perfectly different from any previous attempts, materially influenced the production of that invitation to the world at large, to
contribute suggestions for the building, which was issued on the
13th March, 1850, by the Members of the Building Committee,
whose zeal and liberality in giving the benefit of their talents and
technical knowledge to the public, on that occasion, cannot but reflect
equal credit on themselves and on the professions to which they
belong.

The response to the invitation of the Building Committee was
remarkable, as producing contributions from upwards of two hundred and forty competitors for honour only. The value and beauty
of many of the schemes thus elicited, and the wildness of others,
must have been apparent to the public, and to the members of the
Institution of Civil Engineers, in whose theatre they were exhibited
by the permission of the Council.

The task of analysing the systems proposed was a laborious one,
and involved the devotion of much time and thought, to thoroughly
examine into the different principles upon which the plans appeared
to be based ; the effort, however, was by no means profitless, since
it contributed to a recognition of the value of the various requisites,
the satisfactory supply of which, in a building constructed to effect
an untried purpose, could not but constitute one of the most important merits of such a structure.

Principles of the Proposed Plans.

The principle of arrangement, by which it was necessary that the stalls should run longitudinally, appeared defective, on account either of the inconvenient length of the stalls, if there were only few transverse divisions, or their great confusion, if intersected by many. Plans on radiating systems crowded the public in counter currents upon the foci, and could scarcely be adapted to the form of the site. Plans of an architectural character were generally too monumental, too much divided, and far too expensive, involving an excess of walling, exactly proportioned to the amount of their sub-division, and rendering proper supervision almost impossible. Plans dividing the building into four distinct exhibitions were objectionable, as the effect of the whole would have been marred, a quadruple staff of superintendents would have been necessary, and one part would have been crowded whilst another was empty, in consequence of the impossibility of accurately predetermining the proportion of space to be allotted to each section ; whilst the disproportionate areas of the spaces demanded for raw products, machinery, manufactures, and fine arts could only have produced an irregular building. Plans showing the whole site covered over with parallel sheds, with spaces between, would have involved great lengths of unnecessary inclosure, were likely to be monotonous, and were devoid of any charm of variety, or grandeur. While from some designs, the lesson was learnt, of what to avoid, from others much information was gained, since many indispensable requisites had been foreseen, and more, or less ingeniously provided for, in the plans submitted by the competitors.

Description of the Site.

As the principles which were first laid down were, to a great extent, dictated by the form and character of the ground, it may be well to premise, that the site consists of a piece of ground, originally pointed out by His Royal Highness Prince Albert, on the occasion of the first private meeting on the subject of the Exhibition, held at Buckingham Palace on the 30th June, 1849, as affording advantages which few other places might be found to possess. It contains about 26 acres, and is of a form nearly approaching that of a parallelogram, of which the sides are as one to four nearly, being 2,300 feet long by 500 feet broad (measured on the central axes), fronting north and south, and having its ends east and west, with an almost uniform fall of about one in two hundred and eighty, from west to east. Several large trees stretch about half across the centre of its length, and two clumps of smaller trees, which it was indispensable to preserve, stand near the northern boundary on the east and west of the central group. Such being the site, and the broad outline of the nature of the Exhibition having been determined, the following requisites for the arrangement of the plan gradually developed themselves, and will be found to have been provided for in the present building.

Requisites finally Assumed.

First, that a main avenue of ample width should extend the whole length from east to west, as near the centre of the structure as the trees would permit; that this avenue should be higher than any other parts of the building, with the exception of a transverse avenue ranging with it in height, leading from the southern entrance, and crossing the entire structure at right angles, as near the centre as possible.

Secondly, that limiting the number of entrances to one at the eastern, one at the western, and one at the southern end of the main avenues, would be convenient to the public, and simplify the supervision of the money-taking, &c., but that it would be desirable to provide numerous exits. That of these three entrances the southern would be the most important, and the one about which it would be best to group the executive offices.

Thirdly, that other longitudinal avenues should extend from north to south, and that transverse gangways between the stalls, numbered to correspond with the Catalogue, should connect them with the main longitudinal avenue, so that any visitor, by passing down one side of a gangway, and up another, or down the centre of one gangway, and up the centre of another, and taking the gangways regularly one after another, might be likely not to omit any portion of the Exhibition, and not to see any part of it twice over ; or so that any visitor, desirous of proceeding directly to a particular object, might be able to pass along the main, or central avenue, until he arrived at the gangway (marked to correspond with the indications of the Catalogue), which would be sure to lead him to the object he was in search of; and so that, in either case, the disposition of the building might rather direct than coerce the motions of the visitors, and might insure the general movement of the public in regular currents.

Fourthly, that round and about the three clumps of trees would be the most convenient spots for the refreshment rooms.

Fifthly, that a fixed dimension of 24 feet should be adopted ; which should serve as the basis of all rectangular lines parallel to the main avenues, on plan ; and that the whole of the supports for the roofing should be placed either at their intersection, or at the intersection of multiples of them ; that the mistakes and consequent delay attending the adoption of irregular dimensions would be thus avoided ;—that the lines of the Building would be rendered agreeable ;—that uniform areas of roofing could be conveniently arranged for drainage through the hollow columns ; and that, to use the common phrase, "the work would run off all the better for it."

Sixthly, that omitting all internal enclosures, or divisions, except-

ing those formed by the stalls, would have the good effect of allowing the eye to range at liberty, and to appreciate the extent, and
the vistas of the building—would afford facilities for any mode of
arrangement best calculated for displaying the goods, and for the
adoption of any system of classification—leaving the hands of the
Executive unfettered ;—would facilitate the police and general supervision—and last, not least, would save a large sum of money.

Many other requisites for the kind of structure likely to be most
desirable, such, for instance as that it must be thoroughly lighted,
ventilated, drained, built simply, economically, and with a view to
ultimate value, are of so self-evident a character, that, to dwell upon
them in detail, would uselessly delay the consideration of the second
part of the subject " an examination of the precise mode in which
the requisites are supplied in,

The Design of the Present Building.

After much deliberation, what were considered the best means of
supplying these requisites were embodied in a series of drawings,
and tenders were invited by advertisement on the 12th June, 1850.
The public were, at the same time, given to understand, that proposals for " methods of construction other than those shown upon the
drawings would be entertained," if made in a bonâ fide form. The
reliance thus manifested in the probability of the urgency of the
demand calling forth valuable suggestions from practical men, was
by no means misplaced,—since it had the effect of stimulating Mr.
Paxton to consider the subject with his usual ability and energy,
giving it the benefit of his great experience in the construction of
buildings of a somewhat analogous character. All that gentleman's
endeavours to supply new remedies for old defects in structures of
glass, to combat the prejudices of conventional construction, and to
develop the capabilities of the combination of glass, wood, and iron,
have been so recently and so ably described by himself, in other
places, that it would be needless here to do more than to refer to
them in general terms.

All his efforts must, however, be looked upon as so many experiments, tried as if for the purpose of enabling England, on this occasion, to exhibit to foreign nations some novel and admirable mechanical appliances, and a fine specimen of the resources she possesses, in
the energy of her individual citizens—the true source of her wealth,
and the key to her industrial position.

It was alike fortunate for the Royal Commissioners—and for Mr.
Paxton, that Messrs. Fox, Henderson, and Co. should have been interested in carrying out the undertaking. From the practical experience which they brought to bear upon the subject, designs
grew into realities,—difficulties were foreseen and remedied,—and a
high order of mechanical contrivance was displayed, in adaptations
of machinery to economise labour and to perfect production.

[Plate 2, × 35%]

The Area covered.

The building, as now erected, provides an area, upon the ground floor, equal to 772,784 square feet, and upon the level of the galleries, 23 feet from the floor, an area equal to 217,100 square feet, making a total area of available space of 989,884 square feet.

The General Features of the Design.

The combination upon so vast a scale, of the materials, glass, wood, and iron, of which alone the building is constructed, and the care, which has been taken, not to exaggerate the proportions of form in which those materials may be best and most economically used, will probably tend to counteract conventionality of style in architecture, and may be expected to produce, hereafter, important changes, alike in the construction and appearance, of many extensive buildings throughout the country.

The general distribution of the design recalls the system of a cathedral structure—a vast nave 72 feet wide, rises to a height of 64 feet above the soil. This is crossed by a transept 408 feet long, equally wide and lofty; but with the difference, that it is crowned by a waggon vault, increasing its height to 104 feet at the centre.

On each side of the nave and transept, a series of aisles, 24 feet wide, by 44 feet and 24 feet high, spread out to a total width of 456 feet.

Some idea may be formed of the leading peculiarities of the building, by recalling the fact, that its main avenue, between the columns, is nearly double the width of the nave of St. Paul's Cathedral, while its length is more than four times as great. The walls of St. Paul's are 14 feet thick, those of the Hyde Park Building are 8 inches. St. Paul's required thirty-five years to erect, the building will be finished in about half that number of weeks.

The Drainage.

It may be conceived, that the arrangements for carrying off, rapidly, the entire roof-water of 17¾ acres, involved considerable preparation. Six rows of cast-iron pipes, each 6 inches diameter, communicating with the hollow columns, supporting the roof, follow the fall of the ground from west to east, and convey the water to three drains running north and south. The latter, communicating with sewers running east and west, outside the building, convey the water to the lowest points, at the east end of the site, from which it is discharged into the main sewer in the Kensington Road, by an egg-shaped culvert of 4 feet 8 inches sectional area. A datum line having been assumed, the level of the flooring of the whole area was arranged to incline 1 inch in 24 feet, approximating to the fall of the ground.

The Flooring.

The floor was arranged to consist of boards 1½ inch thick, laid half-an-inch apart, upon joists 7 inches by 2½ inches, bearing upon sleepers 13 inches by 3¼ inches, at intervals of 8 feet apart.

The interstices were left between the boards to permit the passage of dust and dirt. This method of flooring has been found to answer well at Chatsworth and in other localities.

THE FOUNDATION AND BASE-PLATES (Figs. 1 & 2).

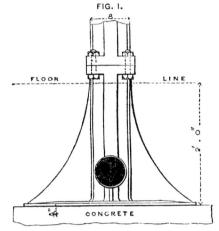

FIG. I.

Elevation of base-plate, showing connexion with column above it.

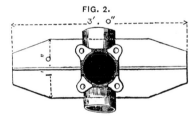

FIG. 2.

Plan of base-plate.

It would have been difficult to have found a better foundation than that which extends over the whole area of the building, with the exception of a few "faults" here and there. Good gravel is reached at a depth of about 3 feet below the surface of the ground, and excavations have been made, in all cases, sufficiently deep to lay bare the gravel. The extent of the horizontal area of the excavation has been determined by a rule, that, making allowance for possible contingencies, the gravel cannot be exposed to a greater load that 2¼ tons per superficial foot. The cavities thus formed, have been, in all cases, filled up with solid concrete, finished with fine mortar. On the surface of this mortar are bedded "base-plates," or foundation pieces, consisting of a horizontal bed-plate, at right angles to the vertical lines of the building, strengthened by shoulders, uniting the horizontal plates to the portion of the base-plate, the section of which corresponds with that of the columns. The exact height, from the top of the concrete foundation to the plane of the junction between the base-plate and the column, has been so precisely calculated, and the casting of the base-plate has been, in all cases, so perfectly performed, that the snugs, cast on the upper portion of the base-plates, have exactly met and corresponded with those on the lower portion of the superincumbent columns, without leaving any interstice, or requiring any packing.

From the vertical portion of the foundation pieces, which carry columns, through which the roof-water passes, sockets branch out, into which are fixed the ends of the cast-iron pipes, for conveying the water descending from the roofs to the transverse drains.

THE COLUMNS AND CONNECTING PIECES (Figs. 3, 4, & 5).

FIG. 3.

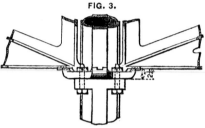

Elevation of lower portion of connecting piece, showing its attachment to a column below, and to the girders at the sides.

FIG. 4.

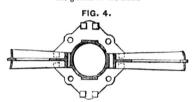

Plan of connecting piece, with girders, &c.

FIG. 5.

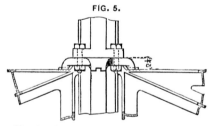

Elevation of upper portion of connecting piece, &c.

The form of the supporting columns bearing upon the upper face of the base-plates was suggested by Mr. Barry. The horizontal section is a ring, of which the external diameter is uniformly 8 inches, and the substance of metal is proportioned to the various areas of roofing, &c., to be supported at each point on the plan. The minimum thickness of the columns thus varies from $\frac{1}{2}$ inch to

1$\frac{1}{8}$ inch; but the sectional area is increased by the addition of what would be equivalent to four fillets 3$\frac{3}{8}$ inches by $\frac{5}{32}$ inch, cast upon the opposite portions of the ring, and facing, when fixed *in situ*, north, south, east, and west. Four snugs are cast on the top and four on the bottom of the columns, between these fillets. Corresponding snugs are cast on to connecting pieces; the snugs alternating upon the same plane, with the projections on the connecting piece which serve to carry the girders. Bolt-holes are cast in the snugs of the columns, and in those of the connecting pieces. All the bedding surfaces are accurately faced in a lathe, and are then fitted together, so as to enable four bolts to pass through the holes in the snugs of the columns and connecting pieces, which exactly correspond to one another. Nuts then secure the bolts in their places. By these arrangements, connecting pieces may be placed on, and attached to columns; and columns may, in turn, be placed on and attached to connecting pieces; the rigidity of the whole being secured, by fixing girders, at right angles to one another, on to the projections cast on the connecting pieces. The detail of these projections will be described in connection with the roof-trusses, which they serve mainly to keep in their places.

The largest number of columns fixed in one week was three hundred and ten.

Various Heights of portions of the Building.

Facilities are thus obtained for varying the dimensions in height of portions of the building, and at the same time for preserving lateral stiffness. The main arms of the cross on plan, that is, the avenues 72 feet in width, or the nave and transept, together with their aisles, 24 feet wide, rise three stories in height; an avenue 48 feet wide, and an aisle 24 feet wide, on each side of the three-story building, rise two stories in height, and the whole of the remainder of the covered area is one story only in height. The gutter level of the three-story portion is 62 feet 2 inches from the floor; that of the two-story, 42 feet 2 inches; and that of the one-story, 22 feet 2 inches.

As a description of the varieties of structure, induced by these several altitudes, necessarily involves an outline of the whole skeleton of the building, it will be well to consider each separately. The horizontal planes, or strata of the building, from the ground-floor upwards to the roof, in the three-story work, will be found to consist, first, of base-plates, the upper bearing surface of which rises 3$\frac{3}{4}$ inches above the ground-floor; secondly, of columns 18 feet 5$\frac{1}{2}$ inches long, fixed on the base-plates; thirdly, of connecting pieces, 3 feet 4$\frac{3}{4}$ inches deep, to which are attached cast-iron girders, 24 feet long, serving to support a gallery floor, at the height of 23 feet from the ground floor; fourthly, of columns 16 feet 7$\frac{1}{2}$ inches long; fifthly, of connecting pieces 3 feet 4$\frac{3}{4}$ inches deep, to which are attached transversely in one direction, and longitudinally in two

directions, cast-iron girders 24 feet long, of similar form and scantling to the roof girders, in order to retain all the columns in their
places; sixthly, of columns 16 feet 7¼ inches long; and lastly, of
connecting pieces 3 feet 4¾ inches deep, to which are attached the
roof trusses and girders.

The corresponding horizontal strata of the two-story portion of
the building consist, first, of base-plates, the upper bearing surface of
which rises 3¾ inches above the ground floor; secondly, of columns
18 feet 5½ inches long, fixed on the base-plates; thirdly of connecting pieces, 3 feet 4¾ inches deep, to which are attached cast-
iron girders, 24 feet long, serving to support a gallery floor, at
the height of 23 feet from the ground-floor; fourthly, of columns
16 feet 7¼ inches long; and fifthly, of connecting pieces 3 feet
4¾ inches deep, to which are attached the roof trusses and girders.

The horizontal strata of the one-story portion consist, first, of
base-plates, the upper bearing surface of which rises 3¾ inches above
the ground-floor; secondly, of columns 18 feet 5½ inches long,
fixed on the base-plates; and lastly, of connecting pieces 3 feet
4¾ inches deep, to which are attached the roof trusses and girders.

THE GALLERIES (Figs. 6, 7, 8, & 9).

FIG. 6. :

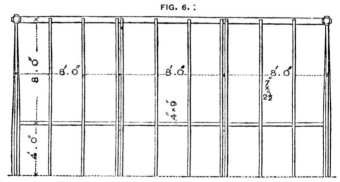

Plan of half of a 24-feet bay of the gallery floor.

FIG. 7.

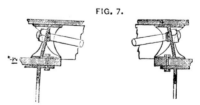

Details of elevation of truss of gallery floor.

From these dimensions it will be apparent, that at 23 feet
above the floor level, galleries are inserted, which form striking
features of both the two and the three story buildings. These
galleries, in two widths of 24 feet each, with frequent connecting
galleries, extend entirely round the upper portion of the building,

and are supported by cast-iron girders 23 feet long, similar in form to those which support the roof, but of somewhat heavier scantling. These single castings, 3 feet deep, are divided into three parallelograms of 3 feet by 8 feet, by vertical struts, connected at the top and the bottom by diagonal ties and struts. The sectional areas of their top and bottom flanges, in the centre of the length of the girder, equal respectively 5·31 inches, and 7·64 inches; those of the diagonal struts and ties average 3·50 inches. All these girders are proved, in the building, to a strain of 15 tons, and in exceptional cases, with extra scantlings, to 22 tons. Their breaking weight is calculated, and has been proved by experiment, to be not less than 30 tons. The binders, which serve to support the floor of these galleries, have been so arranged by under-trussing, by means of cast-iron shoes, rods, and struts, as to take their bearing upon four, instead of upon two girders; and thus any possible accumulated load, or vibration on a portion of the gallery, will be transferred to double the number of points of support that would have been available, had it been constructed in the ordinary manner. Joists of 7 feet 9 inches clear bearing, bridge these binders; and on them is laid a floor of boards 1¼ inch thick, with iron tongues, to prevent the passage of dust, &c. Ten double staircases, each 8 feet wide, enclosed by an iron railing, designed by **Mr. Owen Jones**, afford access to these galleries.*

Next to the internal supports of the building the external enclosures present themselves for consideration. It is obvious from the widths and heights given, that the north and south elevations, with the exception of the transept front, must consist of three stories, set back at various distances from each other.

---

* Several experiments were subsequently tried, to ascertain the action of these galleries under the strain of a moving load. A complete bay, 24 feet square, was constructed, and raised slightly from the ground. Its area was covered with labourers packed as closely together as possible. No action of walking, running, or jumping of three hundred men did any injury to it. Soldiers, of the corps of Royal Sappers and Miners, were then substituted for the contractors' men, and although the perfect regularity of their step, in marking time sharply, appeared a remarkably severe test, no damage resulted from their evolutions.

Subsequently a very ingenious apparatus was devised by Mr. Field, the late President of the Institution of Civil Engineers, for the purpose of testing the stability of the galleries *in situ*, and on being applied over the greater part of the building, not a single bolt, or girder gave way under its action. The apparatus consisted of eight square frames divided into a number of compartments, each just capable of containing a 68-pound shot, and allowing it to rotate. The surfaces of the balls, placed in each of these compartments, came in contact with the gallery floor, the frames themselves being attached to one another, and running upon the floor by means of castors fixed at the angles. The whole apparatus being drawn along by a number of men, two hundred and eighty-eight 68-pound shot, confined in a limited area, were thus set rolling over more than half the whole extent of the galleries, when, not the slightest mishap having occurred, the experiment was considered decisive, and a persistance in it was deemed unnecessary.

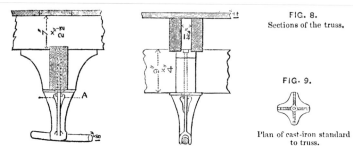

FIG. 8.
Sections of the truss.

FIG. 9.

Plan of cast-iron standard
to truss.

These three stories are, the first, or ground floor ; the second, or gallery floor ; and the third, or clerestory floor.

On the ground floor, the cast-iron columns which carry the transverse roof-girders of the one-story building, constitute vertical divisions, at 24 feet from centre to centre ; two wooden columns of precisely similar form, placed between the cast-iron ones, divide the 24-feet space into three bays of 8 feet each. The first horizontal line above the ground is a cill 9 inches by 3 inches, and 1½ inch above the floor level ; beneath this cill, an enclosure of boards forms a plinth, against which rests a slope of turf, at an average level of 2 feet above that of the adjacent ground line. A second cill, 9 inches by 4 inches, is placed at a clear height of 4 feet 3½ inches from the lower one, the space between forming a kind of dado, and being filled in with louvres, which will be described under the head of ventilation. At 10 feet 6 inches from the upper surface of the second cill is the springing line of a light cast-iron arch, which spans from column to column, and assists in supporting the " filling-in frames."

These frames, sufficiently deep to supply the idea of an entablature, and yet so light and open as not to appear to overload the slender proportions of the columns, are 3 feet high, and are backed with louvres similar to those in the plinth. The parallelogram, bounded by the sides of the columns, the top of the dado, and the underside of the " filling-in frame," is filled in, on an inner plane, behind the arch pieces, with ploughed, tongued, and beaded boarding, stiffened by stout ledges on the inside. Small castings, spanning the inner face of the column, screwed to these ledges, connect them together ; and are themselves fixed to the columns by bolts, passing completely through. On the top of the " filling-in frame " runs a boxing, with external mouldings, and behind the boxing is a small gutter. The whole is surmounted by a cast-iron ornamental cresting, 1 foot 6 inches high, attached to the boxing.

On the gallery-floor the upper parts of the columns supporting the two-story roof, constitute the main vertical lines. The space between is divided and filled up in a similar manner to that of the ground-floor, with two exceptions ; first, that there is no dado, and secondly, that for the vertical boarding of the ground floor a

The Facework (Figs. 10, 11, 12, & 13).

FIG. 10.

FIG. II.

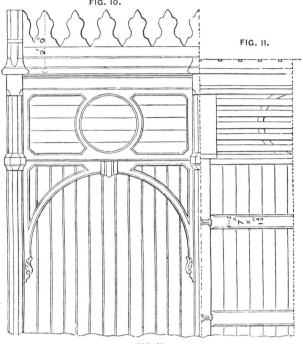

FIG. 12.
Section.

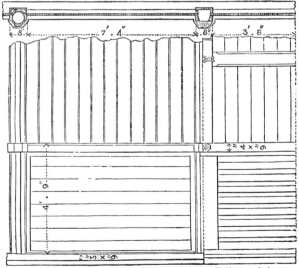

External elevation of an 8-feet bay of the facework of the lower tier.

Half internal elevation of the same.

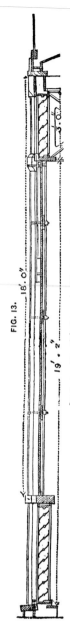

FIG. 13.

18' 0"

19' 2"

Vertical section of the facework of the lower tier.

glazed sash is substituted. The frame of the sash is fixed to the columns by castings, similar to those which secure the ledges.

THE SASHES.

As these sashes form an important portion of the building, no fewer than 1,500 of them being required, a short description of them may be given. The sash-frames are $2\frac{1}{2}$ inches thick, with seven bars in their width; the sash-bars are $2\frac{3}{8}$ths inches deep, double-grooved for the glass; three bolts, $\frac{3}{8}$ths inch diameter, pass completely through the bars and frames, at the points where they are attached to the columns, and thus a chain tie is kept up all round the building, in order to prevent the displacement of the sashes, either bodily, or in portions, by the pressure of the wind. To further guard against the same action, timber bridges, $3\frac{1}{2}$ inches by $1\frac{1}{2}$ inch, in the centre, are fixed across the middle of the length of the sash; and at the internal angles, where the wind will exert its greatest force, iron rods, $\frac{1}{2}$-inch diameter, are fastened from column to column, pressing against the wooden bridge, and converting it into a continuous strut, bearing up against any force applied to the exterior of the sash. In order to glaze the sashes, the glass is slipped down between the bars, and provision is made for the repairs by causing one groove to be cut deeper than the other, so that the glass may be slipped in from either side, and puttied into its exact place. Similar provision is made for mending the roof-glass.

On the third, or clerestory floor, the external main vertical divisions are formed by the upper portion of the three-story columns, and the filling-in between them corresponds exactly with that of the gallery floor.

The east and west elevations are simply vertical sections through the main building, filled in with facework similar to, and ranging with that of the three stories of the north and south elevations.

The elevations of the transept ends correspond with those of the east and west, with the exception of the addition of a semicircular head filled with concentric and radiating tracery.

The Exits.

In the circuit of the whole building there are fifteen exits, symmetrically disposed ; wherever they occur, a pair of doors, 8 feet in width, occupy the centre of the space, and the two bays of 8 feet each, on either side of the doors, are glazed instead of being boarded.

The Roof-Girders and Trusses
(Figs. 14, 15, 16, 17, 18, 19, & 20).

The net-work of girders and trusses immediately supporting the roof next demands attention. The main gutters, upon which the " Paxton gutters" are fixed, run transversely, spanning the various avenues leading from end to end of the building, except where it is crossed by the transept.

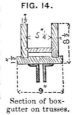

FIG. 14.

Section of box-gutter on trusses.

These avenues are all either 24 feet, 48 feet, or 72 feet wide ; of these avenues there are six 24 feet wide, five 48 feet wide, and one (the central) 72 feet wide. To span these widths at least three kinds of trusses are necessary. All the trusses, with the exception of four, are 3 feet deep, and have perpendicular struts of cast-iron, fixed at distances of 8 feet from centre to centre, connecting the top and bottom bars. The whole parallelogram, formed by the length and width of the trusses, is thus divided into smaller parallelograms of 8 feet by 3 feet, the four angles of which are diagonally connected by various materials, but of uniform width on the face, and thus regularity of form is obtained. The trusses of 72 feet and 48 feet span consist of cast-iron standards and vertical struts, an upper portion formed of two pieces of angle iron, set 1 inch apart, a bottom portion of two bars, increasing in sectional area as they approach the centre of the bearing, and tie-bars, which, passing diagonally between the two pieces of angle iron in the upper portion and the two bars in the lower, are riveted to them, and form a complete suspension truss. The remaining diagonals in the opposite direction, which would, if in action, be under compression, are constructed of wood, and are only inserted for appearance, it being thought better to resist the diagonal strains by tension bars alone, rather than partly by diagonal suspension bars, and partly by diagonal struts.

The girders of 24 feet long are single castings, corresponding in form to those which support the galleries, the arrangement and scantlings of the various parts of which have been elaborately studied and balanced. Every one of these trusses has been proved, in the building, with a strain of nine tons. The largest number of girders cast in any one week was three hundred and sixteen.

THE EXPERIMENTS TRIED ON THE ROOF-TRUSSES AND GIRDERS.

Previous to deciding upon the scantling of the trusses to be used in the building, Mr. Charles Heard Wild and the Contractors entered into an elaborate series of calculations, as to the adjustment

FIG. 16.

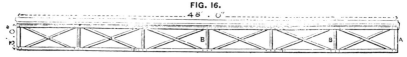

Elevation of ordinary 48-feet truss.

FIG. 17.   **FIG. 18.**

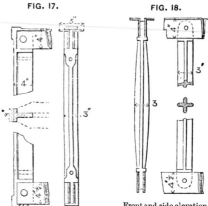

Front and side elevations of end standards to 72-feet and 48-feet trusses.

Front and side elevation of vertical struts, or intermediate standards to 72-feet and 48-feet trusses.

FIG. 19.

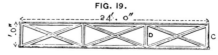

Elevation of 24-feet cast-iron girder.

FIG. 20.

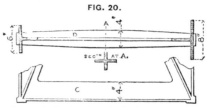

Front and side elevations of ends of cast-iron girder.

and proportions of the various parts. These calculations were submitted to the President of the Institution of Civil Engineers, and their correctness was so completely justified, by the results of some experiments on the trusses and girders, made in his presence and in that of the Author, that a summary must be interesting.

A 72-feet truss, cambered 4⅛ inches, and weighing complete about 35 cwt.,

The maximum sectional area of the two top
angle-irons being . . . . . 5·71 inches.
The maximum sectional area of the two bottom
bars being . . . . 6·75 ,,
The maximum sectional area of the principal
diagonal tie being . . . . . 3·38 ,,

when loaded with a weight of—

4 tons, deflected 1¼ inches.
6 ,, 2½ ,,
8 ,, 3⅜ ,,
10 ,, 4⅛ ,,
12 ,, 5 ,,
14 ,, 5⅝ ,,
16 ,, 6¼ ,,

A 48-feet truss, cambered 4 inches, and weighing complete about 13 cwt.,

The maximum sectional area of the two top
angle-irons being . . . . . 3·0 inches.
The maximum sectional area of the two bottom
bars being . . . . . . 3·38 ,,
The maximum sectional area of the principal
diagonal tie being . . . . 2·75 ,,

when loaded with a weight of—

2 tons 10 cwt. deflected ½ inch.
5 0 ,, 1½ ,,
7 10 ,, 2⅛ inches.
8 15 ,, 2⅜ ,,
10 0 ,, 3 ,,

A 24-feet girder, weighing complete 11 cwt. 3 qrs., exactly similar in construction to the 24-feet roof-girders, but 2 cwt. 1 qr. heavier, bore 30 tons, but broke down with 30½ tons, flying so completely to pieces that doubts existed as to the point at which fracture commenced.

THE EXTRA-STRONG TRUSSES (Figs. 21, 22, 23, 24, 25, 26, 27, & 28).

The four 72-feet trusses which have been alluded to, as differing

63

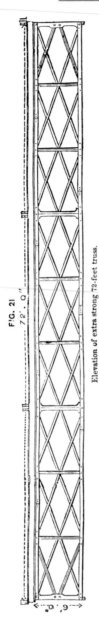

FIG. 21

72' 0"

Elevation of extra strong 72-feet truss.

from the others in depth, perform such important functions, and are consequently so different in form, as to warrant a separate notice. They support the lead flat, covering two bays (each 24 feet by 72 feet) of the main avenue, where it abuts upon the eastern and western sides of the transept, and a pair of them carry, in addition, the two semi-circular ribs, which, at 24 feet from centre to centre, form the main beams on which the semi-cylindrical roofing rests, over the square where the transept roof crosses the main longitudinal avenue.

These trusses are made twice the depth of all the others, and the scantlings are considerably increased. In this extra depth the vertical struts remaining at 8 feet from centre to centre, and the tension bars continuing the same in number, and being set at the same angle as those in the ordinary trusses of 72-feet span, the lines arrange themselves into a lattice-form two diamonds in depth, the intersecting diagonal bars passing through slots cast for them in the middle of the cast-iron struts. Although the form would appear to be that of a compound truss, the strength of all the parts is calculated so as to render these trusses suspension trusses only. In order to relieve the ordinary columns of much of the weight which is supported by these trusses, additional columns are placed beneath their two ends, secured, at frequent intervals, to the ordinary columns by wrought-iron clips.

THE SEMICIRCULAR RIBS (Figs. 29, 30, & 31).

In order to form an idea of the nature of the work the extra-strong trusses have to perform, the structure of the semicircular ribs must be defined. They are made in three thicknesses of timber, each 9 feet 6 inches long, cut into segments of a circle 74 feet extreme diameter, the central thickness being 4 inches by 13½ inches, and the outer flitches, breaking joint with the centre, being 2 inches by 13½ inches. The flitches are nailed to the centre thickness, and bolts ⅝ths of an inch in diameter, and about 4 feet apart, traverse and bind together the three thicknesses; on the extrados of the wooden arch thus formed, two planks, serving as the gutter-board, each 11 inches by 1 inch, and a bar of iron 2 inches by ⅜ths of an inch,

FIG. 22.

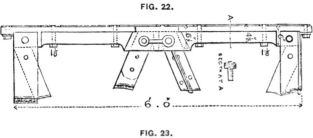

FIG. 23.

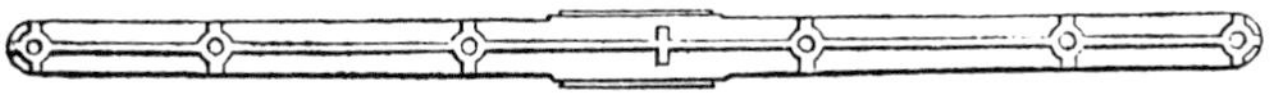

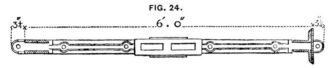

FIG. 24.

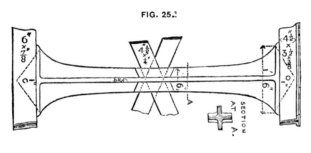

Side, front, and back elevations of the end standard to extra strong 72-feet truss.

FIG. 25.

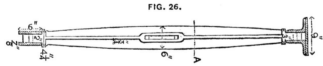

FIG. 26.

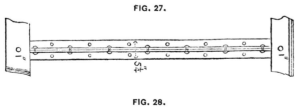

Front and side elevations, with plan of the cast-iron vertical struts, or intermediate standards, to extra strong 72-feet truss.'

FIG. 27.

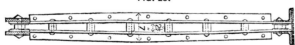

FIG. 28.

Elevations of wrought-iron vertical struts, or intermediate standards to extra strong 72-feet truss.

FIG. 29.

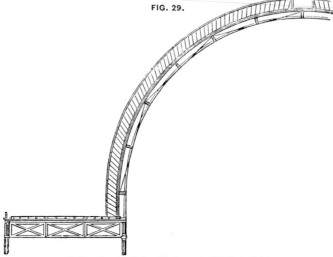

Half section of arched roof to transept, with the lead flat.

FIG. 30.

IRON

8"

1'. 6"

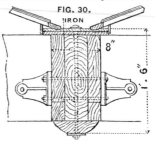

Section of arched rib, showing the attachment of the purlins, &c.

FIG. 31.

TIE   BAR

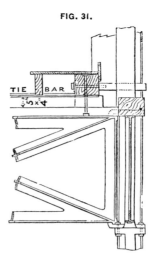

Detail of the foot of arched rib on column, and the adjoining parts.

are bent to the curve; and on the intrados a piece of timber, 7 inches by 2 inches, moulded to correspónd with the form of the columns, and a bar of iron 3¼ inches by ⅜ths of an inch, are also bent to the curve; bolts passed through the depth of the rib, at intervals of 2 feet from centre to centre, unite these additions to each other and to the main rib, which, thus increased in scantling, measures when complete 8 inches by 1 foot 6 inches. The ends are stepped down upon a plate 9 inches by 6 inches, bearing on the top of the two trusses, on each side of the transept.

The Transept Roofing (Fig. 32).

In order to steady the ribs, purlins 4½ inches by 9 inches to 13 inches, and 9 feet 2 inches apart, are introduced between them; and on the top, from end to end, a narrow path of lead flat runs the whole length of the transept, for the purpose of affording convenient access for any repairs which may be necessary. Diagonal rods, intersecting each other in planes parallel to a tangent to the curve, also connect the ribs, and serve to bind every portion together; while, at the same time, their lines form reticulations over the surface of the vault, producing an agreeable effect in perspective.

FIG. 32.

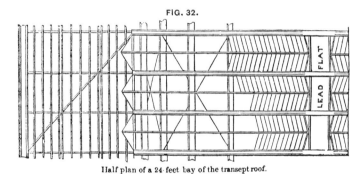

Half plan of a 24-feet bay of the transept roof.

The Connexions of the Roof Trusses, &c.

Having indicated the general construction of the roof trusses, there remain to be noticed the arrangements for fixing and for steadying them longitudinally. In the 72 feet and 48 feet trusses, respectively, the standards forming their ends are cast with a projection on their top and bottom faces, and with a bolt-hole through the upper portion of their length; a hollow " connecting piece," corresponding in the form of its section to that of the columns, and 4¾ inches longer than the height of the truss, pierced through with a bolt-hole to agree with that of the truss standard, has cast upon its upper and lower ends a projection corresponding with those cast on the top and bottom faces of the truss standards. The truss being hoisted above its ultimate position, is lowered down until it can be slipped between the projections on the connecting piece, when the projections on the bottom faces of its two standards take a bearing, and clutch on to those cast on the lower ends of the connecting pieces. A screw bolt, 1 inch in diameter, passed through the bolt-hole of the standard, and completely through the connecting piece, secures the upper part of the truss from lateral motion, and together with the stiffening of the "Paxton-gutters," counteracts any tendency to buckle. The means provided for fixing the cast-iron roof girders of 24-feet span, into the connecting pieces, are precisely similar to those above described, but the mode of securing them from lateral movement is somewhat different. Instead of the bolt-fastening of the trusses of 72 feet and 48 feet spans, a groove is sunk in the middle of the top and bottom projections of the connecting piece, and a corresponding tenon is cast on the bottom of the standard of the 24-feet girder. The bottom of the truss is thus held in its place, by the fitting of its tenon into the lower groove of the connecting piece, while the upper projection of the truss, having a groove cut in it, to correspond with that on the under side of the upper projection of the connecting piece, is secured by the insertion of a wrought-iron key, which acts as a dowell, and prevents the surfaces from sliding laterally upon one another.

The Provisions for Stiffening the Building.

In order to maintain the stiffness and steadiness of the building longitudinally, girders 24 feet long are inserted between the connecting pieces, in the direction from east to west, and are attached to them in a similar manner to the other girders. Of these there are eighteen rows on the various levels of the building.

The influence of the "Paxton-gutters," and of the facework giving additional stiffening to the whole, adds considerably to the good results obtained by the insertion of these longitudinal girders.

In thus providing for the rigidity of the connexions of the various portions of the building, care has been taken, by the substitution, in certain places, of oak for iron keys, to provide for the play of the metal, incident to any sudden variation of temperature.

In the transverse direction, it was determined, that the whole of the keys should be of iron, for two reasons, first, because the length, divided into two portions by the nave, was not sufficiently great to render the probable amount of expansion, or contraction, of any practical importance, and secondly, because it was upon the side of the building that the currents of wind would impinge with the greatest force.

In the longitudinal direction, iron keys are inserted for six bays from the extreme east and west ends, and for six bays east and west of the transept, the intervening girders being keyed up with oak keys: and thus rigidity was maintained in those parts exposed to strain, whilst elasticity was provided in the portions of the building least subject to strain from without.

FIG. 33.

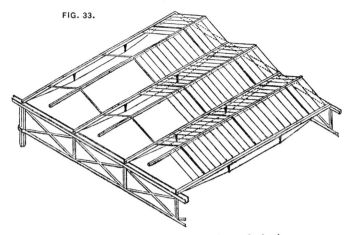

Isometrical view of one 24-feet bay of roofing, partly glazed.

FIG. 34.   FIG. 35.

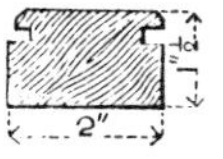

FIG. 36.

Sections of extra strong and ordinary sash-bars.   Section of the ridge.

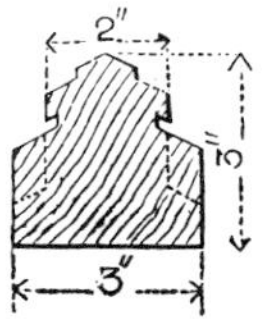

FIG. 37.

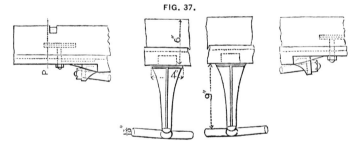

Elevation of portions of a " Paxton-gutter. '

FIG. 38.

FIG. 39.

Section of " Paxton-gutter " through the centre.   Section of " Paxton-gutter " at the end.

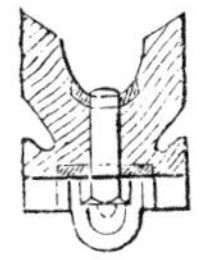

Twenty-two sets of horizontal, and two hundred and twenty sets of vertical diagonal bracing, consisting of wrought-iron rods secured by wrought-iron links to the columns and connecting pieces, and meeting in adjustment plates, are inserted as a measure of extra precaution, tying the main masses of the structure together.

THE "PAXTON" ROOFING (Figs. 33, 34, 35, 36, 37, 38, & 39).

The roof of the building is perhaps the most novel and interesting portion of the whole structure, and exhibits in a remarkable manner the ingenuity of Mr. Paxton's design. In order to convey the rain water to the hollow columns, transverse gutters 24 feet apart extend the entire width of the building. These transverse gutters are capacious wooden boxes, strongly framed and attached to the upper flange of the main trusses, which cross the building, false bottoms being, in some cases, inserted to assist the flow of the water. At intervals of 8 feet from centre to centre, with their ends resting on the box-gutters, are fixed those ingenious contrivances known as "Paxton-gutters" for conveying away simultaneously the rain-water falling on the roof, and the condensed vapour formed inside the building, and of them a length of 24 miles is required. Each one of these consists of a piece of the best crown timber, 5 inches by 6 inches and 24 feet long. The form is given by passing it through an ingenious machine, worked by Mr. Birch of the Phœnix Saw Mills, Camden Town. At one operation, this machine scoops from the middle of the upper surface of the timber, and throughout its whole length, a nearly semicircular groove about $1\frac{3}{8}$ inch radius, and at the same time cuts two smaller grooves downwards at an oblique angle to its sides; the object of the larger groove being to receive and convey to the box-gutters the roof-water, and that of the smaller grooves to receive the moisture, which, condensing upon the inside of the roof, would trickle down, adhering by capillary attraction, and finally deposit itself in the smaller grooves, by which it would be conducted to the box-gutters. On leaving the machine, the "Paxton-gutter" is too slight for a bearing of 24 feet, and is straight, so that the water in it would not have any fall; both these defects are remedied by trussing it into a curve, by means of a wrought-iron bolt, $\frac{13}{16}$ inch diameter, threaded at both ends, and bent so as to pass under and press up, to the underside of the wood, two cast-iron struts 9 inches long; the ends of the bolt being passed through holes in the two cast-iron shoes, fixed at the ends of the gutters, and the nuts on the ends of the bolts being screwed up, the bolt is tightened, and a camber of $2\frac{1}{2}$ inches is given to the gutter, so that the whole becomes a truss, requiring a weight of $1\frac{1}{2}$ tons to break it. A semicircular cut is then given through the depth of the gutter at both ends, so that when two are placed end to end, the water will flow down into the box-gutter through a circular cavity; two oblique cuts being also made, to connect the condensed water with this cavity, and twenty-seven notches are marked from a template, and worked on each side of the upper edge of the " Paxton-gutters," whose ends are then attached to a flanged plate bolted on to the edges of the box-gutters. Of the notches on each side of the " Paxton-gutter," three are larger than the others; and on them bars of wood 2 inches by 1½ inches, grooved for glass on both sides, are notched down; these bars form principal rafters, and being set at a pitch of two and a-half to one, are fixed to a ridge 3 inches by 3 inches grooved for glass on both sides; the long edge of a sheet of glass 4 feet 1 inch by 10 inches is then inserted into the groove of the principal rafter, and a sash bar 1 inch by 1½ inch, also double grooved, is then put on to the other long edge of the glass; the sash-bar is then brought down, and secured to the ridge, and to the edge of the gutter; the lower edge of the glass, bedding on putty about ¾ inch wide, a little force applied at the lower end brings the upper edge of the glass home into the groove in the ridge. The glass being then pressed down, the putty is made good in the grooves externally, and thus simply is this system of roofing put together. Its lightness is one of its remarkable qualities, since the entire weight of one superficial foot averages only 3¼ lbs.

The largest quantity of " Paxton-gutters," each 24 feet in length, planed and grooved by one machine in one week, was four hundred and forty-two.

The " Paxton " Roofing over the Transept.

The area of 29,376 feet, forming the transept, is covered with roofing, similar in many particulars to that adopted by Mr. Paxton in the great conservatory at Chatsworth. The width which is spanned by the semicircular ribs, at intervals of 24 feet from centre to centre, is 72 feet. Purlins 9 feet 2 inches apart. connect the semicircular ribs, and between them, at distances of 8 feet from centre to centre, are framed smaller ribs, the backs of which, as well as those of the main ribs, form water-courses, and convey the rain on to the lead flat, 24 feet in width, on each side of the base of the semicircular ribs of the roof. These latter, which stand at 8 feet apart, are then connected by ridge and furrow roofing, the construction of which is nearly identical with that previously described as employed in the smaller roofs. Beneath the lead flat is constructed a horizontal truss consisting of bars, calculated to transfer the strain to the points most securely tied and abutted, and thus to counteract any tendency of the ribs to spread, or to shift under the action of wind.

In connexion with the design for the building, there are still three important items to be considered:—the ventilation,—the mode to be adopted of tempering the intensity of the sun's rays,—and the supply of water immediately available for the extinction of fire.

THE VENTILATION (Figs. 40 & 41)

Is obtained by means of louvres set in boxings, inserted behind
the "filling in" frames of each of the three stories of the building—
and in the dado, between the lower and upper cills on the ground
floor. At the springing of the transept roof, a line of louvres is inserted on both sides, 3 feet 8 inches high, running the whole length
of the transept; and at the very summit of the curved roof, ventilation is obtained in the gables of the roofing, where it is interrupted
by the narrow path of upper lead flat. The total quantity of ventilating area in the louvres equals about 45,000 feet, in addition to
which, large volumes of air will necessarily be introduced at the
numerous doorways. The louvre frames on the ground floor consist
of boxes, in which eight louvre blades of galvanized iron 6½ inches
wide, are fixed on pivots at 6 inches from centre to centre, and so
curved as to offer the minimum interruption to the ingress, or egress
of air when open, compatible with keeping them weather tight.

FIG. 40. FIG. 41.

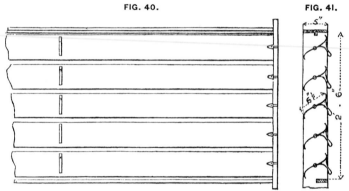

Part elevation and section of one of the louvre frames.

Small iron brackets, attached to the centre of each blade, are furnished with eyes, through which are inserted pins, passing also
through holes bored at equal distances from one another, in a species
of rack: by drawing these racks up and down, the opening and
closing of the ventilators is effected. A number of these racks will,
of course, be attached to levers, and set in motion by rods and cranks;
Mr. Fox has designed an ingenious method of producing the simul-
taneous action of a considerable number, and at the same time of
securing the uniform position of the louvre blades at any desired
angle.

Should it ever be found necessary to reduce, by artificial means,
the internal temperature of the building below that of the exterior,
Mr. Paxton has proposed a system of cooling, applicable to these
ventilators, somewhat on the principle of the Indian "tatties."

THE CANVAS COVERING.

In order to diminish the intensity of the light and heat of the sun's rays, it is proposed to cover the whole of the roof and of the south side of the building with canvas, which will be attached to the sashes on the side, and span from ridge to ridge on the roof, the seam being arranged to occur directly over the gutters.

THE WATER SUPPLY.

The water is supplied by the Chelsea Water-works Company, through a main pipe 9 inches in diameter, branching into three pipes 6 inches in diameter, at the centre of the building, on the south side, at about 35 feet from the entrance.

These latter pipes go entirely round the building, and across the centre; twenty cocks of 3 inches diameter are attached to these pipes externally; eight pipes, 4 inches diameter, branch from the pipe of 6 inches diameter, at eight points on each side of the building, and run inwards to a distance equal to one-fourth the width of the building. On the ends of these pipes fire-cocks, with water-ways 3 inches diameter, are fixed in such situations, that circles drawn from them as centres, with a radius of 120 feet, would intersect one another, and pass considerably without the limits of the building. From the pipes, 6 inches in diameter, crossing the building, it is proposed to draw the principal supply for the fountains, which will probably be distributed along the central nave and line of the transept. An ample supply of water, connected with efficient drainage, will be provided for the steam-boilers, which will be fixed in a detached building, at the north-west angle, and for the refreshment-rooms, &c., which will be placed in immediate proximity to the trees beneath the transept.

It can scarcely be expected, that the limits of the present paper should comprise all that is worthy of remark in a building, the vast size of which involves considerable complexity of parts; it is hoped, therefore, that indulgence will be exercised, if, in this hasty description of the design of the building, much that is worthy of comment should have been lightly passed over, or altogether omitted.

THE EXECUTION OF THE WORKS.

In proceeding to the third part of the subject, the power and dexterity with which the design has been realized, or, in other words, the actual construction of the building, the feature that first claims attention is the celerity with which the various operations have proceeded. When it is remembered that Messrs. Fox, Henderson, and Co.'s tender was only verbally accepted on the 26th of July, 1850, that possession of the site was only given on the 30th of the same month, that the first column was fixed on September 26th, exactly two months after the acceptance of the tender, and that at the present moment but little of this vast building remains to be finished, it must be felt, that England possesses mechanical appliances and physical energies, far exceeding those which gave form and being to the most celebrated monuments of antiquity.

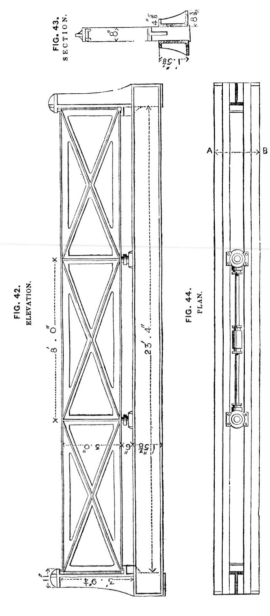

FIG. 42.
ELEVATION.

FIG. 43.
SECTION.

FIG. 44.
PLAN.

Plan, elevation, and section of the frame in which the cast-iron girders were fixed for proving by the hydraulic press.

The total number of men employed in each week varied from thirty, in the week ending August the 3rd, to two thousand two hundred and sixty in the week ending December the 6th.

Modifications of the Original Design.

Previous to the acceptance of the tender, various modifications of the design were made, and from Mr. Barry's refined perception of form and proportion, valuable structural improvements were derived. These modifications involved the preparation of an entirely new set of general drawings, while the rapid flight of time demanded that the details should be at once got out, in order that the work might be commenced without delay. The energy and ability displayed by Messrs. Fox, Henderson, and Co., in the preparation of these details, and in the completion of the necessary arrangements for carrying on the work, were very remarkable. Mr. Charles Heard Wild went into minute calculations with Mr. Fox, and under the supervision of Mr. Cubitt, President of the Institution of Civil Engineers, fixed the scantlings of the various parts of the building. Mr. Wild's calculations were based upon an analysis of the amount of weight to be borne by every column throughout the building, and the area of roofing depending for support upon each truss, making liberal allowances for the additional weight of snow. At an early stage in the proceedings, the Author, with Mr. Wild, and Mr. Owen Jones, had been selected by the Building Committee to assist them in their labours, and to superintend the erection of the building. Under the supervision of Mr. Cubitt, the Chairman of that Committee, they have been constantly employed up to the present time. Mr. Owen Jones went carefully over every form in the building susceptible of harmonious combination, and has zealously occupied himself with every detail of arrangement likely to benefit by the exercise of his taste and knowledge. While the general drawings were quite incomplete, various details were so far settled, that the patterns for much of the ironwork could be made, and the trusses and girders be experimented upon. The celerity with which the girders, columns, &c., have been executed and forwarded is remarkable. In one week as many as three hundred and eight girders were delivered at the building.

The Proving of the Girders (Figs. 42, 43, & 44).

To prove the girders, a very ingenious apparatus, connected with an hydraulic press and register, was contrived by Mr. Wild, by means of which the girders are perfectly gauged, and in which they are retained in an inverted position. Pressure is then applied upwards from two pistons, at the points in the upper table of the girders upon which, in the roof-girders, the "Paxton-gutters" will bear, and in the gallery-girders, the binders, and thus the proof is applied in a similar manner to that in which the girders will be eventually loaded. One of Mr. Henderson's patent cranes, and a weighing-machine, have been so conveniently arranged, in connexion with this apparatus, that a girder has been lifted from the waggon, deposited for weighing, weighed, lifted up again, conveyed to the proving machine, slipped into its place, and secured,—proved, released, taken up again, deposited on the ground, and stacked, in less than four minutes.

The whole of the light iron-work, with the exception of some of the gallery railing, has been cast by Messrs. Fox, Henderson, and Co., at their works, near Birmingham, and the principal castings, consisting of the columns, girders, &c., were supplied all ready turned and fitted from the works of Messrs. Cochrane and Co., of Woodside, and Mr. Jobson, of Holly-hall, both near Dudley.

The wrought iron has been principally supplied by Messrs. Fothergill and Co. ; the glass by Messrs. Chance, Brotherton, and Co., of Oldbury ; the timber by Messrs. Dowson and Co. ; and the machine cutting of the " Paxton-gutters" has been entirely executed at Messrs. Fox, Henderson, and Co.'s mills at Chelsea.

The Setting Out and Progress of the Work.

The perfection with which the lines of the building were set out by Mr. Brownger will be easily tested in the building, by remarking the precision with which the columns range and cover one another diagonally as well as rectangularly. To this correctness, and to the careful setting of the base-plates (of which one thousand and seventy-four were required), may be attributed, in a great measure, the

The Glazing Machines.
FIG. 45.

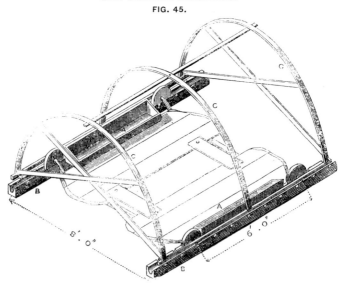

Travelling stage for glazing the roofs.
A. Box for glass.   B. Trussed girder.   C. Frame to support the covering used in wet weather.

uniformity of the lines exhibited by the columns from whatever points they are viewed.

One of the most striking peculiarities of this building is the skill with which it has been arranged, so as to form the scaffolding for its own construction. The columns were raised by a fall descending from shear-legs, steadied by guy-ropes: so soon as two columns were fixed, two falls, descending from two pairs of shear-legs, raised a girder with the connecting pieces attached; then, when four columns, four connecting pieces, and four girders had been raised, the whole became self-supporting, and the tackle and apparatus, used to erect it, could be moved off to do its work in constructing a similar bay elsewhere. The raising of much of the upper tiers was effected by suspending falls from poles lashed to columns. The trusses of 48 feet and 72 feet spans were raised by means of derricks, steadied by guy-ropes, the derricks being moved on from spot to spot in a perpendicular position. The way in which the men managed to retain the derricks in a perpendicular position, by alternately tightening, slackening, and shifting the guys, was really admirable. By this means as many as seven of the great trusses of the nave have been raised in one day: the derricks (for one was at work at each end of the building) thus travelling 168 feet.

The active superintendence and direction of the whole of the labour devolved upon Mr. John Cochrane, Mr. Earee acted as clerk of the works to the Commissioners, and Mr. Harwood as their surveyor.

During many weeks upwards of two thousand men were constantly employed upon the ground; four steam-engines assisting in the various operations, and affording motive power to a variety of machinery for facilitating production. Ingenious arrangements of circular saws, and revolving gouges, &c., cut and bored different portions of sash-bars, ridges, and " Paxton-gutters." Huge shears, and punching and drilling machines combined to prepare the truss-bars for being riveted, and portable forges supplied the means of heating the rivets for the three hundred and seventy-two wrought-iron trusses, of which as many as sixteen have been riveted up in one day.

It was of great importance that arrangements should be made for carrying on the glazing of the roofs independently of weather. To effect this purpose a travelling stage was devised by Mr. Fox, which superseded the necessity of any scaffolding for glazing, and by means of seventy-six of these machines nearly the whole of the work has been executed. The stage is about 8 feet square, and it rests, on four small wheels, which travel in the " Paxton-gutters." It thus embraces one bay of a span of 8 feet of·the roof, with one ridge and two sloping sides; each bay in width requiring a separate stage. The stage, occupied by two workmen, is covered by an awning of canvas, stretched over hoops to protect them in bad weather, and is provided with two boxes, to contain a store of glass.

The sash-bars and other materials are piled upon the stage itself, the centre of the platform being left open, for the convenience of hoisting up materials.

Whilst working, the men sit at one end of the platform (the ridge having been previously placed in position by means of the extra-strong sash-bars), and fix the glass in front of them, pushing the stage backwards as they complete each pane. On coming to the strong sash-bars previously fixed, they temporarily remove them, to allow the stage to pass: in this manner each stage travels uninterruptedly from the transept to the east and west ends of the building.

The average amount of glazing hitherto done by one man per day has been fifty-eight squares, or about 200 superficial feet, and the largest amount done by any one man, in a working day, has been one hundred and eight squares, or about 370 superficial feet. The largest amount of work done in one week was by eighty men, whose time amounted to 309 days, and who put in eighteen thousand three hundred and ninety-two squares, containing 62,584 superficial feet.

The machine for glazing the transept roof was also designed by Mr. Fox. It consists of a kind of long wooden box, with wheels running against the semicircular ridge. In each of these boxes eight glaziers can stand at their work. The machine is lowered and raised by means of ropes attached to the purlins at the summit of the roof.

FIG. 46.

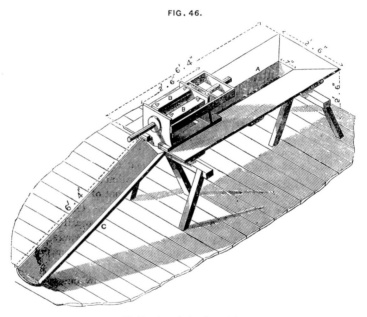

Machine for painting the sash-bars.

A. Trough for holding paint.   B. The brushes.   C. Spout for waste paint.

A platform, with wheels also travelling upon the ridges, has been contrived for the performance of any repairs that may be necessary, after the flat roofing is completed.

The Painting Machine (Fig. 46).

An ingenious machine has been adopted for painting the sash-bars. A trough being filled with liquid colour, the sash-bars are dipped into it, and when taken out, are passed through a series of brushes set at such angles to each other as to entirely remove the superfluous paint, and to leave the sash-bar as neatly finished as it could have been by hand.

Mode of Raising the Transept Ribs (Figs. 47, 48, & 49).

The operation about which most anxiety had been felt was the hoisting of the arched ribs of the transept. These ribs were constructed horizontally on the ground, and when completed with all their bolts, two of them were reared on end, and maintained in a vertical position, at a distance of 24 feet from each other, by guy-ropes. As the ribs possessed little lateral stiffness, they were framed together with the purlins, intermediate small ribs, and diagonal tie-rods, forming a complete bay of the roof, 24 feet long. Two complete sets of temporary ties were also introduced, to provide for the strains incident to the variations in position of the ribs, during the

FIG. 47.

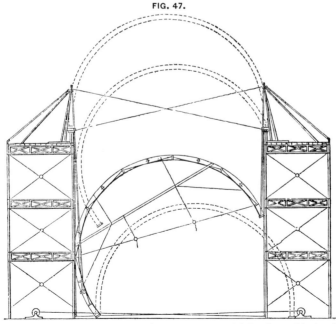

Section through the transept, showing the arrangements for hoisting the semicircular ribs. The dotted lines indicate the various positions of the ribs during the hoisting.

FIG. 48.

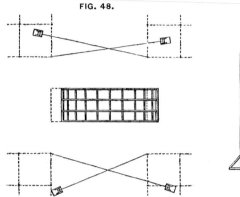

FIG. 49.

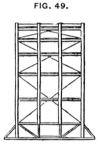

Plan of centre of transept, showing the position of the crabs for hoisting the ribs, &c.

End view of a pair of ribs, framed together, previous to being hoisted,

hoisting : the feet of the ribs were bolted on to a stout cill, and the lower purlins were strutted up from it. The whole framework was then moved on rollers to the centre of the square formed by the intersection of the transept, and the main avenue, whence it was hoisted ; all the ribs were landed over this square, and were afterwards moved on a tramway to their permanent positions. This tramway, formed of half balks, was constructed over the columns on each side of the transept, at a height of about 4 feet above the lead flat.

The hoisting tackle consisted of four crabs, each one being placed on the side of the transept, opposite to the part of the ribs to be lifted by it, so that the men at the crabs might watch the effect of their exertions with greater convenience. The hoisting-shears were placed on the lead flat, immediately over the deep trusses of 72 feet span ; each set consisted of three stout scaffold-poles, lashed together at the top, bearing on planks laid across the flat, and secured by the necessary guy-ropes. The hoisting rope passed from each of the crabs, across the transept to a leading block attached to the foot of the column in the opposite angle of the square ; it then passed up to a treble block attached to the shears, and from thence down to a double block, secured by chains, to the bottom part of the ribs. The extreme width of the frame-work to be hoisted was 74 feet, and the clear width apart of the trusses, above which it had to be hoisted, was only 71 feet 4 inches ; it was, therefore, necessary to raise one side to a height of 35 feet, before lifting the other, so as to diminish the horizontal width. The diameter of the semicircle being maintained at this angle, the whole was then hoisted, until the highest end could clear the tramway. The foot of the ribs was then passed over the tram-way, high enough to allow the other side of the ribs to clear the opposite truss, after which the whole was hoisted to the full height, and rested on rollers of hard wood, placed between the cills attached to the framework and the tramway, by means of which it was moved to its permanent position. There it was again raised by another set of shears, while the cill and tramway were removed, and the ribs were then lowered into the sockets prepared for them, which, in fact, formed a continuation of the columns above the level of the lead flat.

Each successive pair of ribs was fixed at a distance of 24 feet, or one bay from the preceding one, and the purlins, &c., were placed in this space by means of jointed ladders, which were adjusted to the form of the roof, and thus all scaffolding was avoided.

The first pair of ribs was hoisted the 4th of December, 1850, and the eighth pair on the 12th of the same month. It took about one hour to raise each pair, from the ground to the level of the lead flat, and the whole was completed without the occurrence of any accident.

About sixty men were employed in the hoisting, there being eleven men to each crab, and the remainder engaged on the lead flats.

CONCLUSION.

In bringing to a close this somewhat lengthy description, the Author cannot but express his sense of inability to cope with the vastness of the subject, and the importance of its scientific details.

He cannot, however, better conclude, than by reminding the members that the weight of responsibility, the arduous duty of supervision, the honour of acting as the master mind, to weigh the requisites, to determine the design, and to govern the construction of this great apparatus, have been reserved for Mr. Cubitt, President of the Institution of Civil Engineers.

Barentin Viaduct, Paris–Rouen–Le Havre Railway; engineer: Joseph Locke; contractor: Thomas Brassey, 1846 (from The Illustrated London News, 27 March 1847, × 74%). The railway was an early example of the export of British civil engineering expertise. The construction of the viaduct was marred by failure during construction. Thomas Brassey accepted full responsibility and it was rebuilt within six months. The viaduct comprises 27 arches of 50 feet span, at a height of 110 feet. It was renamed the Joseph Locke Viaduct in 1950

Presidential address

J. LOCKE, MP

Reprinted from Min. Proc. Instn Civ. Engrs, 1858, vol. 17, 128-152

In the 150 years of the Institution's proceedings, there have been a great many presidential addresses of note and significance. The choice of Joseph Locke's rests largely on his key place as one of the 'triumvirate of the engineering world' as the London *Times* once described him. Since the other two were Isambard Kingdom Brunel and Robert Stephenson, Locke's place in the pantheon of engineers can be seen to be of the highest. For all that, Locke has always been less well known than his great contemporaries, even though his close relationship with the contractor Thomas Brassey gave rise to the construction industry as it is now.

The Victorian engineering world was a small one, and it was George Stephenson, 'the father of the railways', who set both Locke and Brassey on their first steps to fame. Stephenson had known Locke's father, and a year after the railway age had begun with the Stockton to Darlington line in 1822; Locke entered Stephenson's office as a 17 year-old pupil. He was to become an assistant, a deputy and eventually — after a quarrel — a rival to Stephenson. Even so, Locke was a firm friend of Robert Stephenson, George's son, and remained one until his death in 1860.

Locke worked for Stephenson on the Liverpool and Manchester Railway as a resident engineer, although very young at the time. His abilities were shown, however, when James Walker and Rastrick recommended using stationary engines on the line instead of locomotives. Almost immediately, Locke and Robert Stephenson responded in a tract which demolished Walker's case and ended the argument in favour of locomotives.

At first it was generally felt that locomotives would always need easy gradients, but Locke disagreed and always went for steeper gradients than any of his rivals. Indeed, he always boasted 'of having been systematically the hardest task-master of the locomotive, by eliciting its powers to overcome the gradients he had submitted to it'. So much is this the case, that it is only fairly recently that trains have been able to travel over Locke's line to Scotland up and over the Lune Valley without additional engines.

This method of construction, of course, meant that Locke's lines were generally cheaper to construct than those of anyone else. Since he added to that great care in specifying and estimating, his popularity with investors was assured.

Despite his successes and importance in the civil engineering profession, Locke differed from his great contemporaries in one important way: whereas they left behind prodigious monumental artefacts, like the Britannia and Saltash bridges, he did not. Locke's railways were, of course, great engineering achievements, but his style was low key. He almost made a cult of ordinariness.

The *Times* said of him, 'The peculiar characteristic of Locke's career was the firmness and decision with which throughout all his projects he avoided the construction of great and too costly works. His viaducts were of ordinary dimensions, though some of them were of admirable construction — such as those across the bold ravines of the north of England and Scotland. In every case they are exactly fitted to the places they occupy; and in the same manner his bridges over the Thames and the Seine are distinguished for their adaptation to their position, the lightness and simplicity of their construction, and the elegance of their design'.

Locke sat in Parliament as Liberal MP for Honiton for many years after 1847. But although he supported his party on most political affairs, he generally addressed the House only on matters where he had special and useful knowledge. That, incidentally, was the course followed by most of the engineer politicians of the period.

The memoir on Locke printed in the *Proceedings* after his death at the age of 55 ends with the words, 'Thus passed away within a few short months the third of the leaders of the engineering world: — Brunel, Stephenson and Locke: — they were born within two years of each other, and within the same space of time they were all removed. They were intended to execute certain purposes, and having fulfilled their mission, they were removed by the same all-wise Providence who rules all things for the general good'.

Of the triumvirate, Brunel was flamboyant and daring, and these characteristics led him to dazzling successes and striking failures; Robert Stephenson was safe and steady but he never shrank from the grandiose when it called to him; Locke was precise and workmanlike and, above all, he was careful with other people's money. If all these characteristics are necessary to some degree in an engineer, it was mainly Locke's example that the profession later followed.

HAVING been called to the office of President for the present session, somewhat unexpectedly, I may be permitted to claim indulgence on this occasion for what I am about to submit to you in that capacity. The duty which has devolved upon me was, until recently, unforeseen ; so that the time for considering and preparing what I might have to offer has been short. This circumstance, I hope, will be allowed in excuse, to some extent at least, of deficiencies which no one can feel more sensibly than myself.

That the Address, which it is a part of my office to deliver to such an audience, should not merely fulfil a formal obligation, but also contain some real substance, would in any case be an object of anxiety. It is one, moreover, which (as was well observed by my predecessor in office) every year becomes more difficult ; as the agency of our profession, in each successive period, covers a wider surface, and is connected with a greater variety of interests— social and financial, as well as scientific.

The extent and complexity of these relations, indeed, are now such, that I might, in any case, deem the attempt to take an adequate view of the whole subject a task beyond my powers. The incident already mentioned, is, at all events, a sufficient reason for not venturing on so large an enterprise. I shall therefore confine myself to a small portion, only, of this vast field, with which my personal experience has rendered me in some measure familiar :—to a sketch of the principles and character of the French railway system. This I am the more encouraged to attempt, by the circumstance of your late President's having, on a similar occasion, so fully discussed the main features of English railways :—the origin, progress and results of which, are, in many respects, strikingly dissimilar to those of the former.

The points in which they are contrasted will suggest various reflections on the past, and might be studied with advantage in regard to the future ; so that what I am about to offer you may

perhaps be acceptable as a sequel to what you have lately heard :—
a supplement, tending, however inadequately, to complete the outline of a general survey, so ably begun by your late President.

The contrast to which I have alluded, as shown in the principle,
has been still more strongly displayed in the practical results of
the respective systems. What these have been, and are, in
England, I need not attempt to detail. They are sufficiently
apparent to you all, and may be briefly summed in these two
positions :—immense convenience and advantage to the public
who use,—inadequate profit to those who have made,—our railways.

In France, we see these terms reversed. The capital has
yielded a fair, or even a handsome profit ; whilst the service to the
public—although far in advance of all its former means of con-
veyance—is still limited in comparison with ours. Such, at all
events, is the state of the comparison at the present moment.
How far it may be modified hereafter, I do not venture to calculate : although I am aware of circumstances which may, before
long, affect the balance, as it now stands, between the respective
systems. Still, as these, again, may be contrasted with other
processes, as yet undeveloped, on the opposite side, it may be
safer to confine our view to the materials which actually lie
before us.

In the first place, however, it should be observed, in pointing to
contrasted results, that the real difference is greater than is apparent on a mere comparison of percentages of income and profit.
Other things being equal, the advantage might fairly be
assumed to lie on the side of England, in all that is essential
to the success of improved communication. Density, movement, and wealth of population ; activity of trade and manufactures ; habits of despatch and intercourse in the natives ; the
resort of strangers ; cost of necessary materials ; practice and
skill in their manipulation :—these, and other points of less
moment, were clearly in favour of our railway enterprises. It
might be difficult, indeed, to say what amount should be added,
on these grounds, to the evidence of actual returns, in order to a
just estimate of the respective systems. But there can be no
hesitation in asserting that, viewing the relative conditions of the
two countries—apart from disturbing circumstances—the result,
as between them, of the experiment of railways, ought to have
been a higher rate of profit in England than in France. So that,
at all events, it is stating the question in the most moderate terms,
to take the actual figures only, without deduction on the score of
local circumstances.

The essential characteristic of the French system, almost from
its beginning, has been the determination by the State of its lines
of railway. In whatever form,—to whatever extent,—private
enterprise has been admitted, or invited, this main principle has
been uniformly preserved. This is the first of the two leading
objects in our present survey. The second, though considerable,

may be termed subordinate. It includes the process which the State,—while adhering to its general rule of absolute control in the selection of lines,—has thought proper to employ, in order to obtain the desired progress in their construction.

The terms of concession have undergone great variations at different stages of French railway history. The successive modifications have largely affected the interests of promoters; and the practical effects thus successively produced, as well as the motives to which their adoption may be traced, will deserve attentive consideration; and must occupy the largest space in the view before us.

The operation of the first, or main principle, is simple,—its effects are obvious. The consideration of the second point necessarily leads into more detail, amidst various successive changes. Throughout all, however, it will appear, that the railway system has been sustained by the conservative operation of that first ruling principle. In this, moreover, we find the secret of much, if not all, that has given the French system an advantage over ours. The rule, we repeat, is, that the State absolutely determines what lines shall be made. Its operation has been exclusively in favour of main arterial communications: protecting these, on whatever terms conceded, from competition in the districts assigned to them.

The conditions annexed to this security have varied at different periods. A complete review of such modifications, and a full explanation of their effects, would embrace nearly all that is peculiar to the French system. In such a review, features of disadvantage, inconvenience, and restriction will present themselves; but it will be seen that, in spite of all such, the security from that species of competition which has been the bane of English railways, has hitherto maintained the French lines in a healthy condition, which they are likely to enjoy, so long as this vital advantage remains unimpaired.

You are all well aware of the preliminary steps that are required in England before a Company can be incorporated for making a railway: and it may be useful to observe at once, that the Parliamentary notices; deposit of plans showing the line; standing-order committees; examinations, &c.; are altogether dispensed with in France, as in that country, the Government has long taken the initiative in all that relates to public works.

It has a corps of engineers well organized, presided over by the Minister of Public Works; who directs the operations of that important body known by the title of *l'Administration des Ponts et Chaussées.*

All railway lines, therefore, must originate with, or be sanctioned by, the Government, before any material steps whatever can be taken. When a ministerial decision is pronounced, declaring that a particular line would be " of public utility," the Minister of Public Works is authorised to enter into communication with such parties as may desire to undertake it; and,—having satisfied himself of the *bona fides* and ability of those who make the most eligible offer,— to enter into a preliminary treaty with them : which treaty, when approved by the Government and the Chamber, or the Senate, is ultimately signed by the Emperor, and becomes law.

The *cahier des charges*, containing the conditions of the concession, fixing the rates of charge, and defining the relative powers of the Company and the State, is settled at the same time.

The Government,—having at its disposal all the means of collecting information respecting the course of the line proposed,— furnishes, at all times, whatever plans, sections and estimates it may have in its possession, to the company thus formed ; who then proceed to lay out the line. The *cahier des charges* allows considerable latitude in this selection ;—the only restriction being that the line shall pass " by, or near to " certain towns therein mentioned. This preliminary survey, or *avant projet* as it is termed, is presented, when completed, either in the whole, or by departments, to the Minister of Public Works, accompanied with a list of curves, and gradients, and a full description of the line generally ;—and the Minister, after conferring with the Conseil Général des Ponts et Chaussées, ultimately notifies his approval, through the Préfet, to the company.

In the meantime, the latter are occupied in preparing plans and *états parcellaires*, (parish plans and references,) for each *commune* separately ; showing how the roads, rivers, or streams are proposed to be crossed, or deviated ; and these, with a description, are sent to the Préfet, who communicates them to the Mayors of the *communes* respectively.

The Mayor announces, by an advertisement on the doors of the *Mairie* and the church, and by beat of drum, that the plans have been received ; and that they are ready for the inspection of any parties whose lands may be affected by any of the proposed works. The plans, &c., remain thus open for inspection for eight days ; during which time any person may examine and comment upon them.

The Mayor then draws up a *procès-verbal*, or report, containing all the objections that have been made ; which is sent, with the plans, to the Préfet. The Préfet then names a commission, or *enquête*,—over which he presides,—composed of members of the *Conseil Général* of the department, the Mayors of the *communes* interested, and the company's engineer ; these meet and deliberate on the observations presented by each *commune*. No person whose land is to be taken can be a member of this commission.

A *procès-verbal*, or report on the Minutes of the Commission, is then drawn up and signed by the parties ; adding any observations they may have to offer. This, with the plans and all documents, is sent by the Préfet to the Engineers of Control ; who are appointed by Government to report on the nature and fitness of the works to be executed by the company, and to superinten'd the fulfilment of all clauses in the Act of Concession. These engineers make their report. All the documents, plans, and references are then sent to the Minister of Public Works, who pronounces, under the advice of the Conseil Général des Ponts et Chaussées, finally on the company's proposition.

The plans are then sent back, definitively corrected, to the Préfet; who makes his *arrêté de cessibilité*, and declares transferable for public utility the different parcels of land shown by the references, which, from that date, are fixed for expropriation. The *arrêté de cessibilité*, with the plans and references, is sent by the Préfet to the Procureur-Impérial of the civil courts of the district in which the properties are situated: whereupon the latter makes a requisition to the tribunal for the expropriation.

The "tribunal civil" examines with care if all the formalities required by the company's *cahier des charges* have been rigorously fulfilled; if the *enquêtes* have been duly completed, &c.; and pronounces the judgment of expropriation.

From this moment, all the parcels of land, houses, &c., shown on the plans and references, become the company's property; and all rights of the proprietor to his estate are merged in a title to compensation. He is legally divested of his property; but retains possession of it until the amount of indemnity is settled by agreement or by the jury, and is paid by the company.

The mode of fixing the value of the land by means of juries, so nearly resembles the process adopted in England, that I need not trouble you with an account of it.

The length of time necessary to enable a company to pass through these various stages is considerable; varying from six to twelve months; but, however tedious, they are not, like the preliminaries of an English railway, expensive. Nor is it necessary to do more than briefly to call your attention to the fact, so much in favour of French railway undertakings, that their mode of concession exempts them from that doubtful and onerous process, which has thrown on similar works in England the enormous dead-weight represented by our well-known term—"Parliamentary expenses."

From the description of what may be termed the "fixed machinery" of railway concessions,—as applied from the commencement, and continued, without alteration, under all changes in the terms on which they have been granted,—we shall now proceed to the latter branch of the subject: in which the variations have been considerable.

The first concession for a railway in France was given in 1823. It was twelve miles long: extending from the coal-fields of St. Etienne to the Loire at Andrézieux. In 1826 and 1828 other extensions from the same district, to Roanne and Lyons, were granted; but it was not till the year 1837 that any great impulse was given to these undertakings: for the concessions, at that date, scarcely amounted to two hundred miles. These were to be constructed wholly at the expense of the promoters.

In 1838 four lines of considerable importance were conceded to private companies: viz.—Strasbourg to Basle; Paris to Hâvre; Paris to Orléans, Lille to Dunkerque;—and it is a remarkable fact, that in the following year (1839), no funds for their construction being forthcoming, the concessions for the three latter lines were cancelled, with the exception of the small part of the Orléans concession, extending from Paris to Corbeil.

Up to this period, therefore, and indeed up to the year 1842, little progress had been made in France in extending the railway system, and in developing the resources of her ample territory; and it is probable that the failure to induce private capitalists to undertake the railways, led the Government to modify the law in regard to the granting of concessions. The Government had as yet afforded little pecuniary assistance to any of the lines; but had given a guarantee of 4 per cent. interest on some of them. The belief, however, that railways would yield in their results any great return, beyond the guarantee, had not yet taken root in the public mind; and the Government became aware that, to obtain railways for France, it would be necessary to attract capital, not only from France, but from England and elsewhere; and to offer greater advantages than they had hitherto afforded. To accomplish this, the law of the 11th June 1842 was passed; which authorised the state to construct the railways up to what is called "formation level;"—including the land, earthworks, works of art, stations, &c.;—and to let out, or farm, for a term of years, the working of the lines to companies; who would have to provide the rails and permanent road, together with the rolling stock, engines, carriages, &c., necessary for carrying on the traffic. This law,—which, it was assumed, would throw nearly three-fifths of the entire cost of construction on the State,—was so far successful, that numerous companies presented themselves for concessions, or leases to work the lines which the Government had determined on making.

These offers of aid, combined with a feeling, which then existed in France, against the making and working of railways by the State, induced the Government to modify, in some instances, the law of June; by granting subventions in money, in lieu of works, —varying the amount to suit the necessities of each case. In this manner, they succeeded in giving a new impulse to the railway system.

The whole extent of concessions existing up to 1842 did not reach 600 miles; whilst in the year 1842 alone, concessions were made, and works were undertaken for more than 1,400 miles.

The lines comprised in these concessions are among the most important in France, viz.:—

	Kilomètres.
Paris to Lille and Valenciennes	310
Rouen to Hâvre	92
Paris to Strasbourg	502
Paris to Lyons	512
Avignon to Marseilles	120
Orléans to Vierzon and Bourges . . .	113
Orléans to Bordeaux	461
Total kilomètres . .	2,110

or about 1,400 miles.

It should be remembered, that the 600 miles conceded before 1842 included the Paris and Rouen and the Paris and Orléans lines. These, after having been cancelled in 1839, were conceded in a modified form in 1840.

Nearly all the concessions since 1842 have either been based on the law of that year, or are in the modified form of granting a certain amount of subvention in lieu of works, with an extension of the term of concession, and, in some cases, with the continuance of the minimum guarantee of 4 per cent. interest.

We may, therefore, safely ascribe to this combination,—of pecuniary aid with a guaranteed minimum of interest,—the rapid increase in the development of the French system since 1842.

This participation of the State in the construction of railways, was, indeed, most opportune ; and must have greatly contributed to their prosperity. The guarantee of interest, whilst it satisfied those who had neither faith in, nor knowledge of, the resources of the country, was a means wisely employed by the Government for bringing out a large amount of capital, which might otherwise have sought investments elsewhere, or have continued, as heretofore, to lie dormant amongst the small landed proprietors.

No claim, meanwhile, has ever been made on account of this guarantee ; which may therefore be said to have completely fulfilled its purposes, without loss to the State.

It remains to show how far this system of "subvention" was carried : and, without detailing each individual grant, I will endeavour to state the gross amounts supplied by the State in successive years, down to the end of 1856.

From 1823 to 1842 the private capital required for the conceded lines amounted to £7,000,000, and the State contributed the sum of £120,000 only.

In the six years including 1842 and 1847, the private capital amounted to £17,000,000, and the State expenditure to £9,280,000.

From 1848 to 1851, inclusive, the private capital was £8,000,000, and the State contribution £12,000,000.

From 1852 to 1854, inclusive, the private capital was £29,240,000, and the State contribution £3,840,000.

In 1855 and 1856 the private capital was raised to £35,520,000, whilst the State contribution had fallen to £1,200,000.

If to these be added the engagements taken for lines already conceded, and not yet executed, but which are spread over from five to ten years, we shall have the whole financial condition of the French railways exhibited in the following table .

The total estimated cost, therefore, of the 7,030 miles conceded, stands at £173,600,000, or about £24,600 per mile ; say, £19,600 per mile contributed by the companies, and £5,000 by the State. It must be borne in mind, that I speak of estimated cost ; and that I am dealing with figures and estimates on which the Government has based its legislation : and since out of the

	Private Capital.	Contributions of the State.	Length of Lines conceded.	Length of Lines opened.
From	£	£	Miles.	Miles.
1823 to 1842. . .	7,000,000	120,000	550	..
1842 „ 1847. . .	17,000,000	9,280,000	2,250	1,156
1848 „ 1851. . .	8,000,000	12,000,000	..	..
1852 „ 1854. . .	29,240,000	3,840,000	5,770	2,900
1855 „ 1856. . .	35,520,000	1,200,000	7,030	4,060
	96,760,000	26,440,000		
Still to complete . .	41,200,000	9,200,000		
	137,960,000	35,640,000		
	35,640,000			
Total . . £	173,600,000			

7,030 miles conceded up to 1856 only 4,060 were then opened to the public, it would be premature to say that the actual cost will correspond with the estimate.

This Table exhibits considerable fluctuation in the proportion granted by the State at different periods; and we observe a rapid decrease in its advances since the year 1851, and a greater expenditure, consequently, thrown on the companies. It appears that from 1842 to 1851 the State contribution was £21,280,000; as against £25,000,000 furnished by the companies; whilst from 1851 to 1856 the State only provided £5,040,000, as against £64,760,000 furnished by the companies.

It might not be difficult to assign a reason for the variations here exhibited; which, however, are more apparent than real; for it will be found that, while making the larger advances,—whether under the law of 1842, or in the modified shape of subventions,—the State was securing an important reversionary interest in the railways; which was afterwards abandoned, in order thereby to get rid of the more pressing demands for money.

The law of 1842 had the advantage (for the State) of engaging companies to work the lines on leases of very short duration, say from 28 to 40 years. But, at the same time, it drew largely on the public treasury; and it was probably found more convenient, as the confidence of private capitalists increased, to attract them, by extending the periods of concession to 99 years, as had been the practice before 1842. To this end, the guarantee of 4 per cent. interest was liberally extended: and a remission made of the right to a share in the profits, after a certain amount of dividend had been paid to the shareholders.

In getting rid, therefore, of the contribution,—which either in works, or in money, in 1851, pressed so heavily on the State,—it was obliged, not only to lend its credit in the shape of extended guarantees, but also to give up some of the advantages expected from a participation in railway profits.

The amount of capital, either in shares, or bonds, guaranteed by the State, in 1851, did not exceed six millions; whilst in 1855 it rose to sixty millions, and is now applicable to 5,200 miles of railway. The companies who partake of it are, chiefly, the Orléans, Lyons, L'Ouest, Mediterranean, Midi, and Grand Central.

In like manner, the right of participation, which had applied to nearly all the lines founded on the law of 1842, has been abandoned as regards the recent concessions, and is retained only on those in which the provisions of that law, or an equivalent, in the shape of subvention, has largely entered into the terms of arrangement. At the present time, the right of participation applies to 3,500 miles; chiefly with L'Est, Lyons, Mediterranean, Midi, and Grand Central companies.

I may add, that in the recent amalgamations of several of the great companies in France, the prolongation of term, with an increased capital guaranteed, and a diminished subvention, seems to have entirely superseded the law of 1842.

Throughout all these changes, however, it will be seen, that almost from the very beginning of the French railway system,—but especially from 1842 down to the end of 1856,—the rule has been, that, in one shape, or another, and with varying degrees of liberality, these undertakings have always received a certain amount of direct assistance from the State; in addition to the protection secured to them by the operation of that general principle of control, to which your attention has been already directed.

An element of considerable importance in the finance of French lines is the proportion of share capital to the amount raised on obligations, or bonds. There will be remarked a great difference in this respect, as compared with the practice in England; and it is interesting to observe how it affects the finances of the former. In the whole of the capital provided by companies, amounting, as we have seen, to £137,960,000, there is less than £50,000,000 in shares; or about 37 per cent. of the whole: whilst the remaining 63 per cent. has been raised on obligations.

There are some notable instances which deserve to be specially mentioned.

The Company " Du Nord " had an original share capital of £8,000,000, on a concession of about 370 miles of railway. It subsequently reduced its shares from 500 francs to 400 francs, making the capital £6,400,000, and it remained so fixed, at the end of 1856, although its engagements were then increased to £13,000,000.

The Company "l'Est" had an original share capital of £5,000,000. It has subsequently doubled its capital; but its engagements by new concessions were more than quadrupled, being nearly £21,000,000.

The Paris and Lyons Company, with an original share capital of £4,800,000, subsequently raised to £5,280,000, has engagements estimated at nearly £14,000,000.

The Company from Lyons to the Mediterranean, in like manner, has a share capital of £1,800,000; whilst its estimated engagements are £6,800,000.

The Orléans and the Western Companies are in a similar condition;—each having a share capital of £6,000,000. The former having £13,000,000, and the latter £17,500,000 of engagements by new concessions.

During the past year some modifications of these respective amounts have occurred; but as no authentic account has appeared of them, and as they would not materially affect the general deductions which moreover are entirely retrospective, I shall abstain from including them in this general statement.

The effect of this mode of providing funds will be seen on examining the net receipts of railways from 1841 to 1854, and the percentage of dividend which has resulted from them. These are stated in the following table; where it will be observed, that the percentage paid on the whole capital expended,—

in 1841 was 3·11 per cent.
in 1847 ,, 6·30 per cent.
in 1854 ,, 6·58 per cent.

You will also find, that, by the operations of the subventions, in reducing the capital subject to dividend, the rate paid to the companies was

in 1841, 3·11 per cent.
in 1847, 7·17 per cent.
and in 1854, 9· per cent.;—

so that the State assistance, at the latter period, gave a benefit of 2·42 per cent. on the whole of the remaining capital.

But by far the largest amount of that capital, as already observed, was raised on loan at a fixed rate of interest; and it is evident, that according as the dividend on the whole capital varied from the interest paid to the bondholder, a profit, or loss would accrue to the company from the operation. In order, therefore, to a just comparison of receipts with our railways, the percentage of net income must, in both cases, be taken on the whole capital raised: a process by which the percentage would be considerably reduced on the French side, and be raised on the English;—preference stock, in the latter, being included in the category of borrowed capital, which it virtually is, although lent by proprietors. The rate of interest on loans may be taken as practically the same, say about 5 per cent. on both sides.

This being premised, it follows that it will depend on the ratio of net profit to the whole capital expended, whether any portion of it raised by loans at a fixed interest, will increase, or lower the rate of dividend on the remaining portion. Take, for instance, two railways, each having cost £1,000,000, one of which would produce on that cost a net profit of 4, and the other of 8, per cent. It results, that in the one case, to borrow half the capital at 5 per cent. must reduce the sum left for dividend, on the £500,000 in shares, to £15,000, viz., from 4 to 3 per cent.; while the other, by borrowing half its capital at the same rate, will raise the dividend, on its £500,000 in shares, to £55,000, *i. e.*, from 8 to 11 per cent.

Such is the operation, when the borrowed capital is the same in both cases. But let us assume that in the former case, as in England, it amounts only to one-fourth, or to one-third, and in the latter to two-thirds. We shall then find that in the first case the reduction from 4 per cent. is only one-half per cent.—viz., to $3\frac{1}{2}$:— whilst in the second the dividend on share capital is raised from 8 to 14 per cent.

It thus appears, that the decisive element in both, is the ratio of net profit to the whole capital spent in a given undertaking : and that the reason why French dividends are augmented by borrowing so much, is solely that the rate of profit earned on the entire cost is in excess of the current rate of interest ; while English dividends are impaired by the same process, because here this condition is reversed.

It has been estimated, that the profit made by the Railway Companies in France, by this mode of raising funds, amounted, in 1854, to 3 per cent. on the whole of their share capital. I am inclined, however, to believe that this estimate is not sufficiently high ; for I find that the average annual dividends paid from 1854 to 1857, by the following companies amounted to :—Nord, 14 ; l'Est, 14 ; l'Ouest, 10 ; Paris to Lyons, 16 ; Orléans, 16 ; Lyons to the Mediterranean, in 1855 (the first year of its entire completion), 17 ;—and in 1856, 23 per cent.

It must not, however, be overlooked, that in all the French lines provision is made by law for extinguishing the capital by what is termed an *amortissement,* payable out of revenue every year during the period of concession. In the origin of railways the law fixed the amount of this at 1 per cent., but it was found more than sufficient for the purpose ; and the Government then consented to a modification of the law, which, spreading over 99 years, did not require more than about one-fourth, or one-eighth per cent. in order fully to redeem the capital within that time.

The mode adopted is to cancel every year by lottery a certain number of shares and bonds. The shares are paid off at par : but the holder receives, in lieu, a share *de jouissance,* which entitles him, at all times during the concession, to receive his dividend like any other proprietor ; excepting only, that 5 per cent. is first paid as interest on the shares not drawn, before the partition for dividend takes place. The bonds, when drawn, are paid off, with a bonus of from 25 to 40 per cent.

The annual pressure of this species of sinking-fund on the dividends cannot, indeed, be considerable ; but something must be allowed for it, in calculating the rate of profit, in the manner already described.

These needful corrections of the nominal returns being made, the final result will be, that the true scale of French railway profits is not, indeed, so high as the dividends would represent; but that, as compared with ours, the actual ratio of profit to expenditure is still in their favour. This, alone, is the material circumstance which enables them to enhance the income of the shareholder by the very means which, on our side, only tend to diminish it. In the one case, borrowing may be dictated by prudence; in the other, it must be excused by necessity.

Proceeding to a comparison of the cost of French and English railways, it will be seen that we exhibit a very unfavourable picture as contrasted with our neighbours. For our 13,111 miles of railways, granted by Parliament, provision has been made for £377,760,000, which is equal to £28,800 per mile; but it appears from a recent return, that 2,845 miles have been abandoned, by allowing the powers of construction to expire, and the capital is thus reduced to £336,684,155, which, for 10,626 miles, gives £31,690 per mile. The French railways, as we have seen, have been estimated to cost £24,688 per mile.

The causes which have tended to swell the expenses of English railways were stated, at some length, by our late President, in his Address from this chair, and I need not repeat them. From many of these, whether directly inflicted by our mode of Parliamentary proceedings, or indirectly by the encouragement of a rivalry which leads to contentious and unprofitable works, the French railway promoter is wholly exempted, by the operation of those rules of the system, which have already been pointed out. He enjoys another advantage in the greater facilities which the physical features of the country present in France, whereby less expensive works are necessary there. Neither in tunnels, nor in viaducts, is there the same magnitude, or cost; nor, with the exception of Lyons and Rouen, do we find that excessive expenditure which is incurred, in almost every provincial town in England, for the alleged "accommodation" of its inhabitants. If we cast our eyes over the North line of France, we discover neither extravagance nor excessive outlay. The same may be said of the Ouest, the Orléans, and many other lines; and if we compare what has been spent on these, with the expenditure at, or near Birmingham, Wolverhampton, Liverpool, Manchester, Bradford, Leeds, and other towns, where the rivalry of companies has duplicated, nay trebled, both lines and stations, we shall see one considerable item of the difference in the cost of the two systems.

Nor let us forget the premiums paid by timid Directors to projectors of hostile lines; such as the Trent Valley, the Leeds and Bradford, the Oxford and Birmingham, the Birmingham, Wolverhampton, and Dudley, the Richmond, and other lines; an extravagance mainly produced by the rivalry to which I have already alluded, and which is unknown in France.

If to these causes be added the exactions of landowners, and the expenses thrown on companies by parliamentary inquiries, we shall perceive very sufficient reasons, independently of greater engineering difficulties, why our railways have been so much more costly than the French.

We have, however, probably passed the maximum of expenditure; and, profiting by experience, are now constructing railways at a much less rate per mile than formerly; whilst in France, they have, perhaps, not yet reached the culminating point. I find that, between the years 1841 and 1854, the cost has gradually increased from £18,600 to £26,664 per mile; and since many of the lines are but recently opened, and others not yet completed, there is, as I have said, reason to believe that the maximum actual cost is not yet reached.

Whilst, however, the direct control of the State has protected French railway enterprise from the rivalries of party interests, and the wasteful expenses of competition, and whilst it has been aided by subventions, loans, and guarantees, the Government has not lost sight of the advantages to be drawn from it in return. It has secured to the State the mail service of France, free of charge; it has laid a 10 per cent. tax on passengers, and on first-class goods; and these two items, alone, are now estimated to yield more than 5 per cent. on the whole of the £36,000,000 given in the shape of subventions.

On behalf of the State, there has, further, been secured the participation in dividends, on many of the lines, after a certain percentage is paid to the shareholders: the low tariffs fixed for soldiers, sailors, prisoners, paupers, &c.: and, finally, the possession, at the end of their concessions, of all the railways in France; which up to this period, are estimated at £173,000,000 sterling.

It would thus appear that the system has, so far, reconciled the two important interests, of the promoters, and of the State, with considerable success:—that while substantial benefits have been secured to the latter, the former have been enabled to derive a liberal return for their outlay; in short,—that the railway interest in France has not, as in England, been made a victim of public exigencies, and of private cupidity.

Before leaving this branch of the subject, let me advert to another of the causes beneficial to railway property in France. The service which there is considered sufficient for public convenience, is more limited, both in frequency of departures, and in speed, than is expected on English lines. How much a limitation in these points generally tends to the ease and economy of working, and thereby decidedly tells on the profits of a railway, I need not detail to you; but I will observe, that it is of especial moment in France, where the cost of coke—for instance—is greatly in excess of ours, and, indeed, all that belongs to locomotive power is more expensive than in this country.

On referring to the ordinary time-tables of main lines, here and in France respectively, the difference on this head, to the advantage of the latter, will be found equal to about 20 or 25 per cent. But were we to introduce into the comparison the departures and speeds, on those English railways which are under the strain of direct competition, the percentage in favour of French economy would be nearly doubled.

When I turn from this part of my subject to that in which, as professional men, you naturally take a great interest, I cannot but feel that, in all that especially belongs to the chapter of engineering, the field before us offers little that is calculated to occupy your attention. The chief cause of this will already have occurred to you. The railway had been in a great measure perfected in England before it was introduced into France:—where, accordingly, the mode of construction, wholly imitative, has been throughout, with scarcely an exception, a repetition of ours. To describe a French line, indeed, would be little more than to repeat details with which you are familiar at home. Something I have already said of the superficial features of the country, as more apt than ours for economical construction; something, too, of the more limited nature of accommodation works, the absence of duplicate stations, &c. What I have further to add, rather turns on some incidental matters, which may perhaps interest you.

I will first advert to some of the advantages which French railways have enjoyed, as compared with ours. Our system began when everything connected with them was new, and every man had his experience to gain. There were few facilities at hand; and mechanical skill was not equal, all at once, to the task which the demand for railways so suddenly made upon it. Our principal engineers, as well as their assistants, had their work to learn; and the locomotive engine, yet in its infancy, was neither generally relied on, nor capable of sustaining the great part which it has since occupied. Our neighbours, therefore, later in the adoption of railways than ourselves, benefited by the experience which we were able subsequently to furnish.

I may mention, as bearing on this subject, one or two circumstances which have come under my own observation. When, in 1840, I became Engineer to the Paris and Rouen Railway, I, of course, very soon turned my attention to the means which that country afforded for enabling me to construct and to maintain my own works: and after the experience of a first adjudication of a contract, in which the French parties demanded prices nearly double those which were asked by Englishmen, I arrived at the conclusion that it would be necessary, if the railways were to be made for the sums estimated, to employ contractors already experienced, who, in carrying out their works, might be able to instruct others in the use of those appliances, which as you all know, are so desirable in operations of that kind. The result of this determination was to engage the co-operation of Mr. Brassey and Mr. Mackenzie, who carried into France the machinery and skilled labour then at their disposal; and I may appeal to the long-continued employment of both those gentlemen, and to the success which has attended their efforts,—more particularly to those of Mr. Brassey,—not only in France, but in nearly every part of the globe, as a justification of the employment, at that time, of my countrymen in France.

Amongst the "appliances" carried there by these gentlemen, there were none more striking, or important, than the 'navvies' themselves. Following in the wake of their masters, when it was known that they had contracted for works in France, these men soon spread over Normandy; where they became objects of interest to the community, not only by the peculiarity of their dress, but by their uncouth size, habits, and manners; which formed so marked a contrast with those of the peasantry of that country. These men were generally employed in the most difficult and laborious work, and by that means earned higher wages than the rest of the men. Discarding the wooden shovels and basket-sized barrows of the Frenchmen, they used the tools which modern art had suggested, and which none but the most expert and robust could wield: and often have I heard the exclamation of French loungers around a gang of navvies—"*Mon Dieu! ces Anglais, comme ils travaillent!*"

The abundance of five-franc pieces, on the Saturday, at all the shops and places of trade, soon made the distributors of them popular; and it was a remarkable fact, well known at the time, that in tunnelling, or other dangerous work, the French labourer could not be induced to join, unless an Englishman was at the head of the operations. The lawless and daring habits of this class of our countrymen sometimes brought them under the special notice of the "Gens-darmes;" who, however, soon discovered that it was better to humour, for a time, rather than to attempt to control them, during the excitement which always followed the receipt of their monthly wages.

There was one complaint, however, which I think it right to notice, regarding the employment of Englishmen in France. It was soon observed and complained of, that the Englishmen earned larger wages than the French; forgetting that the latter, at that time, were physically unequal to much of the work which had to be performed in constructing railways. A piece of coarse bread and an apple or pear, which then formed the ordinary meal of a French labourer, could not be set up against the navvies' beef or bacon; and none knew the difference so well as the contractors themselves; who always obtained the greatest amount of labour from the highest-paid workmen. Three or four francs a-day were then expended more profitably on an Englishman than two francs on a Frenchman: whilst now, it is fair to state, that, by force of imitation, both in the mode of living and in the implements used, there is little, if any, difference in the relative values of the labour obtained from each. The Frenchman has learnt the effects of nourishing food, and the consequently higher wages he can obtain for his labour; so that the result is, that this class of work is now entirely supplied by the native population. Thus it appears, that the introduction of English railway labour, so far from having been a grievance, has, in fact, as previously, in the cases of the iron trade and the machinery manufacture, considerably improved the condition of the French working class.

I found, too, that France had then only two, or three places where a small number of locomotive engines had ever been made, the rest being obtained from England; and all these, at that time, were of a very inferior description.

Knowing that the railway system, there, was then just starting and that France could not, and ought not, to remain without the means of repairing, and consequently, of constructing its own engines, I at once determined on establishing workshops at Rouen; by which that Company, at least, might be able to rely on resources entirely under its own control.

In this matter I engaged the assistance of Mr. Buddicom; who constructed, at fixed prices, all the engines, carriages, waggons, and other _matériel_ required by that Company, and subsequently agreed to keep them in repair at a fixed rate per kilomètre. The success of this experiment has been complete, both to the company and to Mr. Buddicom, who still continues his labours, and in a much wider field,—for he now supplies engines and carriages to most of the Companies in France,—and I think I may add, that no company, even at the present day, possesses a _matériel_ better adapted for railway service, than that which has emanated from the workshops of Rouen.

The only other important Railway company at that time existing in France was the Orléans, which obtained most of its engines from England: but as the railway system became developed, establishments sprang up, which have since kept pace with the demand; and the native manufacture of these machines is now equal to the wants of the country. English mechanics, therefore, are now little employed on French railways; and the enginemen, who, at one period, were chiefly English, are now rarely met with on any of the lines, with the exception of that of Rouen.

In excellence of manufacture, however, or in manipulation, I do not think that they have yet quite reached the English standard; although it is fair to suppose that they may do so. Nor is the economy of working yet brought so low as in England; notwithstanding that the speed is not so high; that the wages of labour and the salaries for attendance are lower; while the trains, being less frequent, are better filled, and consequently carry less dead weight than on English lines. Still, there are elements of disadvantage on the French side, such as the dearness of coke and iron, which tell largely against them: but as it is not my present object to compare minutely the working expenses of the two systems of railways, I shall content myself with this general statement of the circumstances which affect them.

I may, however, add that the engines generally employed on French railways are becoming very heavy; and this is not surprising when we find that the manufacturers are paid for them _by weight_. The influence of this excessive pressure on the permanent way, as in England, has already been felt: and, notwithstanding that engines lighter, by several tons, are performing as much work, at equal cost, as their heavier competitors, there seems no sufficient check on a practice which tends to the premature destruction of the permanent way, and a heavy liability for its renewal.

In the construction of their railways, there is little to remark; the French engineers, as already observed, having generally imitated our practice.

In masonry they are perhaps somewhat more lavish in quantity than we are: on the other hand, in their cuttings they rarely give sufficient flatness to the slopes; the surface of which is being constantly denuded by the weather. To remedy this, it is their practice to pitch, or pave the slopes with stone; a process, you will probably think, neither so economical nor so good as flattening the slopes, covering them with soil, and thus obtaining a surface of permanent vegetation.

The rails, both as to form and weight, resemble those which are chiefly adopted in this country;—I mean the double and equal headed rail, first used on the Grand Junction Line. The gauge is the same as our standard; and its uniformity throughout France is another of the benefits derived from State control; which has thereby obviated all the inconveniences and contentions incident to discrepancies of system in the great highways of a country. The permanent way generally, both as to sleepers, chairs, and fastenings, differs little from our own.

I will name, before concluding, a peculiarity in the working service of the French lines, which, though trivial in itself, bespeaks a difference in national habits that may be worth noticing. I allude to the employment of females, which prevails on several of the French railways, especially in certain offices of the booking department, as well at the principal, as at minor stations. At the level crossings, too, females are employed: the head of the family being engaged on the line, whilst his wife, or daughter opens and shuts the gates when required. They are found quite equal to the men in the performance of the duties assigned to them, while they are content with lower wages. The usages of the country, where this kind of substitution takes place in many other departments of business, find nothing strange in a practice, which, however convenient and economical, would be thought in many respects questionable in ours. As the trait, though slight, is characteristic, I may be excused for mentioning such a matter of detail:—the last I have to offer in this department.

As regards the conduct of their works by French engineers, there may be observed a difference between their proceedings and ours, which cannot be wholly excluded from a comparative survey of this kind.

The object, common to both,—of taking the utmost advantage of the ground in tracing lines, and in making them, when laid down, in the most effectual manner,—is not pursued by both in the same way. With us, as you well know, the work is planned and carried through every stage by the immediate operation of the chief Engineer; who searches with his own eyes the whole field of his labours; familiarizes himself, by frequent and minute inspection, with all its features; and continues, throughout the progress of his work, in close personal contact, so to speak, with every form of its material requirements. Constantly on the ground, he at once perceives whatever demands attention; of all exigencies, as they occur, he judges for himself on the spot; determining, in fact, every essential circumstance on the evidence of his own senses; seizing advantages and meeting obstacles, as they present themselves to a view thoroughly conversant with the district, and instructed by the experience of similar phenomena elsewhere. To him it never occurs, in matters of the least consequence, to depend on the information of any judgment but his own; least of all, to rely on the reports of subordinates only. In short,—all that is material in the business in hand is alike designed and governed by the direct agency and actual presence, as it were, of the chief;—in other words, by the person presumed to be the best qualified to devise and control them.

The French practice, in general, may be described as the reverse of ours. What the English engineer pursues in the field, in immediate view of his object, the French engineer, in a great measure, seeks to accomplish in his study, through the medium of others. The reports of assistants,—transmitted in various shapes to head quarters, classified and manipulated in a central office by the diligence of clerks;—such are the materials upon which, to a great extent, he decides on lines and sections, designs the working plans, and provides for such incidents as arise in the course of operations.

This method you will not think altogether favourable to the consummate performance of a task subject to an infinite variety of conditions, and calling, from its outset to its close, on many occasions, for the immediate action of the best judgment available. By it, indeed, the ability of the head in no small measure becomes dependent in its exercise on materials furnished by others, who, at best, cannot be supposed equally able. Nor, indeed, in many cases, can any report, however able, supply all that is required for a thorough mastery of critical points. The experienced eye, on such occasions, sees more than any pen can describe;—and elicits, by inquiries and inspection, much that would never occur from the perusal of a statement in writing.

It is further to be remarked, that,—whereas this system does not apply to the chief only, but descends, through all ranks, to the lowest departments,—it must often happen, that the details on which the chief Engineer ultimately acts, really originate with subalterns of very moderate qualifications: from whom they pass, through various ascending stages, with little effectual modifications, —though with various marks of control,—until, at length, they reach the Engineer in chief.

This method, indeed, presents a show of organization, which our offices do not exhibit. On paper it is highly methodical and imposing:—copious details are amassed, and every transaction has its special document: all is minutely recorded, and easily referred to;—whatever, in short, can be conveyed and classified in writing, is done in great perfection. But this will hardly be deemed an efficient substitute for the less formal, but more direct, process, by which the engineer is thrown into constant personal relation to the realities with which he has to deal, attacking them, as we have said, face to face, with the full weight of his own proper energies; doing nothing of importance at second- or third-hand; but directly grappling with all that is material to the success of his undertaking.

In the same department, another peculiarity may be mentioned, which, also, is not without its detrimental effect on the engineer's proceedings in France. I allude to a species of influence, rather incidental to the system than expressly enjoined by it; but which, in practice,—as well while lines are making, as in working them, when made,—is apt to cause both needless trouble and useless expenditure.

Every administrative province is superintended by a Government Engineer, one of the department of *Ponts et chaussées*, whose presence affects the railway system somewhat in the following manner:—He is naturally disposed to assume as much authority as he can acquire over the public works in his district; and this, in the case of railways, does not make itself felt the less, that it is, in many cases, an encroachment beyond the proper limits of his office.

By the terms of concession, indeed, the plans being settled and approved, the responsibility for their execution rests with the engineer appointed by the promoters; and the Government official,—except on some particular occasions, and at the requisition of the Minister,—has no positive right to interfere with the details of construction, working, or maintenance. But it often happens that he will, nevertheless, take upon himself to do so; and, as a general rule, his demands, or suggestions, although of no legal force, are submitted to. It is in the nature of such interference that its action should, in every way, be inconvenient and onerous to those whom it affects: a cause of delay and waste, whether the mandate be to undo, or to alter what has already been done, or to adopt needless extras.

The official person is, of course, in no way concerned for the trouble, or expense which his notions may entail on the promoters: he is mindful, chiefly, to keep himself free from all responsibility, without regard to the consequences resulting from his orders. When it is remembered that most of the native engineers on the lines in progress belong to the *Ponts et chaussées*, from which these State inspectors, also, proceed,—and that the country is accustomed to the pressure of official control, on nearly every point of social and industrial action,—it will readily be conceived how much, under these circumstances, may be assumed and endured, beyond what is really incumbent on those who bear the cost of interference.

It is proper, however, to say that, so far as concerns my own employment in France, I have no personal complaint to make on this head : having never been required to yield to unauthorized pressure from public officers ; but having, on the contrary, always found sufficient support and protection, both from my own Directors and from the State authorities, whenever I have found it necessary to resist undue encroachments.

I have now laid before you the main features of the economy of the French system as compared with ours. These, and the comments upon them, introduced at different stages of the review, will, I trust, have enabled you to form a tolerably clear idea of the causes to which its prosperity may be ascribed, and of the points in which its pecuniary successes may be contrasted with our failures.

On a retrospect of the whole, some leading points will be noticed. The difference in estimated cost per mile of the lines hitherto conceded, or made in France, as compared with ours, may be taken at from £5,000 to £7,000. To this must be added, in the French promoters' favour, the £5,000 per mile furnished by the State. If, however, from the English rate were taken the outlay solely due to disadvantages from which the French are exempt, the difference in favour of the latter, making every allowance for the more even surface of their country, would be considerably reduced. In extent of lines granted, the comparison of about 7,000 miles of French with 10,000 miles of English, would not, of itself,—considering our priority in the field,—result much to the disadvantage of the former.

But if the respective character of the lines be considered, there can be no doubt where the advantage decisively lies. On a glance at the map of French lines (Plate 3), we find them nearly all in the nature of leading communications ; each draining an important district, and free from the pressure of rivals. The result of a similar inspection here, I need not describe ; but it may be asserted, that the comparative advantage of the French system really consists far more in the class of lines on which its funds have been employed,—and in the assistance given in raising those funds,—than in the expense per mile at which they have been made.

These are the two cardinal points on which the superior prosperity of that system has hitherto turned. As to the rest, without recapitulating details, it may generally be stated, that there is no special circumstance, whatever, of any moment,—with the single exception of a more limited accommodation to the public,—that would explain its superiority. And that exception is, perhaps, balanced by the greater cost of working supplies ; the higher passenger-tax ; the 10 per cent. on a portion of the merchandise receipts ; and the carriage of mails, &c., gratis.

In short, whatever real circumstance of advantage is examined,

TABLE showing the Proportion of the Net Produce of the Working of each Line to the Expense of the Prime Cost.

YEARS.	Length.		Expense, or First Cost, per Kilomètre.			Net Working Receipts per Annum per Kilomètre.	Per Centage upon the Capital on the First Cost.		Receipts from Taxes levied on Passengers.	
	Works Opened to 31st December.	Mean Lengths Opened in the Year.	By the State.	By the Companies.	Total.		Total.	Shared by each Company.	Total.	Per Kilomètre.
	Kilomètres.	Kilomètres.	Fr.	Fr.	Fr.	Fr.			Fr.	Fr.
1841	569	517		290,681	290,681	9,040	3·11	3·11	316,741	612
1842	597	580		305,484	305,484	8,613	2·81	2·81	313,649	540
1843	827	763	11,117	301,132	312,249	13,031	4·17	4·32	501,216	656
1844	829	847	12,327	310,804	323,131	16,819	5·20	5·41	665,364	785
1845	881	901	15,741	315,700	331,441	18,277	5·54	5·78	679,247	753
1846	1,320	1,137	10,927	290,426	301,353	19,064	6·32	6·56	850,205	747
1847	1,830	1,537	37,526	307,054	344,580	22,040	6·39	7·17	1,136,221	739
1848	2,222	2,034	49,730	309,219	358,949	13,121	3·65	4·24	1,094,720	538
1849	2,861	2,508	108,176	272,807	380,983	14,706	3·86	5·39	1,407,976	561
1850	3,013	2,962	112,681	271,537	384,218	17,168	4·46	6·32	1,903,275	642
1851	3,558	3,299	129,705	249,356	379,061	17,754	4·68	7·11	2,125,514	644
1852	3,872	3,694	107,001	280,064	387,065	21,627	5·58	7·72	2,469,564	668
1853	4,063	3,978	104,783	287,956	392,739	24,591	6·26	8·57	2,855,183	717
1854	4,660	4,348	109,154	291,988	401,142	26,415	6·58	9·00	3,098,756	713

the result of the inquiry will be to arrive at one, or the other of the two principal conditions above mentioned.—In other words, the source of the present good fortune of French railways lies in their favourable treatment by the State. The Government of France, as we have seen, while strongly controlling, has also liberally fostered this kind of enterprise ; while the English legislature, on the contrary, unable to guide, has suffered, if not encouraged, hostile, or selfish interests to encumber and pervert it. This, briefly, is the sum of the qestion.

In whatever detail the particulars of the comparison may be pursued, the contrast in this point of view, alone, is remarkable. It is, in fact, a contrast between method and confusion, in a matter of supreme national interest :—there, led and guarded by the sovereign power :—here, ungoverned and undefended ; left to the chances of competition ; abandoned to every kind of attack ; and only conscious of authority in the shape of exactions.[1] This view suggests many grave and difficult considerations ; some of which are too obvious to need express mention : others rather invite the study of philosophers and statesmen, than lie within the province of the practical Engineer. It will, on every account, therefore, be more becoming in me to abstain from venturing into this field of speculation.

Let me, however, in conclusion, say a few words on a topic that more directly concerns us. It may perhaps be objected that my sketch, as designed for a professional audience, brings into undue relief the financial elements of the subject. To this I would reply—recalling its expressed purpose, of offering materials for a comparison of the French railway system with ours—that it is here, precisely, that their essential distinction will be found :— that whatever is peculiar to the former,—from the commencement of its proceedings to the development of its finished works,— practically resolves itself into a control of the application of capital to a given end ; and, beyond this, into questions of the amount and productive effect of the outlay thus controlled. But, further, it may be observed, independently of particular objects, that this side of the railway question, so far from being foreign to the Civil Engineer's province, must, on the contrary, under existing conditions, be always deemed an important part of it : so important, indeed, that it cannot now be excluded from even the most limited view of his professional studies.

Let us consider the principle on which public works are now undertaken :—the motives that supply those abundant means by which, alone, they become possible. It must be seen, that the problem proposed, on such grounds, to practical science, is, not merely the execution of certain works, but rather their arrangement and construction in a manner calculated to realize the objects in which they originate.

If the " adjustment of means to ends " be truly described as

---

[1] *Vide* the late President's " Reply to the Postmaster-General's Report."— Minutes of Proceedings Inst. C.E., vol. xv., pp. 470—496.

the right aim of the Engineer, that aim, it is evident, would be but half reached, were the end, contemplated by the promoters of a given enterprise, overlooked in devising the means of carrying it into effect. The proposition here is ;—not simply that railways should be made, but be so made as to produce to their proprietors the benefit, in expectation of which the funds for their construction were contributed. The profitable effect of capital, directed to a given object in the hope of profit, is thus a main element of the subject on which the modern Engineer has to exert his skill and judgment. It may, indeed, be termed,—taking a general view of this matter,—as much a part of the whole, to be dealt with by practical science, as the method of construction, or the choice of materials.

Beyond this—observing the springs from which our profession draws its support, and the relation which it bears to the voluntary employment of private means in public works—the significance of financial results, as final exponents of their success, or failure, must be apparent.

The practical science of our day, as enlisted in the service of monied enterprise, must indeed confess itself at fault, if, by any defect of its own, that enterprise were defrauded of its fair reward. Thus it is concerned, not only in guarding against this default, but also in the discovery and indication of whatever influences—(beyond its sphere of action, but of which it may unjustly bear the reproach,)—tend to frustrate the hopes of attainable benefit ; and thereby to dry up the source, or to divert to other channels, the current of future enterprise. For it is obvious that, when the employment of science by wealth is mainly actuated by the stimulus of gain, the spur being withdrawn, the occupation must cease. Public works will no longer be attempted, where experience proves that their result, instead of profit, is ruin. Confidence gives place to distrust ; capital seeks its harvest elsewhere ; and the cause of past disappointment and loss becomes the object of a prejudice, which years may not eradicate.

In every point of view, therefore,—whether especially considering that it is the triumph of science to solve the whole of every problem submitted to it, and not a part only,—or regarding its general relations to the objects of modern society in inviting its exercise ;—it will be seen, that the financial result of their joint operation is not their least important feature :—and that the appreciation of this side of the question really concerns the Engineer, no less than the Statesman, or the Capitalist.

On the main drainage of London, and the interception of the sewage from the River Thames

J. W. BAZALGETTE, MInstCE

*Reprinted from Min. Proc. Instn Civ. Engrs, 1865,
vol. 24, 280-314*

London in the middle third of the 19th century was the scene of widespread building activity. In the years between 1840 and about 1880 a remarkable amount of large-scale construction work was carried out in the capital. Not only were the main railways brought into London, but also such important edifices as the new Palace of Westminster and the Crystal Palace were built and a start was made on the London Underground railway system.

As important as any of these were two major projects with which Sir Joseph Bazalgette was closely connected. These were the main drainage scheme for London and the Thames Embankment.

Bazalgette was born at Enfield in 1819. His family, as his name suggests, was originally French, but his father had had considerable service in the British navy during the Napoleonic wars. Bazalgette entered the civil engineering profession as a pupil at 17 and, like so many of his engineering contemporaries, was practising on his own account by the age of 23. Although he had been engaged in drainage and reclamation work, much of his practice was at first concerned with railways.

Addiction to work was the major Victorian virtue, so much so that many of the great Victorian engineers and industrialists literally worked themselves to death in middle age. Bazalgette did not do that, but he over-exerted himself as a young engineer to such an extent that he was obliged to take an entire year off to recover his health. This was even before he was 30.

On resuming work, he was appointed to the Metropolitan Commission for Sewers — an arrangement which eventually led him to the two major projects mentioned above.

When Bazalgette took up his post, the condition of the Thames was the despair of the capital. The river was virtually an open sewer and, apart from its being extremely disagreeable to anybody who was obliged to be nearby, it presented a continuing health hazard. The eight municipal authorities which were responsible for drainage were combined to form the Metropolitan Commission for Sewers, and a succession of schemes were prepared and discussed with the object of improving the drainage arrangements which then existed.

Despite these discussions, nothing much happened until the Metropolitan Board of Works was formed in 1855 with Bazalgette as its first chief engineer. Even then no great progress was made until 1858 when Disraeli removed from the Board the need to obtain Government sanction for its detailed plans.

Disraeli's views were refreshing for a politician although they have largely gone out of fashion since his day. Since the metropolis paid for the works, he said, it had the right to construct them in any way it pleased. As the First Commissioner afterwards said, 'He who pays the fiddler has a right to call the tune'. That was not original perhaps even then, but Disraeli settled the matter and Bazalgette was able to prepare detailed designs and get contracts let.

The drainage works were immense. There were 83 miles of large intercepting sewers, draining more than 100 square miles of built-up land and dealing with over 420 million gallons a day. The cost of the works was £4.6 million. The project was opened by the Prince of Wales in 1865, but the latter portions of the work took longer than might have been expected and final completion did not take place until 1875. That was 26 years after Bazalgette had first become concerned with London's drainage.

His other great London project was the Thames Embankment. First proposed by Sir Christopher Wren after the Great Fire, embanking the Thames became a real proposition in 1860 when a House of Commons Committee took up the idea. The following year a Royal Commission supported the committee's views and the Metropolitan Board of Works was asked to execute the work; Bazalgette saw it through at a cost of £2.15 million.

Bazalgette was connected with the Institution for 53 years, and at the time of his death there were only four surviving members of longer standing than he. He was President in 1884. Bazalgette was knighted in 1874 and he died in 1891.

THE majority of the inhabitants of cities and towns are frequently unconscious of the magnitude, intricacy, and extent of the underground works, which have been designed and constructed at great cost, and are necessary for the maintenance of their health and comfort. It is, however, impossible for large numbers of the human species to congregate and live upon a limited space, without provision being made for the rapid removal of the refuse thereby produced. This necessity is perhaps most forcibly illustrated, by the fearful destruction of life from malaria, produced amongst troops suddenly encamped upon ground not previously so prepared for human habitation. The ravages of disease, thus engendered, became a subject of serious alarm amongst the allied troops in the Crimea ; and there are many instances of the mortality in armies arising from this cause, having far exceeded the deaths from actual warfare.

Various methods have been, and still are, adopted in different parts of the globe, for obviating the dangers which thus force themselves upon the attention of mankind. The Jews, it is known, kept a furnace called " Gehenna," or " Hell-fire," constantly burning in the Valley of Hinnom, into which the refuse of the city of Jerusalem was daily cast, as well as the dead bodies of criminals ; and even the most savage nations are unable entirely to neglect these considerations. The Chinese, sacrificing to a large extent the delicacy and comfort so highly prized by more civilized nations, but with a sound appreciation of the value of town refuse, apply it in the most direct and rude manner to the reproduction of their growing crops. The solid refuse of Paris has also, for many years, been separated and removed for agricultural manure ; but the drainage of that city, and of most of the continental towns, has, until of late years, to a large extent flowed over the surface of the streets. The drainage of English towns has in this respect been mostly in advance of those of other countries ; and London, even prior to the introduction of the improved system, was probably the best-drained city of the present age. One important feature, which it is not the object of this communication to dwell upon, has however, up to the present time, been altogether neglected—the Utilisation of Sewage for agricultural purposes. This subject is now occupying much of the consideration of scientific men, and of the public generally, and is deserving of special consideration in a separate Paper.

Before proceeding to describe the modern works for the improved drainage of London, a glance at the early history of its sewerage may not be uninteresting. The Minutes of Proceedings of some of the earlier Commissions of Sewers contain many curious entries, showing that the subject of sewerage received the attention of the Legislature from a very early date. Amongst others, a proposal by Sir Christopher Wren for improved drainage, nearly two hundred years ago, is preserved in MS. in the records of the ancient Westminster Commission.

"Saturday, yᵉ 13th April, 1678.

" Proposalls delivered by Sᵣ Christopher Wren touching the new street in St. Margaret's, viz.—

" It is proposed, That whereas yᵉ new sewer in Westminster, now proposed to be carryed through George yard to Stories corner, and thence through Long ditch to Sre Rob Pyes sluice, by an uniforme riseing frome yᵉ Thames to the sayd sluice, so as to receive a flush of water from the Mill ditch, by meanes of the sayd sluice, for the scouring and cleansing of the sayd sewer. Now, if the sayd sewer which is already brought to Stories corner by a riseing levell, should be carried with a fall yᵉ otherway' through Long ditch, and so through Deane's yard, and all along by the Mill ditch, and then be vented into yᵉ Thames, neare yᵉ sluice of the Mill. And if a small branch with a sluice should be brought from the King's canall with His Majesty's allowances. It is conceived this way would be far more advantageous to cleane yᵉ sewer, than yᵉ antient ways of receiving a flush from the Mill pools, and may be done at any ebbe, and the charge will be lesse than yᵉ scouring and wharfeing the Mill poole, because ten times the quantity of water may be afforded from the canall without drawing downe canall above 4 inches, which will be immediately supplyed again at flood, and yᵉ water taking the sewer in the middle and driveing downe two waies to each end of the sewer will more effectually cleanse it.

" That a Draught of a Decree be made according to yᵉ proposalls aforesayd."

"Saturday yᵉ 30th of Nov., 1678.

" Upon readeing a paper intituled, An Estimate of yᵉ Charge of several Works to be done in relation to yᵉ Back Waters in St. Margarett's, Westminster. It is ordered, That the worke therein mentioned, to be done in Brasbyes alley in Gardener's lane, be forthwith done and performed. And that the other particulars in the sayd paper mentioned, be referred to Sir Christopher Wren, who is desired to consider the same and make report what is fitt to be done therein."

Commissioners of Sewers were in those days persons of considerable importance, for on the 4th February, 1663, it was ordered " that yᵉ kinges Majestie (Charles II.) beare one halfe of yᵉ charge of yᵉ carrying away of yᵉ rubbish at the sluice by his said Majesties bouling green," and on the 17th April, 1669, " That Francis Crassett, clerk to this Commission, doo attend his Majesties officers concerning the Kinges arreares which are in arreare upon his said Majestie for casting yᵉ comon sewers synce yᵉ thyme of his Majesties happy restauration," and again in 1768, His Majesty George III. was permitted by an order of Court of the Westminster Commissioners of Sewers, at his own cost, to alter the line

[Plate 14, × 27%]

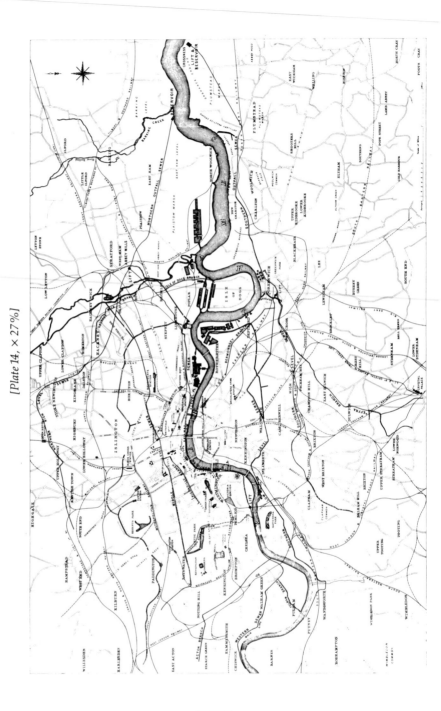

of the King's Scholars' Pond Sewer from under Her Majesty the Queen's palace in St. James's Park, and it was—

"Ordered that His Majesty may remove the sewer from under Her Majesty's the Queen's Palace in St. James's Park, by making a new sewer from the north side of this said Palace to the road leading from Buckingham Gate towards Pimlico, at His Majesty's expense if His Majesty so pleases."

Up to about the year 1815, it was penal to discharge sewage, or other offensive matters, into the sewers; cesspools were regarded as the proper receptacles for house drainage, and sewers as the legitimate channels for carrying off the surface waters only. Afterwards it became permissive, and in the year 1847 the first Act was obtained making it compulsory, to drain houses into sewers.

The Fleet Sewer, formerly known as the River of Wells, or the Old Bourne (now called Holborn), was fed by several springs, from which originated the names of many of the populous districts of London, such as Sadler's Well, Bagnigge Well, Lamb's Conduit, Chad's Well, and Clerk's Well or Clerkenwell, which latter derived its name from the parish clerks of the City of London, who used to meet there annually to represent certain parts of Scripture in a theatrical manner, and thither the nobility, the lord mayor and citizens repaired to see the performances.

In 1218, the Fleet supplied the people residing west of Chancery Lane, then called "Foreigners," with water; and in 1307, a mill, the property of the Templars, was removed on the ground that it disturbed the water. The Fleet Sewer was at that time navigated up to Holborn Bridge, and it was not until 1732 that it was, by Act of Parliament, covered in between Holborn Bridge and Fleet Bridge.

The waters from a spring at Tye Bourne and from the Bayswater Brook (now called the Ranelagh Sewer) were also conveyed, in 6-inch leaden pipes, into the neighbouring dwellings; and, in 1730, Queen Caroline fed the Serpentine in Hyde Park with water from the Ranelagh. Of late years, however, the water so polluted the lake that it has been diverted by a new sewer through the Park.

The Ranelagh and the King's Scholars' Pond Sewers, the Fleet Ditch, and other main valley lines were at this time, and for many subsequent years, open brooks, ponded up at various points along their route, so as to form ornamental waters in the pleasure-grounds of the gentry, who lived in what still continued to be the suburbs of the metropolis. Plate 15 Fig. 2, represents the condition and appearance of the Ranelagh sewer, as taken from actual surveys in 1809. The Commissioners of Sewers of those days were wont to make an annual personal inspection of the sewers under their charge, a duty which has of late years been discontinued.

As the population of London increased, the subsoil became thickly studded with cesspools, improved household appliances were introduced, overflow drains from the cesspools to the sewers were constructed, thus the sewers became polluted, and covered brick channels were necessarily substituted for existing open streams.

Prior to the year 1847, the sewers were under the management of eight distinct Commissions, viz., the City, Westminster, Holborn and Finsbury, Tower Hamlets, Poplar and Blackwall, Surrey and Kent, Greenwich, and St. Katherine's Commissions of Sewers. These were independent bodies; each appointed its own officers, and carried out its drainage works, frequently regardless of the effect thereby produced upon the neighbouring districts, through which the sewage flowed. The works were not constructed upon a uniform system; and the sizes, shapes, and levels of the sewers at the boundaries of the different districts were often very variable. Larger sewers were made to discharge into smaller ones; sewers with upright sides and circular crowns and inverts were connected with egg-shaped sewers; and egg-shaped sewers with the narrow part uppermost were connected with similar sewers having the smaller part downwards.

In the year 1847, these eight Commissions of Sewers were superseded by one Commission, termed "The Metropolitan Commission of Sewers," whose members were nominated by the Government. That Commission entertained opposite views respecting the use of sewers to those which had been previously held, and directed its energies mainly to the introduction of pipe-sewers of small dimensions, in lieu of the large brick sewers previously in vogue, to the abolition of cesspools, and to the diversion of all house drainage (by direct communications) into the sewers, making the adoption of the new system of drainage compulsory; so that, within a period of about six years, thirty thousand cesspools were abolished, and all house and street refuse was turned into the river.

Similar systems were, about the same period, to a large extent adopted in the provincial towns, by which means their drainage has been vastly improved, but the rivers and streams of the country have become very generally and seriously polluted.

During the existence of this Commission, the Author first became officially connected with the drainage of London; but, within nine years after its formation, the Metropolitan Commission of Sewers was six times superseded, and six new and differently constituted Commissions were successively appointed. These were however unable, during their limited period of office, to mature and carry out works of any magnitude.

The second of these Commissions was issued in 1849. The Thames at that time was becoming full of sewage; and as several of the Water Companies then obtained their supply from the river at or near London, the public press began to agitate for a remedy for this rapidly increasing evil. The Commissioners, by advertisement, invited designs for the purification of the river, in answer to which they received one hundred and sixteen different schemes, proposing various methods for the accomplishment of that object, and in the midst of the perplexity of selecting from these designs,

112

[Plate 15]

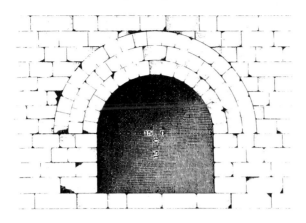

CLOACA MAXIMA
ROMA.

RANELAGH SEWER, CHELSEA.
1809.

EAST ELEVATION OF PRIVATE BRIDGE.

and of the public excitement thereby produced, the Commission resigned. The late Mr. Robert Stephenson, Mr. Rendel, and Sir William Cubitt were appointed members of the third Commission, and they undertook the classification and investigation of the merits, of these competing plans, and eventually, after much careful consideration, arrived at the conclusion, that whilst the plan of Mr. M'Clean (President Inst. C.E.) was the best, none could be recommended for execution as a whole.

In 1850, Mr. Frank Forster was appointed Chief Engineer of the Commission; under his direction, Messrs. Grant and Cresy commenced the preparation of a plan for the interception of the sewage of the area south of the Thames, and Mr. Haywood, the Engineer of the City Commissioners of Sewers, assisted Mr. Forster in the preparation of a similar plan for the districts on the North side.

In 1851, the fourth Commission was appointed, when one of its members prepared and advocated a plan of his own, in opposition to the plan of Mr. Forster. Mr. Forster's health giving way under the excitement of protracted opposition, he resigned his position, and shortly afterwards died.

In 1852, the fifth Commission was issued, and the Author succeeded Mr. Forster as Chief Engineer. Fresh plans for intercepting the sewage of the metropolis still continued to be laid before the Commission, and were from time to time examined and reported on, without any practical result. In 1854, the Author was directed to prepare a scheme of intercepting sewers, intended to effect the improved Main Drainage of London, and Mr. Haywood was associated with him for the northern portion. The late Mr. Robert Stephenson and Sir William Cubitt afterwards devoted much time and attention to the consideration of the plan so prepared, and eventually recommended its adoption.

In February, 1854, Mr. Cubitt reported that—

"After a very careful examination of the reports and plans, and the elaborate set of sections and details which they (Messrs. Bazalgette and Haywood) have produced, together with the estimate founded thereon, that the whole are worthy of every attention as regards the capacities and inclinations of the various intercepting drains, in relation to the quantities of water they have to carry and discharge. The matter is, in fact, so clearly and minutely set forth in report, plans, and sections, that the Engineers have laid themselves entirely open to detection by any persons who understand practical engineering, inasmuch as, in their present state, the documents would enable such a person to make a correct estimate of the amount at which any portion of the works might be contracted for; a fact highly creditable to the Engineers."

The sixth Commission, formed in 1855, continued to discuss the subject, without coming to any practical result, up to the time of its dissolution, and of the formation of the present 'Metropolitan Board of Works,' in 1856.

But it was not alone the anomalies of the old Commissions, and the necessity for providing for the great increase in drainage matter caused by modern improvements, which compelled the adoption of a general system of Main Drainage. The metropolis had suffered severely in the cholera visitation of 1831-2, again in 1848-9, and lastly in 1853-4. In 1849 the deaths were 18,036, and in 1854 nearly 20,000 ; and although great differences of opinion existed, and continue to exist, as to the causes of the disease, yet an inspection of the houses in which deaths occurred was sufficient to show that, however occult might be the connection between death and defective drainage, the places formerly most favourable to the spread of disease became quite free from it, when afterwards properly drained.

Acting on the indications afforded by the Registrar-General's return, the Commissioners of Sewers endeavoured to afford an outlet into a good sewer for every suspected locality ; but they speedily found that a limit had been put to their operations, by the carelessness and cupidity of preceding generations. Builders had in many cases, especially on the south side of the Thames, availed themselves of the comparative cheapness of the land, and placed their houses in spots not only sewerless, but where no outlets for sewers existed. In designing a system of Main Drainage, these points had to be kept in view,—to provide ample means for the discharge of the large and increasing water supply consequent on the universal adoption of closets, and of the ordinary rainfall and surface drainage at all times, except during extraordinary storms, and to afford to the low-lying districts a sufficiently deep outfall to allow of every house being effectually relieved of its fluid refuse.

For centuries there had existed Sewers Commissions appointed by the Government, and irresponsible to the ratepayers, upon whom they levied rates, and for whose benefit they expended them, and the substitution of the Metropolitan Board of Works was the first introduction of the system of local self-government. Under this Act London is divided into thirty-nine districts. The City of London and the larger parishes, such as Marylebone and Lambeth, each form one district, and minor parishes are united to form other districts. The ratepayers of each parish, or district, elect from among themselves a prescribed number of representatives, to form a board, who manage the local drainage, paving, lighting, and other improvements, and these district boards select from their body one or more members (proportionate to the population and extent of the district) to form the Metropolitan Board, which consists of forty-five members, presided over by a Chairman, and has control over the Main Sewers, the Thames Embankment, all new streets, and metropolitan improvements, and makes bye-laws for the direction and control of the different vestries and district boards.

The Author, having been appointed Engineer to the Metropolitan Board, was again instructed to prepare a plan for the drainage of the metropolis, and, when completed, it was approved and adopted by the Board. Her Majesty's First Commissioner of Works, however, having a veto under the Act constituting the Board, refused, upon a technical point, to sanction this plan. His decision was resisted by the Board, and the difficulty was ultimately removed. He had, however, referred the plan for examination to a

Commission of Engineers named by him, which Commission substituted and recommended a design of their own, in lieu of that approved by the Board. The Royal Commissioners' plan was, in its turn, submitted by the Metropolitan Board of Works to Mr. Bidder, Mr. Hawksley, and the Author, upon whose Report the Board's plan was, after much discussion and delay, eventually adopted, and the works were commenced in 1859. It was through the influence of Lord John Manners, who afterwards became the First Commissioner of Works, that the Board was left free to carry out their system of Main Drainage.

The works involved in that design are now practically completed and in operation. They are illustrated more particularly by the contract drawings and specifications herewith presented to the Institution, and a description of the works forms the more immediate subject of this Paper.

The objects sought to be attained in the execution of the Main Drainage works were the interception of the sewage (as far as practicable by gravitation), together with so much of the rainfall mixed with it as could be reasonably dealt with, so as to divert it from the river near London ; the substitution of a constant, instead of an intermittent flow in the sewers ; the abolition of stagnant and tide-locked sewers, with their consequent accumulations of deposit; and the provision of deep and improved outfalls, for the extension of sewerage into districts previously, for want of such outfalls, imperfectly drained.

Having these objects in view, it is easier and more economical to originate a new and complete system of drainage, than to adapt existing and defective sewers to a uniform and more perfect system.

According to the system which it was sought to improve, the London Main Sewers fell into the valley of the Thames, and most of them, passing under the low grounds on the margin of the river before they reached it, discharged their contents into that river at or about the level, and at the time of low water only. As the tide rose it closed the outlets, and ponded back the sewage flowing from the high grounds; this accumulated in the low-lying portions of the sewers, where it remained stagnant in many cases for eighteen out of every twenty-four hours. During that period the heavier ingredients were deposited, and from day to day accumulated in the sewers; besides which, in times of heavy and long-continued rains, and more particularly when these occurred at the time of high water in the river, the closed sewers were unable to store the increased volume of sewage, which then rose through the house drains and flooded the basements of the houses.

The effect upon the Thames, of thus discharging the sewage into it at the time of low water, was most injurious, because not only was it carried by the rising tide up the river, to be brought back to London by the following ebb-tide, there to mix with each day's fresh supply,—the progress of many days' accumulation towards the sea being almost imperceptible,—but the volume of the pure water in the river, being at that time at its minimum, rendered it quite incapable of diluting and disinfecting such vast masses of sewage.

In the system now adopted, it has been sought to remove these evils by the construction of new lines of sewers, laid at right angles to the existing sewers, and a little below their levels, so as to intercept their contents, and convey them to an outfall 14 miles below London Bridge. As large a proportion of the sewage as practicable is by this means carried away by gravitation, and for the remainder a constant discharge is effected by pumping. At the outlets, the sewage is delivered into reservoirs situate on the banks of the Thames, and placed at such a level as will enable them to discharge into the river at or about the time of high water. By this arrangement, the sewage is not only at once diluted by the large volume of water in the Thames at high water, but is also carried by the ebb tide to a point in the river, 26 miles below London Bridge, and its return by the following flood tide, within the metropolitan area, is effectually prevented.

At the threshold of any inquiry into this subject, the following important points required to be solved :—

1st. At what point and state of the tide can the sewage be discharged into the river so as not to return within the more densely inhabited portions of the metropolis ?

2nd. What is the minimum fall which should be given to the intercepting sewers ?

3rd. What is the quantity of sewage to be intercepted, and does it pass off in a uniform flow at all hours of the day and night, or in what manner ?

4th. Is the rainfall to be mixed with the sewage, in what manner and quantities does it flow into the sewers, and is it also to be carried off in the intercepting sewers, or how is it to be provided for ?

5th. Having regard to all these points, how are the sizes of the intercepting and main drainage sewers to be determined ?

6th. What descriptions of pumping engines and of pumps are best suited for lifting the sewage of London at the pumping stations?

So comprehensive a subject, involving not only the above, but many other important topics, cannot be fully considered within the limits of an ordinary Paper, in which these questions can only be briefly touched upon.

The position of the outfalls and the time of discharge into the river were arrived at in the mode described in the following extract from the Report of the late Mr. Robert Stephenson and Sir William Cubitt, dated the 11th December, 1854 ; wherein they give a brief summary of a series of experiments made by the late Mr. Frank Forster, and subsequently repeated by Captain Burstal, R.N., and the Author, upon this subject—

" On the 13th of July, 1851, a float was put into the centre of the river opposite Barking Creek two hours after high water. This time was chosen, because it was found that sewage discharged into the river two hours before high water arrived at about the same point above Barking Creek as sewage discharged two hours after high water did by the next flood tide. At low water the float reached 11¾ miles below that point, and returned with the next flood tide to 1 mile above it, having gone 12¾ miles that flood, it being then the period of spring tides.

"As the neaps came on, the float continued to work lower down at each succeeding high water, and by the 24th of July it was 13 miles below Barking Creek at high water, having gone down the river 14 miles during the falling off of spring tides to neap tides. As the floods again became stronger, it worked up the river each succeeding tide until the 29th July, when it again came within 5 miles below Barking Creek at high water, having worked up the river 9 miles from high water neap tides to high water spring tides, the excess of the ebbs over the floods being only 5 miles in fourteen days."

"Another experiment was tried at the same place on the 6th of August, 1851, it being then lowest neaps, and the float being put down two hours after high water. It worked up each succeeding high water till top springs on the 12th of August, when it reached 6¼ miles above Barking Creek at high water. The float then again worked down the river, till the 20th of August, 9½ miles below Barking Creek, being a distance of 16 miles during the falling off of spring tides to neap tides. The excess of ebbs over the floods would in this case have been about 7 miles in fourteen days. The wind and other causes would vary the result, but it may be roughly assumed, that a substance in suspension works up the river about 1 mile a day at each high water as the springs strengthen, and down the river 2 miles a day as they fall off."

The main object was of course to determine, how near to London the sewage could be discharged into the river, at or near high water, without finding its way back again to the inhabited parts of the town. The experiments proved, that it was essential to go as far as Barking Creek; and also, as regards the level of the discharge, they demonstrated that it should take place at or as near high water as practicable.

Now, although it is desirable to fix the place of discharge as far below the metropolis as possible, it will be found that a practical limit to this point is imposed on the north side of the river, by the advantages gained from a discharge by gravitation, and by the necessity of maintaining a sufficient fall in the sewers; and on the south side, in order to preserve as a safety outlet a discharge into the river at low water by gravitation, in case of accident to the pumps, as well as during excessive floods.

As regards the time of discharge, it is demonstrated by the same series of experiments that—

"The delivery of the sewage at high water into the river at any point is equivalent to its discharge at low water at a point 12 miles lower down the river, therefore the construction of 12 miles of sewer is saved by discharging the sewage at high instead of low water."

As to the velocity of flow and the minimum fall, though it is necessary to economize the fall of the sewers in order to save pumping, yet a sufficient velocity of flow to prevent deposit must at the same time be maintained, and the question—What is a sufficient flow? must be determined.

Upon this point Mr. Wicksteed, in his Report upon the Drainage of Leicester (p. 19), states—

" From experiments made by me with great care, I find that with a bottom velocity of 16 inches per second only (or 0·90 mile per hour) heavy pieces of brick, stone, &c., will be removed, and that with a velocity of 21¾ inches (or 1·24 mile per hour), even iron borings and heavy slag will be removed. The above minimum velocity will therefore be sufficient."

Mr. Beardmore, in his work on Hydraulics, states (p. 8) that "a velocity of 150 feet per minute (or 1¾ mile per hour) will generally prevent deposits in pipes and sewers."

Mr. John Phillips states (see First Report of Sanitary Commission, 1847, p. 177),—

" From observation and experiment, I find that it requires a constant velocity of current to be running through the sewers equal to about 2½ feet per second, or about 1¾ mile per hour, to prevent the soil from depositing within them."

Professor Robison, in his " Theory of Rivers," states, at page 465, that—

" We learn from observation, that a velocity of 3 inches per second at the bottom will just begin to work up fine clay fit for pottery, and however firm and compact it may be, it will tear up."

" A velocity of 6 inches will lift fine sand, 8 inches will lift sand as coarse as linseed, 12 inches will sweep along fine gravel, 24 inches will roll along rounded pebbles an inch diameter, and it requires 3 feet per second at the bottom to sweep along shivery angular stones of the size of an egg."

It is difficult to lay down any general rule upon this point, because the conditions of sewers, as to the quantity of deposit passing into them, and the ordinary volume of the sewage flowing through them, vary considerably. But the Author does not hesitate to rely upon these opinions, confirmed as they are by his own observations and experience, which lead him to regard a mean velocity of 1½ mile per hour, in a properly protected main sewer, when running half full, as sufficient, more especially when the contents have previously passed through a pumping station.

Having thus determined the minimum velocity, it becomes necessary to ascertain the quantity of sewage to be carried off, before the fall requisite to produce that velocity can be estimated. This quantity varies but little from the water supply with which a given population is provided; for that portion which is absorbed and evaporated is compensated for by the dry weather underground leakage into the sewers. The water supply to various parts of London in 1856 varied from 20 gallons to 25 gallons per head per diem; but a more liberal supply was contemplated, and that supply was likely to be further augmented, by an increase in the population in certain districts not then wholly built upon. It was ascertained that a district of average density of population, when wholly built upon, contained 30,000 people to the square mile, so that in districts containing that, or more than that number of people to the square mile, the actual numbers were ascertained and provided for; but in districts where the population was below that number, provision has been made for an increase of population up to 30,000 people to the square mile, except over the outlying districts, where provision has been made for a population of only 20,000 to the square mile.

An improved water supply, equal to 5 cubic feet, or $31\frac{1}{4}$ gallons, per head for such contemplated increased population, has moreover been anticipated. The effect upon the Thames of the diversion from its channel of water for the supply, not only of London but also of other towns, appears already to have attracted the notice of the Legislature.

Experience has shown, that sewage is not discharged into the sewers at a uniform rate throughout the twenty-four hours, nor even throughout the day. Mr. Lovick, the Assistant Engineer, made some careful observations on this subject for the late Metropolitan Commission of Sewers. The habits of the population in various parts of London are indicated by the flow of sewage through the sewers; the maximum flow in the more fashionable districts of the West end being two or three hours later than from the East end. Taking, as before, a liberal margin beyond the results of actual measurements, provision has been made for one-half of the sewage to flow off within six hours of the day; and thus the maximum quantity of sewage, likely hereafter to enter the sewers at various parts of the metropolis, has been arrived at.

How to dispose of the rainfall is a question of considerable difficulty, and has given rise to much diversity of opinion. This arises from the fact that, whilst it is in itself harmless, and even advantageous, to the river, it sometimes falls suddenly in large quantities. These considerations have induced theorists to advocate, that the rainfall should not be allowed to flow off with the sewage, but should be dealt with by a separate system of sewers. This theory is, however, most impracticable. It would involve a double set of drains to every house, and the construction and maintenance of a second series of sewers to every street. Applied to London, it would involve the re-draining of every house and every street in the metropolis; and, according to a moderate estimate, it would lead to an expenditure of from ten to twelve millions of money, while the interference with private property would alone render such a proposition intolerable.

Careful observations of the quantity of rain falling on the metropolis within short periods have been made by the Author for many years. Taking an average of several years, it has been ascertained that there are about one hundred and fifty-five days per annum upon which rain falls; of these there are only about twenty-five upon which the quantity amounts to $\frac{1}{4}$ of an inch in depth in twenty-four hours, or the 1-100th part of an inch per hour, if spread over an entire day. Of such rainfalls a large proportion is evaporated or absorbed, and either does not pass through the sewers, or does not reach them until long after the rain has ceased.   In the Report of Mr. Bidder, Mr. Hawksley, and the Author, in 1858, on this subject, it is stated that continuous observations, and as far as practicable protected from disturbing influences, had been taken at the close of the previous year, and that these observations, which were recorded in the Appendix to the above Report, had enabled them to arrive at some reliable conclusions, and that,—

" The result of these observations distinctly establishes the fact, that the quantity of rain which flowed off by the sewers was, in all cases, much less than the quantity which fell on the ground ; and although the variations of atmospheric phenomena are far too great to allow any philosophical proportions to be established between the rainfall and the sewer flow, yet we feel warranted in concluding, as a rule of averages, that ¼ of an inch of rainfall will not contribute more than ⅛ of an inch to the sewers, nor a fall of $\frac{4}{10}$ of an inch more than ¼ of an inch.   Indeed, we have recently observed rainfalls of very sensible amounts failing to contribute any distinguishable quantity to the sewers."

But there are, in almost every year, exceptional cases of heavy and violent rain-storms, and these have measured 1 inch, and sometimes even 2 inches, in an hour.   A quantity equal to the 1-100th part of an inch of rain in an hour, or ¼ of an inch in twenty-four hours, running into the sewers, would occupy as much space as the maximum prospective flow of sewage provided for ; so that, if that quantity of rain were included in the intercepting sewers, they would, during the six hours of maximum flow, be filled with an equal volume of sewage, and during the remaining eighteen hours additional space would be reserved for a larger quantity of rain.   Taking this circumstance into consideration, and allowing for the abstraction due to evaporation and absorption, it is probable that if the sewers were made capable of carrying off a volume equal to a rainfall of ¼ of an inch per day, during the six hours of the maximum flow, there would not be more than twelve days in a year on which the sewers would be overcharged, and then only for short periods during such days.   But exceptional rain-storms must be provided for, however rare their occurrence, or they would deluge the property on which they fell. As it would not have been wise, or practicable, to have increased the sizes of the intercepting sewers much beyond their present dimensions, in order to carry off rare and excessive thunderstorms, overflow weirs, to act as safety-valves in times of storm, have been constructed at the junctions of the intercepting sewers with the main valley lines : on such occasions the surplus waters will be largely diluted, and, after the intercepting sewers are filled, will flow over the weirs, and through their original channels into the Thames.

Having thus determined the quantities of sewage and rainfall to be carried off, and the rate of declivity of the sewer required for the necessary velocity of flow, the sizes of the intercepting sewers were readily determined by the formulæ of Prony, Eytelwein, and Du Buat ; and the sizes of the drainage sewers by the useful formula of Mr. Hawksley, which, with some modifications, may be

121

applied to a variety of conditions and circumstances, and with respect to which the Author would again quote from the Report of the late Mr. R. Stephenson and Sir William Cubitt of the 11th December, 1854, in which it is said :—

" No part of Engineering science has been more industriously investigated than the laws that govern the flow of water in pipes and open channels; and it is probably not too much to say, that the formulæ which represent these laws rank amongst the most truthful that the professional man possesses. They have been the subject of laborious experimental investigation of the most elaborate character, and their results have been tested by the practical man under every variety of conditions, without their truth being impugned in the slightest degree. The principles upon which they are founded have been sanctioned and adopted by Prony, Eytelwein, Du Buat, and others ; and it is to them that we are indebted, in a great measure, for the simple practical form which they present. Our own Engineers have modified them to suit particular circumstances, and given them more extensive usefulness. Mr. Hawksley, amongst others, has especially contributed to render the principles which they embrace applicable to almost every variety of condition which the complete drainage of large towns involves ; and we shall have occasion, almost immediately, to adduce some instances within the metropolis, where the facts confirm theoretical deductions in a very remarkable manner, and lead irresistibly to the conclusion that they may be implicitly depended on."

With respect to the description of pumping engines and pumps to be employed, various opinions existed as to the comparative advantages of Cornish or rotative engines, and as to the respective merits of centrifugal and screw pumps, chain pumps, lifting bucket wheels, flash wheels, and of every variety of suction or plunger pump and pump valve for raising the metropolitan sewage. In 1859, numerous competing designs, involving all these principles, were reported upon by Messrs. Stephenson, Field, Penn, Hawksley, Bidder, and the Author ; and the pumping engines and pumps subsequently designed for, and adopted by, the Metropolitan Board of Works are based upon the recommendations contained in that Report. The engines are condensing double-acting rotative beam engines, and the pumps are plunger or ram pumps, the sewage being discharged from the pumps through a series of hanging valves.

The contractors for the engines at Crossness and at Abbey Mills guarantee that the engines shall, when working, raise 80 million lbs. one foot high, with one cwt. of Welsh coal.

A primary object sought to be attained in this scheme was the removal of as much of the sewage as practicable by gravitation, so as to reduce the amount of pumping to a minimum. To effect this, three lines of sewers have been constructed on each side of the river, termed respectively the High Level, the Middle Level, and the Low Level. The High and the Middle Level Sewers discharge by gravitation, and the Low Level Sewers discharge only by the aid of pumping. The three lines of sewers north of the Thames converge and unite at Abbey Mills, east of London, where the contents of the Low Level will be pumped into the Upper Level Sewer, and their aggregate stream will flow through the Northern

Outfall Sewer, which is carried on a concrete embankment across the marshes to Barking Creek, and there discharges into the river by gravitation.

On the South side, the three intercepting lines unite at Deptford Creek, and the contents of the Low Level Sewer are there pumped to the Upper Level, and the united streams of all three flow in one channel through Woolwich to Crossness Point in Erith Marshes. Here the full volume of sewage can flow into the Thames at low water, but will ordinarily be raised by pumping into the reservoir.

With respect to the form of the sewers, as the intercepting sewers carry off only the 1-100th part of an inch of rain in an hour, and the volume of sewage passing through them is at all times considerable, the flow through these sewers is more uniform than in drainage sewers constructed to carry off heavy rain-storms. The form, therefore, generally adopted for the intercepting sewers is circular, as combining the greatest strength and capacity with the smallest amount of brickwork and the least cost. In the minor branches, for district drainage, the egg shape, with the narrow part downwards, is preferable ; because the dry weather flow of the sewage being small, the greatest hydraulic mean depth, and consequently the greatest velocity of flow and scouring power, is obtained by that section in the bottom at the period when it is most required, and the broader section at the upper part affords room for the passage of the storm-waters, as also for the workmen engaged in repairing and cleansing.

Having thus briefly glanced at the early history of the drainage of London, and the circumstances which led to the adoption of the main intercepting scheme, and a few of the considerations and general principles upon which that scheme is based, a more detailed description of the works will now be given, as well as of some of the peculiarities or difficulties met with during their construction.

THE NORTH SIDE OF THE THAMES.

The High Level Sewer was constructed under one contract. It commences by a junction with the Fleet Sewer, at the foot of Hampstead Hill, and passes along Gordon House-lane, and across the Highgate-road. It is carried through Tufnell-park-road, Holloway-road, under the Great Northern Railway, and the New River to High-street, Stoke Newington, at Abney Park Cemetery. It then passes under the Rectory and Amhurst roads to Church-street, Hackney ; under the North London Railway, through Victoria-park, and under Sir George Duckett's Canal to a junction with the Middle Level Sewer. (Plate 16.) Up to this point it is a drainage sewer, that is to say, it is a substitute for the open Fleet and Hackney Brook main sewers, which have since been filled in and abandoned ; and it has been constructed of such dimensions, as to be capable of carrying off the largest and most sudden falls of

[Plate 16]

SECTION OF OVERFLOW CHAMBER AT JUNCTION OF NORTHERN HIGH & MIDDLE LEVEL SEWERS.

rain. It is about 7 miles long, drains an area of about 10 square
miles, and intercepts the sewage of Hampstead, part of Kentish
Town, Highgate, Hackney, Clapton, Stoke Newington, and Hollo-
way. A portion of the district adjoining the Hackney Marshes
is so low, that it was necessary to drain it through a branch passing into the Low Level Sewer. The form of the High Level Sewer
is mostly circular, and it varies in size from 4 feet in diameter to
9 feet 6 inches by 12 feet; its fall is rapid, ranging at the upper
end from 1 in 71 to 1 in 376, and from 4 feet to 5 feet per mile at
the lower end.

It is constructed of stock brickwork, varying in thickness from
9 inches to 2 feet 3 inches, and the invert is lined with Staffordshire blue bricks, in order to withstand the scour arising from the
rapid fall. One tunnel, from Maiden-lane towards Hampstead, is
about ½ a mile long, and great care was necessary in tunnelling
under the New River, its channel being on an embankment where
it intersects the line of sewer; also under the Great Northern
Railway, at a place where its embankment is 30 feet high, the
sewer being 7 feet 6 inches in diameter, and the brickwork 14
inches in thickness.

Much house-property was successfully tunneled under at
Hackney. One house, adjoining the railway station, was underpinned and placed upon iron girders, and the sewer, being there
9 feet 3 inches in diameter, was carried through the cellar without
further injury to the house. The sewer is carried close under the
bottom of Sir George Duckett's Canal, the distance between the
soffit of the arch of the sewer and the water in the canal being
only 24 inches. The bottom of the canal and the top of the sewer
are here formed of iron girders and plates, with a thin coating of
puddle, and no leakage from the canal has taken place. This
was the first portion of the Main Drainage works executed, and it
was completed in the year 1854. The whole of the High Level
Sewer, including the Penstock Chamber, was completed in May,
1861, and has been in full operation since that date.

The Penstock Chamber, which is formed at the junction of the
High and the Middle Level Sewers at Old Ford, Bow, is provided
with five large iron penstocks worked by machinery, by which the
sewage can be diverted at will either into the two lower channels
formed for the discharge of the storm-waters into the River Lea,
or into the two upper channels constructed over that river, and
forming the commencement of the Northern Outfall Sewer. As a
rule the lower channels will be closed, and the sewage will flow
through the two upper channels to Barking Creek; but in times
of heavy rain, as soon as the waters have risen to the top of the
upper channels, the surplus will flow over five weirs, constructed in
the chamber, into the lower channels, and be discharged by them
into the Lea. In case of any sudden accident to the intercepting
sewers, the whole of the sewage could, by raising the lower penstock, be diverted in a few minutes into the Lea.

The penstock and weir chamber is a novel arrangement, which

has proved to be simple and satisfactory in its operation, and it places three-fourths of the Northern sewage completely under command. It is built in brickwork, is about 150 feet in length, 40 feet in breadth, and, in places, 30 feet in height.

The principal difficulties to be overcome during the construction of this line of sewer arose from the continued combinations and strikes, which at that time prevailed amongst the workmen, in various parts of England. It is to be hoped that the good sense and good feeling of both the parties concerned will find means for avoiding a recurrence of these public calamities. It is curious to notice, that the injury thus produced was considered so serious in the reign of Edward VI. as to induce the Legislature to pass a statute for the repression of strikes and combinations amongst the workmen. The statute provided that, upon conviction, the offenders should be punished by means not quite consistent with the policy of the present age, viz.—by the infliction not only of fine or imprisonment, but also, for repeated offences, by the punishment of the pillory, having an ear cut off, and being rendered infamous and incapable of giving evidence upon oath.

A long-continued wet season prevented the manufacture of bricks, while the demand for them was greatly increased by the formation of several metropolitan railways and other public works at the same period ; the prices of building materials and labour rose therefore considerably, and the combination of these untoward circumstances rendered this an unprofitable work for the contractor.

The Middle Level Sewer was formed under one contract, and is carried as near to the Thames as the contour of the ground will permit, with the object of intercepting as much sewage as possible by gravitation, and of reducing to a minimum the low level area which is dependent upon pumping. The area intercepted by this sewer is $17\frac{1}{2}$ square miles in extent, and is densely inhabited. The sewer commences near the Harrow Road at Kensal Green, passes under the Paddington Canal into the Uxbridge Road at Notting Hill, along Oxford Street, Hart Street, Liquorpond Street, and across Clerkenwell Green ; thence by way of Old Street Road to High Street, Shoreditch, along Church Street, Bethnal Green Road, and Green Street, under the Regent's Canal and the North London Railway, to a junction with the High Level Sewer at the Penstock Chamber at Bow. (Plate 16.) In order to enlarge the area drained by gravitation, a branch, 4 feet by 2 feet 8 inches, with a fall of 4 feet per mile, is carried along Piccadilly, passes through Leicester Square and Lincoln's Inn Fields to the main line at King's Road, Gray's Inn Road. The length of the main line is about $9\frac{1}{2}$ miles, and of the Piccadilly Branch 2 miles, besides which there are minor branches and feeders. The fall of the Main Sewer varies from $17\frac{1}{2}$ feet per mile at the upper end, by a gradual reduction, to 2 feet per mile at the lower end.

The sizes vary from 4 feet 6 inches by 3 feet, to 10 feet 6 inches in diameter, and lastly to 9 feet 6 inches by 12 feet at the outlet. About 4 miles of the main line, and the whole of the Piccadilly

Branch, were constructed by tunneling under the streets, at depths varying from 20 feet to 60 feet. This sewer is formed mostly in the London clay; to the east of Shoreditch it is constructed through gravel, and during the execution of the works under the Regent's Canal, the water burst into the sewer, fortunately giving sufficient warning to prevent any loss of life. The sewer was afterwards constructed under the canal, first by enclosing one-half of the width of the tunnel at a time within a coffer-dam, and then by open cutting.

The Middle Level Sewer is carried over the Metropolitan Railway by a wrought-iron aqueduct of 150 feet span, weighing 240 tons; the depth of construction between the under side of the aqueduct and the inverts of the double line of sewers being only 2½ inches. As the traffic of the railway could not be stopped during the construction of the aqueduct, which is only a few inches above the engine chimneys, the structure was built upon a stage, at a height of 5 feet above its intended ultimate level, and was afterwards lowered into place by means of hydraulic rams. This stage was

[Plate 17]

NORTH SIDE.

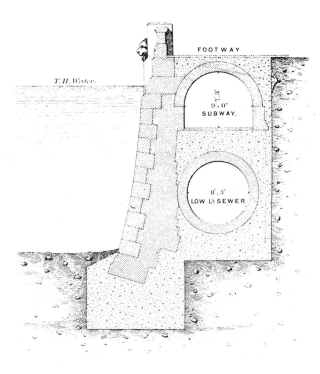

SECTION OF THAMES EMBANKMENT, SUBWAY & LOW LEVEL SEWER.

127

necessarily of great strength and was carefully constructed ; the sewers being formed by wrought-iron plates riveted together.

The Middle Level Sewer is provided with weirs, or storm-over-flows, at its various junctions with all the main valley lines. It has recently been completed, and is now in active operation.

The Low Level Sewer, besides intercepting the sewage from the low level area, which contains 11 square miles, is also the main outlet for a district of about $14\frac{1}{2}$ square miles, forming the western suburb of London, which is so low, that its sewage has to be lifted at Chelsea a height of $17\frac{1}{2}$ feet, into the upper end of the Low Level Sewer. This sewer commences at the Grosvenor Canal, Pimlico, and passes along Lupus Street and Bessborough Street, to and along the river side from Vauxhall Bridge. From Westminster Bridge to Blackfriars it is being formed as part of the Thames Embankment (Plate 17) ; and thence it will pass under a portion of the new street to the Mansion House, and will pro-bably take the line of the Inner Circle Railway to Tower Hill. From Tower Hill it is being formed mostly by tunneling along Mint Street, Cable Street, Back Road, Commercial Road, and under the Limehouse Cut and Bow Common. It is now being tunneled under the River Lea, on its route to the Abbey Mills pumping station, where its contents will be raised 36 feet by steam power. It has two branches :—one from Homerton, and the other from the Isle of Dogs. This island was formerly a dismal marsh, and re-ceived its name from the circumstance of the king's hounds having been kept there, when the Court was at Greenwich. It is now the site of extensive factories and works, and is largely populated by artisans and workmen. Its drainage can only be perfected by the aid of pumping, the beneficial effect of which was so well described by the late Mr. R. Stephenson and Sir W. Cubitt, when they compared it to the lifting of the whole district out of a hollow, on to high ground above the level of the river. The length of the main line is $8\frac{1}{4}$ miles, and its branches are about 4 miles in length. Its size varies from 6 feet 9 inches to 10 feet 3 inches in diameter, its inclination ranges from 2 feet to 3 feet per mile, and it is pro-vided with storm-overflows into the river.

The Western Division includes Fulham, Chelsea, Brompton, Kensington, Shepherd's Bush, Hammersmith, and part of Acton. It was originally intended to deodorise, or utilise, the sewage of this district in its own neighbourhood, rather than to incur the heavy cost of carrying it to Barking, and lifting it twice on its route to that place. But strong objections to this having been raised, the latter and more costly plan has since been adopted, and now forms part of the Low Level system of drainage.

In this district a new system of main sewers has been laid, the sewers being conveyed into one channel passing under the West London Extension Railway, and the Kensington Canal, near to Cremorne Gardens, where a temporary pumping station has been

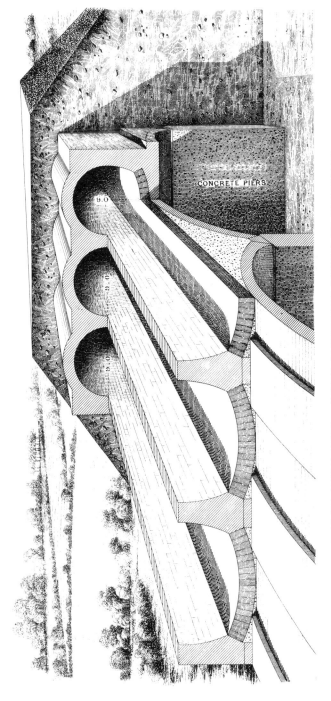

[Plate 18]

NORTHERN OUTFALL SEWER. SECTION OF EMBANKMENT, CULVERTS AND SUBSTRUCTURE.

Concreting plant for the northern level outfall sewer in the early 1860s (from a contemporary photograph, × 68%)

erected, and the sewage is, and will continue to be, lifted into the river, until the Low Level Sewer is completed.

The Chiswick Line commences at Chiswick Mall, and passing near to the river and along the Fulham Road, and Walham Green, again skirts the river to Cremorne Gardens, and will be extended eventually to the permanent pumping station near the Grosvenor Canal.

The Fulham branch commences at Fulham Bridge, and joins the Chiswick line at the King's Road.

The size of the main line varies from 4 feet by 2 feet 8 inches to 4 feet 6 inches in diameter, with a fall of 4 feet per mile, the depth below the surface being from 14 feet to 30 feet. The branch varies in size from 3 feet 9 inches by 2 feet 6 inches to 4 feet 6 inches by 3 feet, its fall being $10\frac{1}{3}$ feet per mile, and its depth about 17 feet.

The Acton branch is carried along the Uxbridge Road from the Stamford Brook, at Wormwood Scrubs, to the Counters Creek Sewer at Royal Crescent, Notting Hill, into which it diverts the water from the higher ground, and which forms a storm-outlet into the Thames, near Cremorne Gardens. The Uxbridge Road Sewer varies from 3 feet 9 inches by 2 feet 6 inches to 4 feet by 2 feet 8 inches ; it has a fall of 4 feet per mile, and is about 14 feet deep.

The Chiswick Sewer is $3\frac{1}{4}$ miles long, the Fulham Sewer 1 mile 720 feet, and the Acton branch $1\frac{1}{2}$ mile. Besides these, there are various other minor branches and works. These for the present discharge into a large well or sump, at the temporary pumping station, near Cremorne Gardens.

The works were executed mainly through gravel, charged with such large volumes of water, that it was necessary to lay stoneware pipes under the inverts of the sewers, to lower the water in the ground, and to convey it to numerous and powerful steam pumps in the line of the works, before the sewers could be constructed. The operation of passing under railways and canals, difficult in so treacherous a subsoil, was successfully accomplished, and no serious accidents or failures occurred.

The Northern Outfall Sewer (Plate 18) is a work of peculiar construction ; as, unlike ordinary sewers, it is raised above the level of the surrounding neighbourhood in an embankment, which has the appearance of a railway embankment, and it is carried by aqueducts over rivers, railways, streets, and roads. Rails upon which the contractors' steam-engines and trucks have been constantly travelling, are at the present time laid along the top of it. It commences by a junction with the High and Middle Level Sewers, at the Penstock Chamber at Bow, and passes immediately under the rails of the North London Railway, which are carried over it on girders. It then passes under Wick Lane, which has been raised 18 feet, and then over the River Lea by a wrought-iron aqueduct of 57 feet span. This aqueduct consists of two wrought-iron culverts of the same section as the brick sewers, and over these is formed a roadway with parapet walls, the whole being supported by three wrought-iron plate girders. Indeed, all the aqueducts on this line of sewer are so constructed as to carry a wide roadway upon plates and girders on the top of them. Four other streams between the River Lea and the Stratford Road are crossed over, by iron tubes, of spans varying from 18 feet to 45 feet; and the sewers pass close under the rails of the Eastern Counties Railway, where it is on an embankment, the work having been executed without any interference with the traffic on the railway. The Outfall Sewer, up to this point, consists of two culverts, each 9 feet by 9 feet, placed side by side, formed with upright sides, semicircular crowns and segmental inverts. These are built upon a solid concrete embankment, carried through the peat soil down to the gravel, which is in many places at a great depth below the surface. Concrete is also carried up with a slope of 1 to 1, so as to form an abutment to the sides of the sewers. The whole structure is then covered with an earthen embankment, with slopes of $1\frac{1}{2}$ to 1, the foot of which is fenced in by a quick-set hedge and a ditch, and presents the appearance of a simple railway embankment. It is executed of sufficient strength to carry a railway or a roadway on the top, and will no doubt, at a future time, be used for some such public purpose. The outer earthen embankment not being carried below the surface, has from time to time subsided into the peat marshes through which it is formed, and these settlements have been made good in the ordinary manner; but the sewer and its concrete embankment have shown no sign of settlement or fracture since their completion. At the Stratford Road, the top of the sewer was depressed and carried under the road by four culverts, each 6 feet high and 7 feet 3 inches wide, covered with cast-iron plates. A large amount of property was purchased, and the road raised 10 feet upon a viaduct to pass over the sewer at an inclination of 1 in 50. From the Stratford Road the double line of sewer is continued over Abbey Mill Lane, by two self-supporting wrought-iron tubes, to the Abbey Mills pumping station, where the contents of the Low Level Sewer will be raised 36 feet. From this point three parallel lines of sewer, of the same form and dimensions as those before described, are continued to the outlet at Barking Creek. Gates and overflow weirs are formed in the line of these culverts, enabling the sewage to be turned into either or all of them at will, and preventing any one of them being at any time overcharged. Just beyond the pumping station, the three lines pass over the Channelsea River and Abbey Creek, by cast-iron culverts, supported by four wrought-iron plate girders of two spans of 40 feet each. They are then carried over Marsh Lane, the North Woolwich and the Bow and Barking Railways, by aqueducts somewhat similar to those already described. These railways were lowered to enable the sewer to pass over them; for the sewer being reduced to a minimum uniform fall of 2 feet per mile, could not be raised or depressed like a railway, to accommodate its levels to those of previously existing works. This, indeed, constituted one of the

great difficulties experienced in laying out the line of the Outfall
Sewer, for the district through which it passes was already closely
intersected by public works. For the same cause, also, the thickness of the ironwork, between the bottom of the sewer and the
under side of the aqueduct, was reduced to a minimum, and it does
not in most cases exceed 5 inches.

For a distance of about 1½ mile at the lower end of this sewer,
so great was the depth of the peat in the marshes, that it would
have been very costly to have excavated the whole of the ground
down to the gravel, and to have filled it in with solid concrete.
The plan therefore adopted for the foundations of this length, was
to excavate cross trenches 6 feet 6 inches wide, at distances of 21
feet from each other, down to the solid ground, and to fill these in
with concrete piers, upon which brick arches of four rings in thickness were turned, and the sewers were built upon these arches.
The top of the bank is 40 feet wide, and in some cases 25 feet
above the level of the marshes.

From the crossing of the Bow and Barking Railway, the triple
sewer is constructed in brickwork to its outlet at Barking Creek;
crossing in its route the five following roads, viz.—Balaam Street,
Plaistow, Barking Road, Prince Regent Lane, Blind Lane, and
East Ham Hall Manor Way, which were raised for the purpose
6 feet, 8 feet, 13 feet, 20 feet, and 16 feet, respectively.

The invert of the sewer at the outlet is about 18 inches below
high-water mark; but before entering the river, the sewage falls
over an apron a depth of 16 feet, and is discharged by nine culverts, each 6 feet high by 6 feet wide, laid at the level of low-
water spring-tides. The three upper sewers are, however, fitted
with penstocks, before reaching the tumbling bay, to afford the
means of closing the river outlet, and of diverting the sewage into
the reservoir, in which it will be stored for about eleven hours per
tide. The reservoir is so situate, that the sewers form one side of
it, and a communication is made between them by sixteen openings, through which, when the penstocks are closed, the sewage
enters the reservoir, and is there stored until high water. The
sluices at the lower part of the reservoir are then opened, and
allow the sewage in the reservoir to be discharged into the river
through the nine 6-feet culverts; and the three penstocks, at
the river outlet, being opened at the same time, the sewage is
simultaneously discharged directly into the river from the outfall
sewers without being first passed through the reservoir. The upper
openings from the outfall sewer into the reservoir are also fitted
with sluices, to enable the communication between the sewer and
the reservoir to be shut off in cases of necessity, and the whole of
the waters to be discharged over the tumbling bay. At the river
end of the nine culverts, a channel is cut in the bed of the river,
the floor of which is formed of concrete, and the sides protected by
campsheathing, so that the sewage is discharged into the bed of
the river at the time of high water. The whole of this line is
practically completed, and has been in operation since March,
1864.

The Barking Reservoir is $16\frac{3}{4}$ feet in average depth, and is divided by partition walls into four compartments, covering altogether an effective area of 412,384 superficial feet, or about $9\frac{1}{2}$ acres. The external and partition walls are of brickwork, and the entire area is covered by brick arches, supported upon brick piers, the floor being paved throughout with York stone. The reservoir, being almost entirely above the general surface of the ground, is covered by an embankment of earth, rising about 2 feet above the crown of the arches. The ground over which it is built being unfit to sustain the structure, the foundations of the piers and of the walls were carried down in concrete to a depth of nearly 20 feet.

The sewage is ordinarily prevented rising above a certain level in the reservoir, by means of a weir or overflow in the partition walls, which are built hollow, the spaces communicating with the discharging culverts below the outfall sewers. In cases of necessity, however, the reservoirs can be filled above the weir level, by closing the penstocks fitted to the discharging culverts at their entrance into the tumbling bay before referred to. A culvert, communicating with the river, is built at the back of the reservoir, having openings into each compartment fitted with penstocks, and by these means any one of the compartments may be filled with tidal water at the top of the tide, and be flushed out by its discharge at the period of low water. This reservoir is completed, and has been in efficient operation since August, 1864.

The Abbey Mills Pumping Station will be the largest establishment of the kind on the Main Drainage Works, providing, as it does, engine power to the extent of 1,140 H.P., for the purpose of lifting a maximum quantity of sewage and rainfall of 15,000 cubic feet per minute a height of 36 feet.

The engine power is here divided amongst eight engines, each being equivalent to 142 H.P. Each engine is furnished with two boilers, making sixteen boilers in all. The engines are contained in one building, cruciform in plan, and are arranged in pairs, two engines in each arm of the cross. These engines, as in all the other pumping establishments on these works, are expansive, condensing, rotative beam engines, but are somewhat more powerful than those used elsewhere, the cylinders being 4 feet 6 inches in diameter with a length of stroke of 9 feet. The pumps differ also in being double acting, a circumstance which allows of the air-pump, &c., being worked from the main beam, instead of from a distinct beam, as at the other stations. Each engine works two pumps, having a diameter of 3 feet $10\frac{1}{2}$ inches and a length of stroke of $4\frac{1}{2}$ feet. The boilers are each 8 feet in diameter, and 30 feet long, with double furnaces.

The engine-house is divided in height into three compartments, the lower one being the pump-well, into which the sewage is conveyed from the Low Level Sewer, the intermediate one forming a reservoir for condensing water, and the upper being more correctly the engine-house, in which are contained the eight engines. The lower part of this building will be laid about 3 feet above the bottom of a thick stratum of clay, overlying a considerable thickness of sand with water, through which the foundations are to be carried, by piling, on to a bed of firm gravel below. The boiler-houses and other portions of the work will be founded upon the clay stratum overlying the sand. As these deep foundations are situate in close proximity to the Northern Outfall Sewer, which is contained in an embankment above the general level of the ground, great caution will be requisite to prevent any settlement in that sewer. The boiler-house and coal stores are to be built between the outfall sewer and the engine-house, keeping the deep excavations as far distant from the sewer as practicable. The coal stores will be built with their floors level with the stoke-holes in the boiler-house, and tramways will be laid from one to the other; one side of the coal stores forming also the front side of the boiler-house. This floor will be only slightly below the present surface of the ground, which is 6 feet below high water. Tramways will be laid from the top of the coal stores to the Abbey Mill River, adjacent to the works, where a wharf wall will be built for landing coals and other materials.

The sewage from the Low Level Sewer, before entering the pump wells, will pass through open iron cages, the bars of which will intercept any substances likely to interfere with the proper action of the pump-valves; and the cages, when requisite, will be lifted above ground, by proper gearing, and the intercepted matter be discharged into trucks, or otherwise removed. The sewage will then pass into the wells, and be lifted by the pumps, through hanging valves, into a circular culvert of cast iron, and thence will be forced into any of the three culverts forming the Northern Outfall Sewers.

It is fortunate that these works were not projected in the year 1306, when coal was first introduced into London, and was regarded as such a nuisance, that the resident nobility obtained a royal proclamation to prohibit its use under severe penalties, for this pumping station alone will consume about 9,700 tons of coal per annum.

The cost of pumping is not, however, entirely in excess of the former expenditure upon the drainage; for the cost of removing deposit from the tide-locked and stagnant sewers in London formerly amounted to a sum of about £30,000 per annum; and the substitution of a constant flow through the sewers, by means of pumping, must necessarily largely reduce the deposit, and consequently the annual cost of cleansing.

THE SOUTH SIDE OF THE THAMES.

The High Level Sewer and its Southern Branch, correspond with the High and the Middle Level Sewers on the North side of the Thames. The Main Line commences at Clapham, and the Branch Line at Dulwich, and they together drain an area of about 20 square miles, including Tooting, Streatham, Clapham, Brixton,

Dulwich, Camberwell, Peckham, Norwood, Sydenham, and part of Greenwich. Both lines are constructed of sufficient capacity to carry off all the flood-waters, so that they may be entirely intercepted from the low and thickly-inhabited district, which is tide-locked and subjected to floods. The storm-waters will be discharged into Deptford Creek, whilst the sewage and a limited quantity of rain will flow by four iron pipes, each 3 feet 6 inches in diameter, laid under its bed into the Outfall Sewer.

The two lines unite in the New Cross Road, near to the New Cross Station on the Brighton Railway, and they are constructed side by side along that road to Deptford; but at the New Cross Station, the Branch Line is 10 feet above the Main Line, but by falling at a more rapid inclination, it arrives at the same level as the Main Line at Deptford Broadway. The Branch is $4\frac{1}{2}$ miles in length, of which 1,000 feet were executed in tunnel, at depths varying from 30 feet to 50 feet. Its size varies from 7 feet in diameter to a form 10 feet 6 inches by 10 feet 6 inches, with a circular crown and segmental sides and invert, and its fall varies from 30 feet per mile at the upper end, to $2\frac{1}{3}$rd feet per mile at the lower end. The soil through which it passes is mostly a mixture of sand and clay, containing cockle and other shells to a large extent. The old Effra Sewer, which fell into the river near Vauxhall Bridge, has been diverted through this sewer to a new outlet at Deptford, and the old line has been filled in and abandoned. Two subsidiary branches have been extended from this sewer at Dulwich—the one to Crown Hill, Norwood, and the other to the Crystal Palace.

The Main Line varies in size from 4 feet 6 inches by 3 feet at the upper end, to 10 feet 6 inches by 10 feet 6 inches, of the same form as the branch by the side of which it is constructed. The double line of sewer occupies the whole width of Church-street, Deptford, and the inverts being below the foundations of the houses on each side of the street, the walls of the houses were underpinned, and the spaces between them and the sewers filled in with concrete. The subsoil here consisted of loamy sand and gravel with large quantities of water, and, to add to the difficulty of the work, the old Ravensbourne Sewer, which passed through the centre of the street, had to be taken up, and its waters diverted during the progress of these operations.

The outlets of the two sewers, 10 feet 6 inches by 10 feet 6 inches, are each fitted with two hinged flaps, one above the other, the lower one being usually fixed close, so as to form a dam to drive the waters through the iron pipes into the Outfall Sewer, but the upper one hanging free, in order to serve as a tide flap, and allow of the exit of the sewage into the Creek, when it rises in the sewer to a sufficient altitude. In cases of heavy floods, however, the lower flap can be opened, to admit of a free and full discharge from the sewers into the Creek. The entrances to the iron pipes are in troughs, or sumps, in the large sewers, a short distance within or behind the outlet flaps, and are fitted with penstocks, to shut off the sewage from the Outfall Sewer in case of need.

The falls of the Main Line are, at the upper end 53 feet, 26 feet, and 9 feet per mile to the Effra Sewer at the Brixton Road, and thence to the outlet $2\frac{1}{3}$rd feet per mile. The sewer is executed in brickwork, varying in thickness from 9 inches to $22\frac{1}{2}$ inches, one-half, that forming the invert, being in Portland cement, and the remainder in blue lias mortar.

The whole of this line is completed, and has been in successful operation since January, 1863.

The Low Level Sewer (Plate 19) does not follow the course of the River, as on the North side, but, commencing at Putney, it takes a more direct line, through low ground once forming the bed of a second channel of the Thames, and drains Putney, Battersea, Nine Elms, Lambeth, Newington, Southwark, Bermondsey, Rotherhithe, and Deptford, comprising an area of 20 square miles. The surface of this area is mostly below the level of high water, and is, in many places, 5 feet or 6 feet below it, having at one time been completely covered by the Thames. The sewers throughout the district have but little fall, and, except at the period of low water, were tide-locked and stagnant; consequently, after long-continued rain, they became overcharged, and were unable to empty themselves during the short period of low water. The waters, therefore, were constantly accumulating, and many days frequently elapsed, after the cessation of the rain, before the sewers could be entirely relieved, the sewage in the interim being forced into the basements and cellars of the houses, to the destruction of much valuable property. The want of flow also caused large accumulations of deposit in the sewers, the removal of which was difficult and costly. These defects, added to the malaria arising from the stagnant sewage, contributed to render the district unhealthy; and it was with reference to the condition of this district, that the late Mr. R. Stephenson and Sir W. Cubitt so forcibly described the effect of artificial draining by pumping, as equivalent to raising the surface a height of 20 feet.

The Low Level Sewer has, in fact, rendered this district as dry and as healthy as any portion of the Metropolis. Its length is about 10 miles. Its size varies from a single sewer 4 feet in diameter at the upper end, to two culverts, each 7 feet high by 7 feet wide, at the lower end, and its fall ranges from 4 feet to 2 feet per mile. The lift at the outlet of the sewer is 18 feet. This sewer was constructed through a stratum of sand and gravel overlying the clay, such as is frequently found in the beds of rivers, and copiously charged with water. Some very successful instances of tunnelling under canals, railways, and house property, occurred in the construction of this work; and a mode of pumping in a quick-sand, and rendering it dry and firm without drawing off the sand, was adopted, which will be more particularly described in another part of this Paper. Much difficulty was experienced in executing a portion of this work close to and below the foundations of the arches of the Greenwich Railway, and under Deptford Creek, owing to the large volume of water there met with. This was,

[Plate 19]

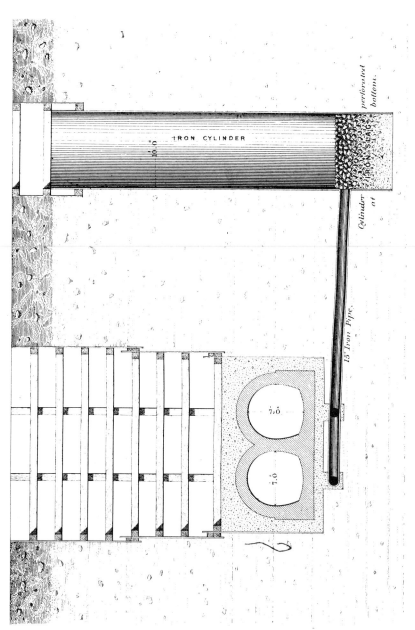

LOW LEVEL SEWER AT GAS WORKS, DEPTFORD. TRANSVERSE SECTION OF SEWER & SUMP.

however, at last surmounted, by sinking two iron cylinders, each 10 feet in diameter, through the sand, to a depth of about 45 feet, the water being kept down by pumping, at the rate of from 5,000 gallons to 7,000 gallons per minute. The sewer was carried under Deptford Creek, and the navigation was kept open, by constructing a coffer-dam into the middle of the Creek, and by executing one-half of the work at a time. All these works were completed with but few and unimportant casualties.

The sewers of this district had been constructed, generally, with a fall from west to east, and had been connected with each other in such a manner that, in case of one becoming first overcharged, it might be relieved by its neighbour, and the sewage be reduced to a uniform level all over the district. Taking advantage of this circumstance, an important branch was constructed from the Low Level Sewer at High-street, Deptford, towards the river to St. James's Church, Bermondsey. This branch, by intersecting the Earl, the Duffield, and the Battle Bridge Main Sewers, relieves a large and populous district. Its length is about 2 miles, its size varies from 5 feet to 5 feet 6 inches in diameter, and its fall is $4\frac{1}{2}$ feet per mile. Its depth varies from 15 feet to 40 feet below the surface, and it has been in successful operation since January, 1864.

The Deptford Pumping Station is situated by the side of Deptford Creek, and close to the Greenwich Railway Station. The sewage is here lifted from the Low Level Sewer, a height of 18 feet, into the Outfall Sewer. An iron wharf wall and barge bed, 500 feet long, has been constructed at the side of the creek, and is provided with a crane and tramways, for landing coal or other materials. Four expansive, condensing, rotative beam engines, each of 125 H.P., and capable together of lifting 10,000 cubic feet of sewage per minute a height of 18 feet, are here constructed. These engines are worked by ten Cornish single-flued boilers, each 30 feet long and 6 feet in diameter. The cylinders are 48 inches in diameter, with a length of stroke of 9 feet, and the pumps, two of which are worked by one engine direct from the beam, are single-acting plunger pumps, the diameter of the plungers being 7 feet and the length of the stroke $4\frac{1}{2}$ feet. One pump is placed on the beam, midway between the steam cylinder and the centre pillars, and the other midway between the centre pillars and the fly wheel. The air, the feed, and the cold water pumps are actuated by a separate beam, attached to the cylinder end of the main beam. The pump valves are leather-faced hanging valves, and the sewage is discharged through them into a wrought-iron culvert placed on the level of the Outfall Sewer, and connected with it by a brick culvert, which receives also the sewage from the High Level Sewer, previously brought by gravitation under the creek, through four cast-iron pipes 3 feet 6 inches in diameter. Both streams enter the Outfall Sewer, and are together conveyed to Crossness, where they are again lifted. The chimney shaft at this station is $7\frac{1}{2}$ feet in diameter at the base and 6 feet at the top ; its height is 150 feet, and the furnaces draw from the sewers and the engine-well to assist in the ventilation of the works. The accommodation for coals is ample, the sheds covering an area of 18,000 superficial feet.

Provision is made, by gratings, for the interception of the larger substances brought down by the sewers, in the same manner as at Crossness.

This Station is completed, and the engines have been in operation since May, 1864.

The Southern Outfall Sewer conveys the sewage which flows into it from the High Level Sewer by gravitation through the four iron culverts laid under Deptford Creek, and that which is pumped into it from the Low Level Sewer, from Deptford through Greenwich and Woolwich to Crossness Point in the Erith Marshes. It is not, like the Outfall Sewer on the North side, constructed above the level of the ground, but is entirely under ground for its whole length of $7\frac{3}{4}$ miles. It is 11 feet 6 inches in diameter, formed in brickwork generally 18 inches thick, and has a fall of 2 feet per mile. The bottom of the sewer is 9 feet below the level of low water at its outlet into the river, so that it can discharge into the river at and near to low water, by gravitation, in case of necessity ; but ordinarily the mode of discharge will be by pumping into the Crossness Reservoir. It has been constructed at a depth of about 16 feet below the surface, except through Woolwich, where the depth ranges from 45 feet to 75 feet. The soil through which it passes is mostly gravel and sand, but the Woolwich tunnel, which is the principal feature of the work, is partly in the chalk. One mile of this tunnel was executed under the town of Woolwich, without any casualties or settlements.

The large volume of water met with in the Marshes, rendered the construction of that portion of the work very costly. These marshes originally formed part of the Thames, and were first enclosed in the reign of Edward I., by the monks of Lesnes Abbey ; 2,000 acres were afterwards flooded, by the bursting of the river banks, in the reign of Henry VIII., and were not again reclaimed until the reign of James I. They would have suffered a similar fate, in the year 1864, in consequence of the breach caused in the river bank by the explosion at Messrs. Hall's Powder Magazine, had not a large number of workmen then engaged upon the Main Drainage works at Crossness, at once, by prompt and energetic efforts, afterwards efficiently aided by the military, repaired the breach before the rising of the following tide.

This sewer was completed in June, 1862, and has been in successful operation since that period.

The outfall of the sewage on the South side of the Thames is at the Crossness Reservoir and Pumping Station. The sewage is discharged into the river at the time of high water only, but the sewer is at such a level, that it can discharge its full volume by gravitation about the time of low water. Its outlet is ordinarily closed by a penstock placed across its mouth, and its contents are raised by pumping into the reservoir, which is built at the same level as that on the North side ; and, like it, it stores the sewage, except for the two hours of discharge after high water. The sewage is thus diverted from its direct course to the river, into a side channel leading to the pump-well, which forms part of the foundation for the engine-house ; from this well it is lifted by four beam engines, each of 125 H.P., and actuating, direct from the beam, two compound pumps, each having four plungers. The engines are condensing, rotative beam engines, the cylinders being 4 feet in diameter, with a length of stroke of 9 feet; they are situate at the end of the main beam, which is 40 feet in length, the fly-wheel connecting rod being attached to the further extremity, and the pump rods situate on either side of the beam centre. The air, the feed and the cold-water pumps are actuated by a separate or counter beam, fixed at one end to a rocking lever, and attached at the other to the main beam. The cylinders are supplied from twelve Cornish boilers, each 6 feet in diameter and 30 feet long, having an internal furnace and flue 3 feet in diameter, and being set so as to have the second heat carried with a split draught along the sides, and the third heat under the bottom of the boiler into the main flue leading to the chimney.

The maximum quantity of sewage to be lifted by these engines will ordinarily be about 10,000 cubic feet per minute ; but during the night, that quantity will be considerably reduced, while on the other hand it will be nearly doubled on occasions of heavy rainfall. The lift also will vary from 10 feet to 30 feet, according to the level of water in the sewer and in the reservoir into which it is lifted. These variable conditions of working led to some difficulty in the arrangement of the engines and pumps, which it has been endeavoured to meet by the arrangement of pump plungers before alluded to. The pumps, which are single-acting, are placed equidistantly on each side of the beam centre, the pump cases being each 12 feet in diameter, fitted with four plungers 4 feet 6 inches in diameter. These plungers are placed in pairs, each pair being worked from a cross-head on the main beam, which is in two flitches with this object, and arrangements are made for throwing either pair of plungers out of gear. By these means the capacity of the pumps may be varied, in the proportion of 1, 2, or 3, as the inner pair, outer pair, or both pairs are thrown into gear. The sewage is discharged into a wrought-iron trough, through hanging leather-faced valves, which are suspended from wrought-iron shackles, and fitted with the wrought-iron back and front plates. Each valve is 12 inches by 18 inches. It should be mentioned, that substances which might prevent the proper action of the valves are intercepted before reaching the pumps, by a wrought-iron grating placed in front of the openings to the pump well, the substances so intercepted being lifted from the face of the grating by an endless chain, with buckets or scrapers and combs attached, working vertically in front of and in close contact with the grating, the teeth of the comb passing between the bars. On the descent of the chain, the buckets are overturned and discharge their contents into a trough, from which they will be removed by manual labour.

141

The sewage, after being delivered from the pumps into the wrought-iron trough, is discharged through brick culverts into the reservoir, or, in case of need, provision is made for its discharge through other culverts directly into the river. After being stored in the reservoir until the time of high water, the sewage is discharged by a lower set of culverts into the river. There are two tiers of eight openings in each compartment of the reservoir, the upper eight for the admission of the sewage from the pumps to the reservoir, and the lower eight for its discharge into the river, the apertures in all cases being opened and closed by penstocks.

The reservoir, which is $6\frac{1}{2}$ acres in extent, is covered by brick arches supported on brick piers, and is furnished with weirs for overflows, and with a flushing culvert. Its height, level, and general construction are similar to that at Barking Creek, already described. Over the reservoir are built twenty-one cottages, for the engineers and other persons employed upon the works.

The ground upon which the whole of these works were constructed consists of peat, sand, or soft silty clay, and affords no sufficient foundation within 25 feet of the surface. To obviate this difficulty, and to reduce the expense of the foundations as much as possible, the culverts on the various levels were built, as far as practicable, in the same trenches, one above the other; the lowest, leading from the Outfall Sewer to the pump-wells, support those discharging the sewage from the reservoir, which latter in turn support those leading from the pumps into the reservoir. The requirements of the pump-wells necessitated that the walls of the engine-house should be carried down to the level of the gravel, independently of the nature of the ground; but such was not the case with the boiler-house. The boilers and stoke-hole floor are supported on arches, which spring from walls brought up from the gravel, and the space below the boiler-house floor is made available as a reservoir for condensing water. The water from the hot and cold wells of the engines is conveyed hither, and one compartment is set apart as a chamber for cooling the water from the hot well, previous to its being used again for condensing water. With the same object, of saving separate foundations, coal stores and workshops have been erected, partly on the external walls of the reservoir, and partly on the culverts in front of them, large coal stores being also provided in front of the boiler-house, and on a level with the stoke-holes, into which the coals will be brought on tramways. A tramway is also provided for the upper level coal-sheds, on the level of the tops of the boilers, whence the coals will be shot into the stoke-holes below. Tramways are also laid from the coal-sheds to the river, and jetties are carried out into the river, to facilitate the landing of coals, and their transfer to the stores. A wharf wall has been constructed along the river frontage of the works, for a distance of about 1,200 feet, by which a large portion of the ' saltings ' has been reclaimed. The wall is of brick, carried upon brick arches, which rest upon piers formed of iron caissons filled with concrete, and which are carried down to the gravel.

The chimney into which the flues from the boilers are conveyed is square on plan externally, being 8 feet 3 inches internal diameter throughout, and 200 feet in height ; it is founded upon a wide bed of concrete, brought up from the gravel, which is here 26 feet below the surface.

The reservoir, as well as the several culverts and the pump wells, are all connected by flues with the furnaces of the boilers, for the purposes of ventilation, in a manner similar to that adopted at the Deptford and other pumping stations.

The outlet into the river from the Outfall Sewer, which was constructed in connection with these works, consists of twelve iron pipes, each 4 feet 4 inches in diameter, carried under the 'saltings' into a paved channel formed in the bed of the river. These pipes are gathered into the single sewer, by culverts in brickwork on the land side of the wharf wall, the culverts being gradually reduced in number, and their dimensions increased, as they approach the junction with the large Outfall Sewer. The whole of these works have recently been completed.

The tunnels successfully completed (Plates 20, 21, and 22), under circumstances of difficulty, and where failure would have been very disastrous, were numerous.

The tunneling, and the formation of the sewers through quicksands charged with large volumes of water, existing under various portions of the metropolis, but more particularly in the low-lying districts on the south side of the Thames, were rendered practicable and safe, by a mode of pumping the water out of the ground, without withdrawing the sand, which was adopted and perfected during the progress of these works.

During the Author's early connection with the Metropolitan Sewers, several disastrous results of pumping in quicksands had occurred, in consequence of the withdrawal of the sand from under the foundations of the adjoining houses. This caused unequal settlements and fissures in the walls, so that the buildings had eventually to be pulled down and rebuilt. The Victoria-street Sewer through Scotland-yard is perhaps one of the most serious instances of this kind ; portions of the War Office, Fife House, the United Service Museum, the Office of Works and other valuable property were then more or less injured. One of the first works executed by the Author, upon his appointment, was the reconstruction of this sewer, from which a branch sewer was subsequently constructed from it, through the same soil, close underneath the Clock Tower of the Horse Guards, without the slightest damage to that important and heavy building.

The sewers in Tothill Street, Duke Street, and other streets in the neighbourhood of Great George Street, Westminster, being in peat and sandy soils charged with water, were not formed without considerable risk. The late Mr. Brunel was at one time under serious apprehension lest his residence should subside into the peat on which it stands, the sewer trench having been opened to a great depth close to it ; and he afterwards expressed much

[Plate 20]

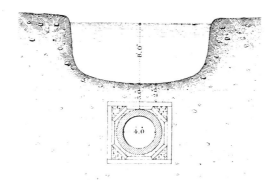

SECTION OF SEWER IN TUNNEL UNDER REGENT'S CANAL, CALEDONIAN ROAD.

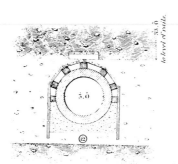

SECTION OF SEWER IN TUNNEL UNDER
WEST LONDON RAILWAY, NEAR FULHAM GAS WORKS.

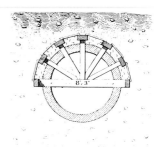

SECTION OF SEWER IN TUNNEL
UNDER NEW RIVER EMBANKMENT.

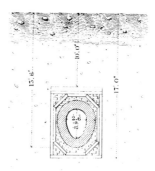

SECTION OF SEWER IN TUNNEL UNDER HORSE GUARDS.

144

[Plate 21]

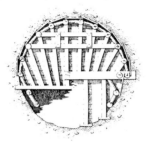 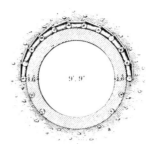

LOOKING WEST.   LOOKING EAST.

TRANSVERSE SECTIONS,

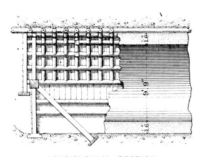

LONGITUDINAL SECTION.

MIDDLE LEVEL SEWER. TUNNEL UNDER NEW INN YARD.

SECTION OF SEWER IN TUNNEL   SECTION OF SEWER IN TUNNEL
NEAR THE UPPER MALL, HAMMERSMITH.   UNDER QUEEN STREET, HAMMERSMITH.

[Plate 22]

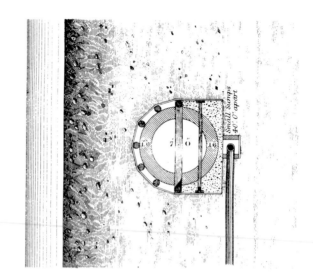

SECTION OF SEWER IN TUNNEL
UNDER GRAND SURREY CANAL.

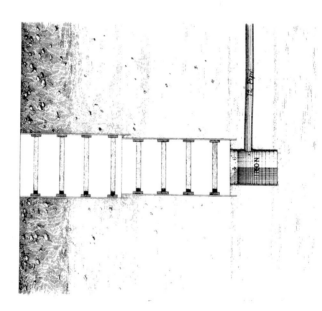

SECTION OF SUMP,
OLD KENT ROAD, NEAR GRAND SURREY CANAL.

satisfaction at the precautions adopted to obviate such a catastrophe.

The cases are too numerous to be here mentioned, but a few of the more prominent may be alluded to. The line of tunnel from Kennington Church to the Old Kent Road, a distance of about 1,000 feet, is close under the basements of a large number of houses, the top of the tunnel being only from 10 feet to 12 feet below the surface, and the diameter being about 10 feet. The water was pumped out of the sand, for this length of tunnel, at the rate of about 8,000 gallons per minute. The same sewer was carried, through similar soil, under the Grand Surrey Canal, and within 8 feet of the water in it; and again under the same canal in the Deptford Lower Road, where the distance between the top of the tunnel and the water in the canal was only 6 feet 4 inches, the whole of the soil being gravel and sand, with 1 foot of puddle in the bottom of the canal.

The Regent's Canal in the Caledonian Road was also tunnelled under, the distance between the top of the tunnel and the water in the canal being only 2 feet, so that the miners could hear the barges as they passed over their heads scrape against the ground; this was, however, executed in clay. Another tunnel has been formed 33 feet under the rails of the West London Railway, and under the Kensington Canal. Sewers were constructed under the London and Brighton, the North Kent, and several other railways, without any interruption to the continuous traffic on them.

The method adopted for pumping out the water, without drawing off the sand, and for building the brickwork in ground so charged with water, was first to sink, in some convenient position, near the intended works, a brick well to a depth of 5 feet or 6 feet below the lowest part of the excavation. In some cases, where the depth was great, an iron cylinder was sunk below the brickwork, and the bottom and sides of the well were lined with shingle, which filtered the water passing into it, and exposed a large surface of this filtering medium. Earthenware pipes were carried from this well and laid below the invert of the intended sewer, small pits being formed at the mouths of these pipes, to protect them from the deposit. By these means, the water has been successfully withdrawn from the worst quicksands, and they have been rendered firm and dry for building on. Iron plates have, in olden times, been laid underneath the brickwork of the invert of the sewers, to support them in such treacherous ground, but concrete forms both a cheaper and a better foundation, and unless the ground is so dry and solid that it can be excavated to the exact form of the sewer to be placed on it, there is no portion of the work more important, than the effectual backing of the invert and the haunches with concrete.

The bricks used in the works have been mostly picked stocks and Gault clay bricks, and the inverts were occasionally faced with Staffordshire blue bricks. The brickwork is laid in blue lias lime mortar, mixed in the proportions of 2 of sand to 1 of lime for one-half or two-thirds of the upper circumference of the sewers, and the remainder has been laid in Portland cement, mixed with an equal proportion of sand. A very considerable length of sewer has been laid entirely in cement. A double test of the quality of the cement has been used, which has been found most effective, and has tended greatly to improve the manufacture of that material, so important in building operations. The specifications provide, that the whole of the cement shall be Portland cement of the very best quality, ground extremely fine, weighing not less than 110 lbs. to the bushel, and capable of maintaining a breaking weight of 500 lbs., on $1\frac{1}{2}$ square inch, seven days after being made in an iron mould, and immersed in water during the interval of seven days.

The total cost of the Main Drainage Works, when completed, will have been about £4,100,000. The works have been executed under the immediate superintendence of the Assistant Engineers, Messrs. Lovick, Grant, and Cooper. The principal contractors have been Messrs. Brassey, Ogilvie, and Harrison; Mr. Webster; Mr. Furness; Messrs. Aird and Sons; Mr. Moxon; Messrs. James Watt and Co.; Messrs. Slaughter; and Messrs. Rothwell and Co. The sum for defraying the cost of these works is raised by loan, and paid off by a 3d. rate levied on the metropolis, which produces £180,262 per annum, the ratable value being £14,421,011, and the principal and interest of the loan will be paid off in forty years.

There are about 1,300 miles of sewers in London, and 82 miles of main intercepting sewers. Three hundred and eighteen millions of bricks, and 880,000 cubic yards of concrete have been consumed, and $3\frac{1}{2}$ million cubic yards of earth have been excavated in the execution of the Main Drainage Works. The total pumping power employed is 2,380 nominal H.P.; and if at full work night and day, 44,000 tons of coals per annum would be consumed, but the average consumption is estimated at 20,000 tons.

The sewage on the North side of the Thames at present amounts to 10 million cubic feet per day, and on the South side to 4 million cubic feet per day; but provision is made for an anticipated increase up to $11\frac{1}{2}$ million on the North side, and $5\frac{3}{4}$ million on the South side, in addition to $28\frac{1}{2}$ million cubic feet of rainfall per diem on the North side, and $17\frac{1}{4}$ million cubic feet per diem on the South side, or a total of 63 million cubic feet per diem, which is equal to a lake of 482 acres, 3 feet deep, or fifteen times as large as the Serpentine in Hyde Park.

The whole of the Main Drainage scheme is now completed, with the exception of the Low Level Sewer on the North side of the Thames, which is being formed in conjunction with the Thames Embankment and the new street to the Mansion House, and will therefore probably not come into operation for two years. The proportion of the area drained by that Sewer is one seventh of the whole.   Some sections of these works have been completed, and have been in working operation, from two to four years, and the largest portion of the work has been completed and has been in operation for more than a year, so that the principles upon which the scheme has been based have already been fairly tested.

Forth Railway Bridge: Fife cantilever under construction, October 1888;
engineers: Sir John Fowler and Sir Benjamin Baker; contractors (structural
steelwork): Tancred Arrol & Co. (from a contemporary photograph, × 39%).
The bridge took eight years to build, and at the time of its completion contained
the largest span in the world (521 m). With an overall length of 2465 m this
cantilever is still one of the world's greatest bridges, and its use of steel (58 000
tons) firmly established the structural value of the new material in Britain

Steel skeleton construction in Chicago

E. C. SHANKLAND, MInstCE

Reprinted from Min. Proc. Instn Civ. Engrs, 1897,
vol. 128, 1-22

The paper presented by Edward Shankland in 1896 combined two of the main interests of civil engineers, namely structural engineering and foundations. Although tall towers had been commonplace in architecture since earliest days, it was not until the advent of the structural steel frame that skyscrapers became possible. The advantage of a skyscraper over a tower is not merely that it is tall, and is therefore a noticeable structure, but that its interior is usable, preferably for offices but possibly for housing as well. It could be argued that the first quasi-skyscraper was the Victoria Tower in the Palace of Westminster, though the architect never claimed that it was, but it is generally accepted that skyscrapers in their modern form were developed in Chicago in the latter part of the 19th century and that their principal progenitor was William le Baron Jenney, an architect-engineer.

Edward Shankland was born in 1854 and was a graduate of Rensselar Polytechnic. He worked on improvements to the Missouri River, and from 1883 on bridge design. In 1889 he joined the Chicago firm of Brown & Root of which he was a partner from 1894 until 1900 when he set up his own practice. Shankland was the structural engineer on many of the early steel frame buildings in Chicago. He died in 1924.

The ground conditions in Chicago's business district, the 'Loop', were difficult and foundations were taken 15 feet down through silt to a stiff clay layer. Differential settlement was common because of varying loads and the presence of a considerable depth of soft clay below the hard layer. In 1873 Baumann developed a method of so designing the foundations to apply equal pressure to the ground. The method now looks elementary, since it was merely a matter of designing independent piers of suitable size. Nevertheless, it was probably the first scientific foundation design.

While the skyscraper — or tower block or high-rise building as it later came to be called — was based on engineering technology, it also presented an architectural solution to a specific building problem. This problem was well explored by Louis Sullivan, the Chicago architect, in a periodical article which he published in 1896. In that article Sullivan considered the tall office building as an artistic entity, or so he said. In fact, he examined the building as an architectural phenomenon not an artistic one, and he came up with a few specific rules which have been followed, more or less faithfully, by the architects of tower blocks even since.

Sullivan's views were put in late nineteenth century 'architect speak' which was more philosophical and aesthetic than was actually necessary. Nevertheless, his message was very clear. Office buildings were needed for business; high-speed lifts made vertical travel easy; steel manufacture had 'shown the way to safe, rigid, economical constructions rising to a great height'; and continued population growth led to high-rise buildings.

Sullivan then described how the problem of the high-rise office building should be dealt with as a problem which involved both the technical and aesthetic characteristics of architecture at that time, as he saw them.

He wrote, 'The practical conditions are broadly speaking these:

'Wanted — 1st, a storey below ground, containing boilers, engines of various sorts etc — in short, the plant for power, heating, lighting etc.

'2nd, a ground floor, so called, devoted to stores, banks, or other establishments requiring large area, ample spacing, ample light, and great freedom of access.

'3rd, a second storey readily accessible by stairways — this space usually in large subdivisions, with corresponding liberality in structural spacing and expanse of glass and breadth of external openings.

'4th, above this an indefinite number of storeys of offices piled tier upon tier, one tier just like another tier, one office just like all the other offices — an office being similar to a cell in a honey-comb, merely a compartment, nothing more.

'5th and last, at the top of this pile is placed a space or storey that, as related to the life and usefulness of the structure is purely physiological in its nature — namely, the attic. In this the circulatory system completes itself and makes its grand turn, ascending and descending. The space is filled with tanks, pipes, valves, sheaves, and mechanical etcetera that supplement and complement the force-originating plant hidden in below ground in the cellar.

'Finally, or at the beginning rather, there must be on the ground floor a main aperture or entrance common to all the occupants or patrons of the building.'

Thus, in these words, Louis Sullivan — certainly the most sensitive and aesthetically-aware of all the early designers of high-rise buildings — justifies the form which these took and for which Shankland provided much of the steel structural skeletons. To be truthful, Sullivan's comments were directed towards office buildings, but they relate to hotel and apartment buildings almost equally well and even, with some reservations regarding the ground and first floors (Sullivan's first and second storeys), to domestic buildings as well.

At the moment high-rise building is under something of a sociological cloud. But it can hardly be doubted that in confined spaces, which most cities or conurbations are or eventually must become, faced with the problems of accommodating large and increasing populations, the spread of high-rise building is inevitable. In that case, Sullivan's formula gives an explanation of the ethos of high-rise building which could scarcely be bettered.

THE main commercial district of Chicago, containing the municipal, county and government buildings, and the large offices, warehouses, hotels and theatres, occupies only $\frac{3}{4}$ square mile. This is a very small area, compared with the 186·4 square miles within the city limits. It is bounded on the north and west by the Chicago River, on the south by the net-work of railways extending to Polk Street, and on the east by Lake Michigan. These natural and artificial boundaries form obstacles to its enlargement, and the erection of many-storied buildings has become necessary in order to accommodate the great and constantly increasing demands of trade.

High buildings having become a necessity, a difficult problem was at once confronted. The soil consists of loam, and is principally made ground, to a depth of 12 feet or 14 feet, about city datum—the mean level of the lake in 1844. Below this there is a layer of blue clay, called " hard pan," between 6 feet and 10 feet in thickness, overlying a very soft and saturated clay, which becomes harder again at a depth of 50 feet or 60 feet. The latter sometimes contains sand- and mud-pockets, but is, for the most part, of the same nature as the hard pan, and saturated for a considerable distance below the lake-level. Rock is found at a depth of between 60 feet and 80 feet. It was found by trial that the load upon the hard pan should not exceed 4,000 lbs., and should preferably be between 3,000 lbs. and 3,500 lbs. per square foot. With such loads the buildings settle between 6 inches and 12 inches. Under the old masonry buildings, however, owing to their heavy walls and the small area of their foundations, the pressure has been found to reach 11,200 lbs. per square foot; that method of construction was therefore rendered impossible. The settlement of these old buildings was much greater than that of the recent structures, but being constructed of wood and brick or stone they would admit of great distortion. They were built immediately after the great fire of 1871, shortly after which the level of the whole of this district was raised 4 feet. For several years steps occurred in the footway, perhaps at several places in the same block of buildings, and at such times a few inches of settlement in a building would not be noticed. By using thin outside walls of brick and terra cotta, or terra cotta alone, simply as a cover for the steel frames, and by spreading the foundations, the pressure on the clay has been greatly reduced, so that the four- and five-storey buildings now standing exert a greater pressure on the clay than do the more recently constructed high buildings.

HISTORICAL.

The Montauk block, ten storeys high, built in 1881 and 1882 from the designs of Messrs. Burnham and Root, was the first of the high buildings. Railway rails were inserted in the walls under the vaults, and this was the first occasion on which an iron and concrete footing was used. The masonry footings nearly filled the basement in the old buildings, and iron and concrete footings were used to give space in the basement for the boilers, engines, and dynamos. In 1883 and 1884 the Home Insurance building, ten storeys high, was built from the designs of Mr. W. L. B. Jenney. It was the first house in which the skeleton construction was adopted, consisting of cast-iron columns and wrought-iron floor-beams. The Rookery, eleven storeys high, designed by Messrs. Burnham and Root, was erected in 1885 and 1886 with isolated footings, but with solid masonry walls; and the Tacoma building, fourteen storeys high, by Messrs. Holabird and Roche, architects, a more complete type of the skeleton construction than any of the preceding, followed; after which the system came into general use.

SUPERSTRUCTURE.

Before the frame of the superstructure can be designed, the positions of the columns must be determined; the architectural considerations being considered as far as is consistent with safe design of the steel frame. A framing-plan of the roof, attic and each floor is then made, and the floor-area supported on each joist, girder and column is computed. A typical framing-plan of the Fisher building, eighteen storeys high, now being erected on Dearborn and Van Buren Streets and Plymouth Place is given in *Fig. 1.*

The live load, consisting of the weight of the tenants, the furniture and the partitions, which are frequently changed, is taken between 60 lbs. and 75 lbs. per square foot, for the upper floors of an office building, and between 75 lbs. and 100 lbs. per square foot for the first and second floors, which are generally used for shops and banks. The weight of the tenants and furniture of a typical office have been found by experiment to be only 6 lbs. or 7 lbs. per square foot; it certainly does not exceed 12 lbs. The average weight of the partitions is 25 lbs. per square foot of floor. The dead weights of the roof and floor are calculated, those of the Fisher building being as follows :—

TABLE I.—WEIGHTS OF THE FLOOR AND ROOF OF THE FISHER BUILDING.

Floor.	Weight per Square Foot. Lbs.
⅞-inch maple floor	4
Deadening, cinder concrete on top of floor arch . . .	15
15-inch hollow tile floor arch	41
Steel joists and girders.	10
Plaster on ceiling	5
Total	75

Roof.	
3-inch book tile	22
6-ply tar and gravel roof	6
T-bars to support book tile	4
Steel roof framing	8
Total	40

Table II, p. 5, shows how the loads are distributed in the same building.

A statement is prepared, showing the live and dead floor-loads, the weights of the outside walls, the lift loads, the weights of the lift and house-tanks, and of the water-closet floors, window-frames, glass, mullions, &c., supported on each column at each floor. The live load, except the partition load, being deducted, the remainder is used in designing the foundations. The sum of these items gives the total weight of the building. In Appendix I is shown how the loads were carried down a few of the columns of the Fisher building.

The unit stresses commonly employed are 16,000 lbs. per square inch for fibre stress in steel $\mathbf{I}$ beams, 15,000 lbs. per square inch for plate girders, and 15,000 lbs. per square inch for short

Fig. 1.

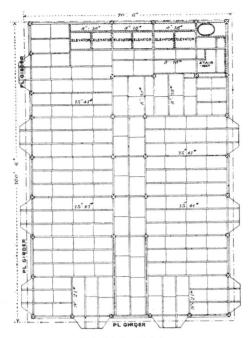

Scale, 1 inch = 32 feet.

FRAMING PLAN IN THE FISHER BUILDING.

columns in compression. In a majority of cases the columns used in a building can be considered short, as they are rigidly held at each floor. When, however, on account of high stories, or for any other reason, it becomes necessary, the unit stress is reduced by one of the standard column formulas, such as $\dfrac{40,000}{1 + \dfrac{l^2}{36,000\,r^2}}$; but sometimes the formula $17,100 - 57\,\dfrac{l}{r}$ is used. When loads are eccentric, the sectional area is deduced from Rankine's formula [1] $f\,S = P + P_1\left(1 + \dfrac{X_0\,X_1\,S}{I}\right)$, in which P is the centre load, P_1 the eccentric load, f the fibre stress, S the section required, X_0 the distance between the neutral axis and the extreme fibre, X_1 the distance between the neutral axis and the eccentric load, and I the moment of inertia of the section. This is for a short column, and is further reduced by the long column formula when necessary. Rivet shear is taken between 9,000 lbs. and 11,000 lbs. per square inch.

[1] " Applied Mechanics," p. 305.

Steel is exclusively used in the best examples of Chicago construction. Box-columns, of plates and angle-bars, and Z-bar columns have been generally used, in which the joints of the columns have been made with a horizontal cap-plate, connected to the column by lugs. The ends of the beams or girders running to the column rested on the cap-plate with $\frac{3}{4}$ inch to $1\frac{1}{2}$ inch between the end of the beam and the face of the columns, Figs. 2, Plate 1. Columns made in this manner are, however, always weak laterally. Recently a column made of eight angle-bars in pairs, connected

TABLE II.—DISTRIBUTION OF LOADS IN FISHER BUILDING.

	Load.	Joists.	Girders.	Columns.	Footings.
		Lbs.	Lbs.	Lbs.	Lbs.
Roof . . . . {	Live . .	20	15	15	..
	Dead . .	40	40	40	40
	Total .	60	55	55	40
Attic . . . . {	Live . .	30	20	20	..
	Dead . .	75	75	75	75
	Total .	105	95	95	75
Eighteenth floor to sixteenth floor. . . . . {	Live . .	60	50	50	25
	Dead . .	75	75	75	75
	Total .	135	125	125	100
Fifteenth floor to thirteenth floor. . . . . {	Live . .	60	50	45	25
	Dead . .	75	75	75	75
	Total .	135	125	120	100
Twelfth floor to tenth floor. . {	Live . .	60	50	40	25
	Dead . .	75	75	75	75
	Total .	135	125	115	100
Ninth floor to seventh floor . {	Live . .	60	50	35	25 '
	Dead . .	75	75	75	75
	Total .	135	125	110	100
Sixth floor to third floor . {	Live . .	60	50	30	25
	Dead . .	75	75	75	75
	Total .	135	125	105	100
Second floor . . . . . {	Live . .	75	60	40	25
	Dead . .	75	75	75	75
	Total .	150	135	115	100
First floor . . . . . {	Live . .	90	75	55	25
	Dead . .	75	75	75	75
	Total .	165	150	130	100

The weights of the fireproofing round the column, and of the column itself, are added to the above column loads.

together by tie-plates, has been used. It can be kept the same size from back to back of the angle-bars, from the basement to the roof, so that the joint can be made with vertical splice-plates. The column has, Figs. 3, Plate 1, hollow spaces throughout its length, in which water-, steam-, and gas-pipes are placed. Beams and girders are connected directly with the faces of the column, a method which gives great lateral stiffness, as has been satisfactorily shown in the Reliance, Wyandotte, Fisher and other buildings. The columns are generally made in two-storey lengths, alternate columns breaking joint at the same floor.

In a building, the height of which is between four and six times its least width, wind-pressure becomes an important element, and several methods have been used to provide for it. In the Great Northern Hotel, fourteen storeys high, and in the Masonic Temple,

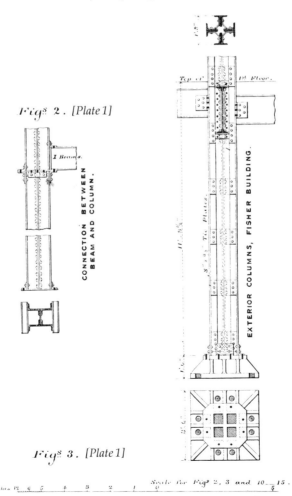

Fig^s. 2. [Plate 1]

Fig^s. 3. [Plate 1]

Fig. 4.

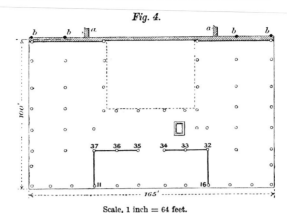

Scale, 1 inch = 64 feet.

GROUND PLAN OF GREAT NORTHERN HOTEL.

Fig. 5.

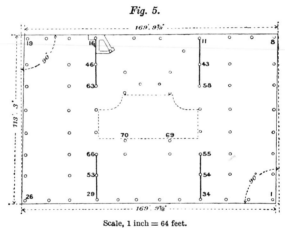

Scale, 1 inch = 64 feet.

GROUND PLAN OF MASONIC TEMPLE.

twenty storeys high, with a roof-garden, vertical systems of lateral rods were used, running from top to bottom of the building, similar to those in an iron pier of a railway viaduct. The ground-plan of the hotel, *Fig. 4*, shows the bracing running from column 16 to column 34, and from column 35 to column 11, forming a tower around the main entrance. A plan of the Masonic Temple, where the rods run between columns 34 and 55, 58 and 11, 29 and 66, and 63 and 16, is shown in *Fig. 5*. This method can never be carried out completely, owing to its interference with the doors and windows, and to its rendering permanent the partitions in which the systems are placed. To show that it is effective, however, the case of the hotel may be cited. The lateral rods, which were shown in the original plans, did not arrive at the building until the frame had reached a height of five or six storeys, and the building of the outside walls had been begun. A travelling derrick was used to set the steel-work, but the vibration which it caused in the building made it impossible to fix the terra-cotta. Work was accordingly stopped until the rods were inserted, when there was no further trouble, although at one time the steel-work was six or seven storeys above the masonry work. Portal bracing,

Fig. 6.

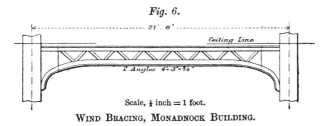

Scale, ¼ inch = 1 foot.
WIND BRACING, MONADNOCK BUILDING.

Figs. 7.

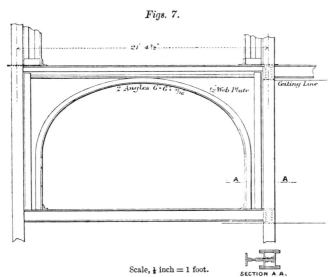

Scale, ¼ inch = 1 foot.
SECTION A A.
WIND BRACING, OLD COLONY BUILDING.

Figs. 8.

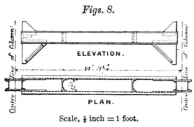

ELEVATION.

PLAN.

Scale, ¼ inch = 1 foot.
WIND BRACING, FORT DEARBORN BUILDING.

between certain columns at every floor, was first used in the Monadnock building, *Fig. 6*, and afterwards in the Old Colony building and others, *Figs. 7*, but its cost is disproportionate to its effectiveness. Knee braces have been used in the New York Life and in the Fort Dearborn buildings, *Figs. 8*. They

159

stiffen the framework, if carefully designed; but they require great exactness in manufacture, and care in erection.

Plate girders, 24 inches deep, running between all the outside columns, and rigidly connected with them, were first used in |the Reliance building, 55 feet wide and 200 feet high, *Figs. 9.* The first storey of this building was slipped under the upper four storeys of the old five-storey building in 1891. In 1894 the upper four storeys were pulled down, and the new fourteen-storey building was erected from the second floor. These plate-girders, the connections of the columns by vertical instead of horizontal plates, and the bolting of the beams and girders directly to the column, instead of resting them on horizontal plates, combine to make each floor rigid in itself, and enable the wind-stresses to be carried to the ground on what may be called the " table-leg " principle.

Figs. 9.

The Author's practice is to construct the frame to withstand a horizontal wind-pressure of 30 lbs. per square foot over the whole side of the building. The resulting stresses are supposed to be taken up by all the columns in each row. If the maximum stress in any column from live, dead and wind stresses exceeds 25,000 lbs. per square inch, the column is enlarged to bring the stress below this limit. This corresponds with the maximum stress allowed for live, dead and wind stresses, in the best bridge practice—between 19,000 lbs. and 25,000 lbs. per square inch.

A typical sprandrel-section, showing the construction of the bay-window framing, is given in Fig. 10, Plate 1, and the construction between the bays is shown in Fig. 11. Fig. 12 illustrates the detail of the cornice of the Fisher building, showing how it is supported. The roof is made of beams and girders, supporting T-bars, spaced 18 inches between centres, between which book-tiles are built. Over

Scale, 1 inch = 64 feet.

RELIANCE BUILDING.

the book-tiles is spread a layer of cement, and on this a six-ply tar-and-gravel roof is laid; the beams and girders supporting the T-bars being fireproofed. The design for carrying the balcony on the front of the Mabley building, Detroit, Michigan, is given in Fig. 13, and in Fig. 14 the design of the bottom of the bays in

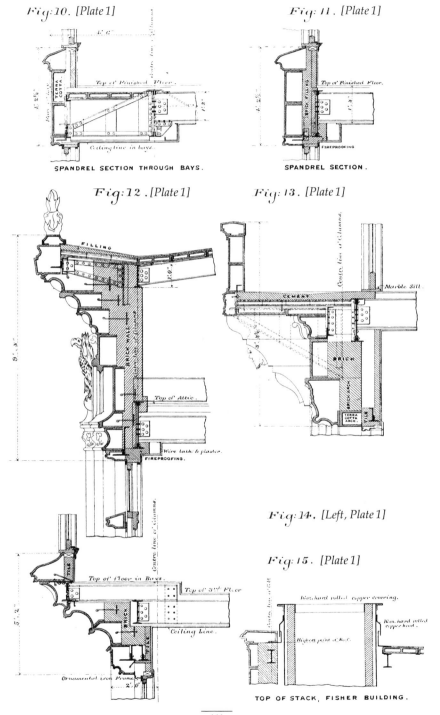

Fig: 10. [Plate 1]

SPANDREL SECTION THROUGH BAYS.

Fig: 11. [Plate 1]

SPANDREL SECTION.

Fig: 12. [Plate 1]

Fig: 13. [Plate 1]

Fig: 14. [Left, Plate 1]

Fig: 15. [Plate 1]

TOP OF STACK, FISHER BUILDING.

161

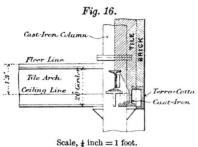

Fig. 16.

Cast-Iron Column

Floor Line

Tile Arch

Ceiling Line

TILE BRICK

Terra-Cotta

Cast-Iron

Scale, ¼ inch = 1 foot.

WALL SECTION, TACOMA BUILDING.

the Great Northern theatre, hotel and office-building. The construction between the columns is shown, and the supporting bracket at the column is indicated in Fig. 13 by the dotted lines. Steel chimney-stacks, lined with firebrick to a height of 60 feet or 70 feet, and with hollow tiles between that point and the top, have

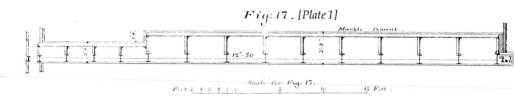

Fig. 17. [Plate 1]

Marble   Cement

12"-50

Scale for Fig. 17.

Feet   5   10   15 Feet.

almost supplanted the old brick chimney, the first having been used in the Home Insurance building. A 2-inch air-space is left between the steel and the brick core. The outside is of steel plates, $\frac{1}{2}$ inch to $\frac{3}{8}$ inch thick at the bottom, diminishing to $\frac{1}{4}$ inch at the top. The stack is not connected with the roof, but passes through it with a sliding joint, Fig. 15, Plate 1, so that the expansion and contraction of the stack will not crack the roof-tile.

A wall or spandrel section used in the Tacoma building, which was one of the first of the high buildings to be erected, is shown in *Fig. 16.* It is interesting to compare this section, used for carrying a plain brick wall, with later sections, which have to support moulded terra-cotta. Fig. 17, Plate 1, is a section through the water-closet floor of the Fisher building, showing how it is furred up, to allow the soil-pipes, &c., to run beneath. A transverse section through the Great

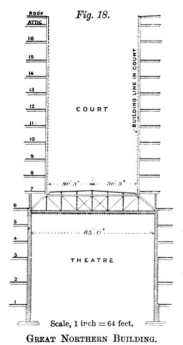

Fig. 18.

ROOF
ATTIC
16
15
14
13
12
11
10
9
8
7
6
5
4
3
2
1

COURT

BUILDING LINE IN COURT

30'.3"   30'.9"

85'.0"

THEATRE

Scale, 1 inch = 64 feet.

GREAT NORTHERN BUILDING.

162

Home Insurance building, Chicago (from 'The Chicago School of Architecture' by Carl W. Condit, × 70%). Normally acknowledged as the first "skeleton" office block, this building was erected in 1884-85, and designed by William Jenney and George Whitney. Its internal frame used cast and wrought iron, and above the sixth floor structural steel. It was demolished in 1931

Northern building, showing the roof-trusses over the theatre, is given in *Fig. 18*. These trusses support the columns extending to the roof, which carry the court walls in addition to the floors.

In order that a building may be absolutely fireproof, every part of the steel frame must be covered with a fire- and water-resisting material, and the outside walls must be made of brick or terra-cotta, instead of stone. Mr. J. J. Webster, M. Inst. C.E., in his Paper on " Fireproof Construction "[1] says : " There is, of course, no such thing as a fireproof structure, if the phrase is taken in a strictly literal sense, no known substance being able to resist a change of state when submitted to intense heat." This is true, but the Chicago high buildings are absolutely fireproof in the sense that they will safely resist any fire which can occur in or around them, as has been shown by severe tests to which certain buildings have been subjected. In one corner of the Rookery building there are janitors' closets, for the storage of supplies and waste paper and containing the gas-meters, one above the other, from the first to the eleventh floor. As there are no windows, the floors consist simply of iron gratings, to allow ventilation. A fire recently started in one of these closets, and in a few minutes there was a sheet of flame from bottom to top of the shaft. The gas-meters were burned, and the escaping gas aided the fire. Although it was reported by the fire brigade to be an intensely hot fire, it did no damage outside of the closets, except on one floor, where the door was opened for access to the fire. On the other floors no damage was done, even the glass transoms across the corridor being uninjured.

During the building of the Chicago Athletic Club, after the floors and fireproofing were erected, and while the interior was being finished, a fire occurred. About 80,000 feet of oak lumber, oiled and finished, was piled in the building ready for use, and was entirely destroyed, the damage to the building being between $50,000 and $60,000 ; but the steel frame was uninjured, with the exception of a few beams between the elevators, which buckled owing to the expansion of the iron guides fastened between them. The tile arches in the floors were uninjured. The fireproofing of the columns was destroyed, but this was through their faulty design. Wooden strips had been wedged between the flanges of the columns every 3 feet or 4 feet, and the fireproofing built between them. These strips were burned out, and the fireproofing fell to the floor.

In addition to fireproofing the beams, the floor-arches must give lateral stiffness to the floor. In this respect, the hard-burned fire-clay, and the porous terra-cotta lumber floor-arches, are the best hitherto devised. Numerous systems of fireproofing have been

---

[1] Minutes of Proceedings Inst. C.E., vol. cv. p. 249.

designed in recent years, nearly all of which are combinations of concrete and iron. Most of them are amply strong as to vertical loading, but none of them, as far as is known to the Author, give the requisite lateral stiffness.

The complete description of floor-arches given by Mr. Webster in the Paper [1] referred to renders it unnecessary to do more than allude to two new arches which have been introduced since that Paper was written. The end construction has been universally used in Chicago for the past four years. In *Fig. 19* is shown a

Fig. 19.

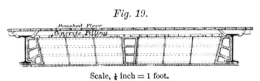

Scale, ¼ inch = 1 foot.

SECTION OF 12-INCH ARCH.

12-inch arch, made by the Illinois Terra-Cotta Lumber Co. The weight of this arch is 41 lbs. per square foot for the 12-inch arch, and 34 lbs. per square foot for the 10-inch arch. A new arch, *Figs. 20*, has recently been introduced by the Pioneer Fireproof Construction Co.; it is deeper than is ordinarily made, and affords much better protection to the bottom of the beam, although it also increases the thickness of the floor.

Figs. 20.

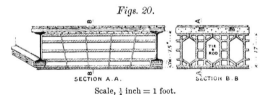

SECTION A.A. SECTION B.B

Scale, ¼ inch = 1 foot.

SECTION OF 17-INCH ARCH, SHOWING DOUBLE AIR-SPACE UNDER BEAMS.

It has been the custom to place the hollow tile fireproofing on the back, and partly on the sides of the outside columns, and to trust to the brick or terra-cotta to protect the remainder, *Fig. 21*. In the Reliance and Fisher buildings the fireproofing is carried entirely round the column, *Fig. 22*, and the brick and terra-cotta front is applied outside it. It is believed that the latter method, on account of the air-spaces, affords better protection against fire, and is much more effective in preventing moisture from reaching the column.

The following is an extract from the fireproofing specification of the Reliance building: "All columns throughout the building, including the attic, shall be fireproofed with 3-inch tiles, special tiles being used having rounded corners, provided with slots to

[1] Minutes of Proceedings Inst. C.E., vol. cv. p. 263 *et seq.*

receive pipes where indicated, set plumb to a line, regularly bonded, having air-space between the fireproofing and the iron keyed in place and to each other, and each piece wired to the column with copper wire." Wherever pipes are run alongside of columns, *Fig. 22*, they are separated from the column by the fireproofing.

For preserving the steel frame from rust, the best practice is to thoroughly scrape off the scale and to apply a coat of oil at the mill or shop, and a coat of red lead, graphite or asphalt after erection. This will suffice for the beams, but additional measures are now taken to insure the safety of the columns.

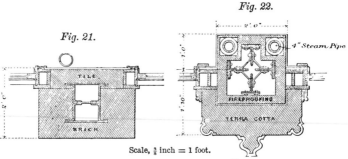

Fig. 22.

Fig. 21.

Scale, ⅜ inch = 1 foot.

PLANS OF OUTSIDE COLUMNS, SHOWING FIREPROOFING.

In the Ellicott Square building, being erected in Buffalo, New York, all the outside columns are filled with Portland-cement concrete, which is generally believed to be an excellent protection to iron. Mr. Eiffel has stated that in cement iron does not rust[1]; and Mr. F. Collingwood has found,[2] from examinations at Niagara, that cement concrete affords an absolute protection to iron against rust. The steel beams used in the foundations are always completely embedded in Portland-cement concrete, and are neither oiled nor painted, as the concrete adheres more to the unpainted iron. When the fireproofing is well fixed and covered on the outside with plaster, the column is in a space nearly air-tight and the danger from corrosion is small. Mr. M. P. Wood, in his Paper " Rustless Coatings for Iron and Steel,"[1] says : " In fact, for all iron and steel requiring protection from corrosion other than by the magnetic oxide processes, and that depend upon paint for their protection, it is an indispensable condition that the scale must be removed in order to secure the best result. When this is done and strictly pure red lead is mixed with pure raw linseed oil that has escaped the manipulations of the whale or menhaden oil-merchant, a paint is produced that will unite so closely to the iron

---

[1] Minutes of Proceedings Inst. C.E., vol. xcvii. p. 431.

[2] Transactions of the American Society of Civil Engineers, vol. ii. p. 337.

[1] Transactions of the American Society of Mechanical Engineers, vol. xv. p. 1013.

or steel surface as to be only secondary in preservative qualities to magnetic oxide in resisting atmospheric effects." The use of magnetic oxide, such as in the Bower-Barff process, for the steel frame of a large building, is now prohibited by its cost, and, further, it weakens the metal. The ironwork of the tower of the new City Hall, Philadelphia, Pa., was electro-plated with copper and aluminium. To quote again from Mr. Wood:[2] " This process is a double one. The first one is designed to protect the iron from rust by an electro-plating of copper of 14 ounces per square foot of surface, and a finishing coat of an alloy of aluminium and tin of $2\frac{1}{2}$ ounces per square foot, for colour to harmonize with the stonework of the lower storeys of the tower; also to prevent oxidation of the copper into a green coating of verdigris."

The process was adopted as a substitute for paint, the periodical renewals of which would have cost $10,000 per annum, the principal amount being due to the use of boiling linseed oil, in which all the material was to be immersed until it had attained the temperature of the bath. The total weight of the wrought and cast iron to be protected is about 500 tons, and comprises 100,000 square feet of surface, the largest single pieces being sixteen columns, 27 feet long and 3 feet in diameter, weighing 10,000 lbs. each. These columns received the copper coating inside as well as outside. The outside coating, being most exposed, is double, requiring two operations or baths, while the aluminium coat is given last as the protective coating to all beneath it. The cost of the whole process varies between 1s. 8d. and 4s. per square foot, depending upon the shape of the piece—simple plates, rods, angles, &c., being the least, while curved pieces with large lugs, flanges with core-holes, are the most expensive. The principal expense is incurred in the cleaning, and the greatest care is necessary to ensure good work.

Mr. Henry M. Howe has advocated the attachment of zinc to iron structures, to oppose corrosion due to differences of electric potential. The following formula has been proposed by Prof. R. H. Thurston[1] for the probable life of steel suffering corrosion. Life, in years, $= \dfrac{W}{C\,L}$, where W is the weight of the metal in lbs. per lineal foot of the surface exposed, L the length in feet of its perimeter, and C a constant, $0\cdot0125$ for steel in air. The method of determining the value of the constant C is not given. According to this formula, a 12-inch 32-lb. I-beam will last 682 years, and a 15-inch 60-lb. bar I-beam will last 1,107 years. A column made of eight 6-inch by $3\frac{1}{2}$-inch by $\frac{3}{4}$-inch L-beams will last 1,640 years, and one of eight $3\frac{1}{2}$-inch by $2\frac{1}{2}$-inch by $\frac{5}{16}$-inch L-beams, such as are used in the upper storeys of a building, will last 620 years.

[2] *Ibid*, vol. xv. p. 1054.
[1] " Materials of Engineering," part ii. p. 331.

FOUNDATIONS.

Spread foundations are used under nearly all the high buildings in Chicago. Before they are designed, borings are made to an average depth of 30 feet below the bottom of the footings, one at the site of each footing. These show whether there are any sand- or mud-pockets, and guide the determination of the load to be carried by the clay. The results obtained from a boring at the Reliance building are given in Table III, and may be regarded as typical.

In Table IV are given the results of two tests made to determine the bearing power of the soil, made in 1890 on the site of the Masonic Temple. A tank, supported on a plate having an area of 2 square feet, was gradually filled with water. In the first test the plate rested directly on the hard pan, and in the second test it was placed in the bottom of a hole 2 feet 4 inches deep in the hard pan. The foundations have in some cases been sunk into the hard pan, so as to give greater basement height. These tests show, however, that it is the safer practice never to descend below the top of the hard pan. If the borings show any sand-pockets or soft spots, the contractor is required by the specification to excavate them and fill the cavity with concrete.

TABLE III.—RESULTS OF BORING AT THE RELIANCE BUILDING.	
Depth. Ft. Ins.	Nature of Clay.
0 0	
	Arenaceous,
2 6	Compact,
7 0	Less compact,
9 6	Gradually changing into a soft and wet condition,
14 0	Somewhat harder,
15 6	Soft and wet,
31 0	Softer,
32 0	Very soft and wet,
42 0	Harder,
44 0	Very soft and wet,
51 0	Somewhat harder,
56 0	Soft and wet.
64 0	

The load per square foot having been deduced, the areas of the footings are determined. The areas of adjacent footings are often found to overlap; they are then combined as one footing, three or four being sometimes treated in this manner. In all such cases the middle of the footing is made the centre of gravity of all the loads upon it. The areas of the bottom-plates of the cast-iron shoes, or bases, upon which the columns rest, are thus derived, and the thickness of the bottom-plate and the other parts of the shoe is calculated. Under the shoes are placed layers of steel I-beams at right-angles to one another, until they cover an area 1 foot or 2 feet smaller in each direction than the required area of the footing. Under the bottom course is spread a layer of concrete between 12 inches and 16 inches thick, and covering the area required for the footing, and each layer of beams is entirely embedded in concrete. The completed footing forms a solid pyramid of steel and concrete, possessing much greater strength than if it were composed

Table IV.—Tests of Supporting-Power of the Soil on the Masonic Building Site.

—	Time of Loading.	Load.	Total Settlement.
		Lbs. per Square Foot.	Inches.
Test 1	10th October, 10 A.M.	267·0	..
	" " 2 P.M.	2,226·5	$\frac{1}{4}$
	11th " 10 A.M.	4,675·5	$\frac{11}{16}$
	13th " 4 P.M.	5,655·0	$1\frac{9}{16}$
	14th " 5 P.M.	5,655·0	$1\frac{13}{16}$
Test 2	18th " 4 P.M.	334·0	..
	20th " 9 A.M.	1,327·0	$\frac{5}{8}$
	" " 2 P.M.	2,280·0	$\frac{7}{8}$
	" " 3.30 P.M.	2,965·5	$1\frac{1}{16}$
	" " 4.30 P.M.	3,767·0	$1\frac{3}{8}$
	21st " 9 A.M.	4,311·5	$1\frac{15}{16}$
	" " 1 P.M.	4,934·0	$2\frac{1}{8}$
	" " 5 P.M.	5,627·5	$2\frac{13}{16}$
	24th " 7.45 P.M.	5,627·5	$4\frac{1}{8}$

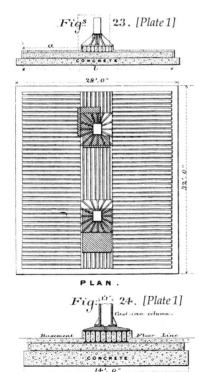

Figs 23. [Plate 1]

a
CONCRETE
l
28'. 0"
32'. 0"
PLAN.

Figs 25. [Plate 1]

CONCRETE
26'. 0"
20'. 6"
PLAN.

Fig. 24. [Plate 1]

Cast-iron column.
Basement Floor Line
CONCRETE
14'. 0"

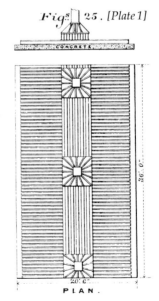

Masonic Temple, Chicago (from 'Architectural Engineering' by J. K. Freitag). At the time of its construction in 1892, this was the tallest building in the world, with a steel frame on reinforced concrete foundations. It was designed by John Welborn Root and Daniel Hudson Burnham. It was demolished in 1939

simply of beams piled in the same manner. This increased strength is taken into account in calculating the sizes and number of the beams in the different layers. The projections of the beams in any layer are regarded as cantilevers, and the portions of the beams covered by the layer above are considered to be subject to shearing stresses only. The total load of both columns in one of the large footings of the Masonic Temple, for example, Figs. 23, Plate 1, including the weight of the masonry in both piers, is 2,750,000 lbs.; the length of the beams in the layer l considered is 25 feet 9 inches; and the projection a from the end of the beams to the centre of the outside beam in the layer above is 10 feet 6 inches. The bending-moment is therefore $\dfrac{2,750,000}{25\cdot75} \times \dfrac{10\cdot5^2}{2} = 5,887,000$ foot-lbs. The layer is composed of forty-two 15-inch 60-lb. I-beams, and their total bending-moment, using a fibre-stress of 20,000 lbs. per square inch, is 6,014,400 foot-lbs. The Author uses a stress of 20,000 lbs. per square inch for foundation beams which are absolutely free from shock or vibration of any kind. It must be remembered that the load on a foundation increases very gradually. The foundations are in place several weeks before any load is applied, and it is eight or nine months before they receive their full load, so that the concrete has time to become perfectly set. The best Portland cement is used, and the greatest precautions are taken in making the concrete. In the Masonic Temple the foundation concrete was made of 1 part of Portland cement, 2 parts of clean sharp torpedo sand, and three parts of clean broken stone which would pass a $2\frac{1}{2}$-inch ring. Between the beams, crushed granite, not exceeding $\frac{1}{2}$-inch cube, was used instead of the broken stone. As the beams must be far enough apart to allow the concrete to be filled and well rammed between them, and as the top layer is covered by the bottom plate of the cast-iron shoe, this layer can have but few beams, and they are therefore short. Each succeeding layer, being able to carry more beams, may be longer. In Fig. 24, Plate 1, is shown a footing under the Tacoma building, and in Figs. 25 a three-column footing under the Masonic Temple. A two-column footing under same building at the main entrance is given in Figs. 23; and Figs. 26 show a double-column footing under the Herald building carrying two of the front masonry piers.

The dead load only is used in designing the footings, in order to secure a more uniform settlement of the building. The amount of the settlement is of small importance, provided it is equal in all parts. If the live load were considered in the calculations, the interior footings would carry a much higher percentage of live load, and it would be impossible for the buildings to settle uniformly. In the case of the Marshall Field warehouse in Adams Street, designed by the late H. H. Richardson, the live load of 75 lbs. per square foot, on every floor, was carried down to the footings, according to the practice in New York and Boston. The

Figs 26. [Plate 1]

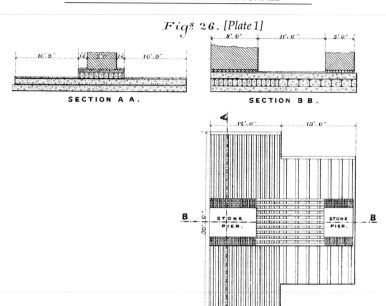

SECTION A A.

SECTION B B.

STONE PIER.

STONE PIER.

PLAN.

Figs 27. [Plate 1]

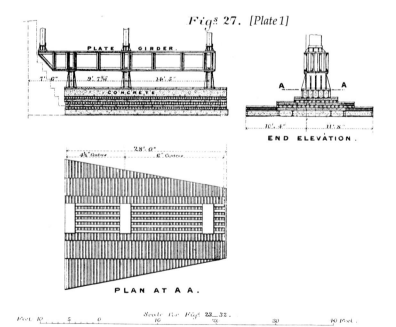

PLATE GIRDER.

CONCRETE

END ELEVATION.

PLAN AT A A.

Scale for Figs 23—32.

Feet 10   5   0   30   40 Feet.

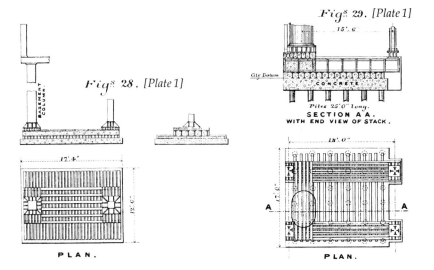

Fig^s 29. [Plate 1]

Fig^s 28. [Plate 1]

Piles 25'0" long.
SECTION A A.
WITH END VIEW OF STACK.

PLAN.   PLAN.

result is that all the floors have risen considerably at the centre. For the most part, the owners of adjacent sites draw up a contract for a party wall. Sometimes, however, this is not done, and the footings along the party line have to be kept entirely within the site, necessitating the use of cantilevers. That used under the Rand and McNally building, ten storeys high, erected in 1889, is shown in Figs. 27, Plate 1. This is a very heavy building, the floors having a live load of 150 lbs. to 200 lbs. per square foot, and the 6th floor, where the printing-presses are placed, 300 lbs. The construction used in the Herald building, built in 1891, is given in Figs. 28.

Pile foundations have been very little used under office buildings, although almost invariably under the warehouses and other buildings on the banks of the river. The Art Institute, Public Library, Schiller Theatre and Stock Exchange rest on piles, 40 feet to 50 feet long, driven in accordance with standard formulas for pile-driving, and treated as bearing piles. At the Stock Exchange, in addition to the piles, wrought-iron tubes filled with concrete were sunk to a considerable depth. The latter form, however, a very expensive foundation. Pile foundations have been used for many years, and the spread foundations are perfectly safe, as the number of large buildings standing on them prove, some of which have been erected ten or twelve years.

In the Fisher building piles were employed, but the principle involved in their use is entirely different from that referred to, for they are essentially spread foundations. On account of the absence of a party-wall contract, it was found impossible to use the ordinary spread footings along the party line. The Author con-

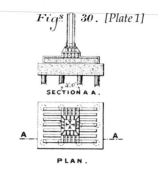

Figs. 30. [Plate 1]

SECTION A A.

PLAN.

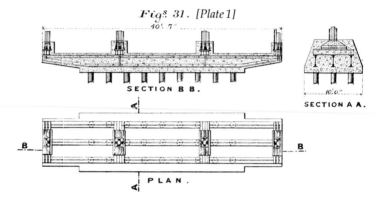

Figs 31. [Plate 1]

SECTION B B.

SECTION A A.

PLAN.

sidered that by driving short piles the clay would be compressed, and would be in the same condition before the building was commenced as it ordinarily assumes after a heavy building has been erected upon it. The clay would therefore stand a greater load than would otherwise be considered safe. Accordingly piles 25 feet long were driven at 3 feet between centres. The load for each pile was 25 tons, the 9 square feet of clay around each pile being loaded to nearly 6,000 lbs. per square foot the pile being disregarded. The piles, however, will act with the clay in bearing the load, for it required between four and eight blows with a 2,500-lb. hammer falling 20 feet or 24 feet to drive the piles down the last foot. A footing of this building carrying two columns and the steel stack, is shown in Figs. 29, Plate 1; and Fig. 30 illustrates a single column-footing under the same building.

A foundation designed by the Author for an office building now being erected in Washington Street is shown in Fig. 31. The building, which will be eleven storeys high, is 40 feet wide by 165 feet long, and is between two buildings, one four, the other seven storeys high. The walls on both sides had formerly been party walls, but new contracts had not been obtained, so the footings had to be kept entirely within the site, the boundaries

Fig. 32. [Plate 1]

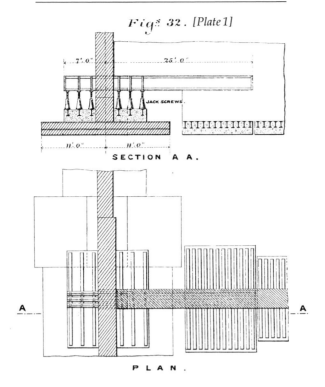

being the middle of the existing walls. To shore up these walls and carry the foundations to the boundaries, would have been a costly and somewhat hazardous operation, as the footings would occur close together along the walls, and would penetrate considerably deeper than one wall. The plan adopted allowed piles to be driven along the centre of the lot, parallel to the walls, with a minimum distance from both walls of 6 feet. On the top of each row of piles a plate girder was placed, upon which the four columns occurring in the width of the building rest. Piles were used in the same manner as in the Fisher building, the tops of the piles being embedded in concrete instead of using a timber grillage.

In the Great Northern theatre, hotel and office building, in course of erection on the east side of the Great Northern hotel, in Jackson Street, the theatre is in the middle of the building. Heavy walls separate it from the office and hotel portions. These walls, each weighing, with the floor loads, 60,000 lbs. per lineal foot, meet the east wall of the present Great Northern hotel at right angles. This east wall had been originally regarded as a party wall, and its footing had been constructed strong enough to carry a floor load from each side. The end of the theatre wall where it meets the east wall could not rest on the footing of the

175

latter, which projects 9 feet 6 inches, as it would overload the footing, besides being only on one side. The old building had practically stopped settling, and the new one would probably settle 7 inches or 8 inches. The floor load, however, from the east side had never been put upon this footing, and in addition it was deemed safe to load it somewhat higher than formerly, as the east wall, fourteen storeys high, had been resting upon it for four years. Plate girders, Figs. 32, Plate 1, were placed lengthwise in the theatre wall, with their ends projecting through the old wall, and resting on 36-ton hydraulic jack-screws, which in turn were supported by I-beams lying on the footing and parallel to the old wall. The plate girders were of such a length, and so situated, as to transfer to the old footing the desired weight. The screws were raised to their full height, so that they could be lowered 14 inches if necessary. As the new building settles these screws will be run down at regular intervals, until the settlement stops, which will probably be in four or five years. Levels will be taken during that period. After the settlement has ceased, the screws will be surrounded with concrete and left. The points dealt with are shown at *aa*, *Fig. 4*; the four other points, *b*, where the new building joins the old, will be treated in a similar manner.

The spread foundations of Chicago have often been referred to as floating, and the soil has been regarded as a fluid, the settlement being constant, with more or less lateral displacement. The Author does not believe that any such lateral movement exists, for it would follow the line of least resistance; and with a heavy building on each side of the street, for example, the Great Northern and Monadock, it would show itself in the disturbance of the network of pipes in the street, and in the forcing up of the pavement itself. The settlement is due to the compression of the clay, the water being pressed out of it. In the Masonic Temple four of the main columns, near the lifts, carry heavy loads and have large footings, and between them are two small columns which only carry the stairs. As these had much smaller footings than any others in the building, they were given a higher load per square foot. During the construction of the building, the four columns had received the greater portion of their loads when the erection of the stairs was begun. It was found at once, that the connections on the stairs would not fit those on the columns, the latter being too high. Levels taken to ascertain whether the small columns had been forced up, showed that they simply had not settled with the rest of the building. About 75 tons of pig-iron were then loaded on both footings, and allowed to remain for a week. Although the load then amounted to 7,000 pounds per square foot, twice the load on any of the other footings, the column only settled about 1 inch less than one-half the desired amount, and so the connections had to be changed all the way up the stairs.

The compression of the soil varies with the load, is greatest when the load is first applied, diminishes and finally stops. Curves of settlement of six columns, four at the corners of and two within the Masonic Temple, are given in *Fig. 33*. The ground plan of the building, *Fig. 5*, gives the positions of the six columns. The levels of the two interior columns could not be taken after the 20th of October, as the old marks had been covered. These curves are rapidly approaching a horizontal line; the amount of settlement since the last levels were taken, almost two years ago, is nearly the same in each case, the maximum variation being only $\frac{1}{8}$ inch, although they had varied considerably before. The auditorium settled more than 20 inches under the tower, but this was due to the fact that several storeys were added which were not in the original design and were introduced after the foundations had been inserted. Probably none of the high buildings on spread footings settled less than 6 inches. The amount of settlement generally is between 6 inches and 12 inches. This settlement is anticipated when construction is begun, by raising the level of the bottom of the footings by the amount it is thought the buildings will settle. This causes the footways to be steep at first, but they approach their proper slope as the build-

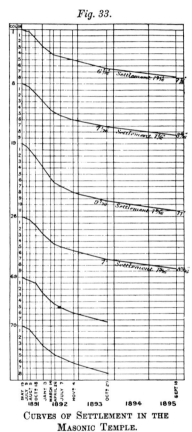

Fig. 33.

CURVES OF SETTLEMENT IN THE MASONIC TEMPLE.

ings settle. The foundations of the Great Northern theatre have been raised 9 inches.

WEIGHT AND COST OF THE STEEL FRAME.

The weight of the steel frame in an office building sixteen to twenty storeys in height, ranges from $1\frac{5}{8}$ lb. to 2 lbs. per cubic foot of the building. The cost is between 4·9 cents and 6 cents per cubic foot, being one-seventh to one-ninth of the cost of the building.

PERIOD OCCUPIED IN CONSTRUCTION.

It requires between seven months and a year to erect and completely finish an office building. At the Reliance building work was begun by pulling down the upper four storeys of the old building, on the 1st May, 1894. Some delay was caused by the construction of a temporary roof over the second floor and making connection to the first storey columns. The first floor was occupied during the whole time of construction. The building was finished and tenanted on the 1st April, 1895. At the New York Life building, twelve storeys high, excavation was begun on the 14th July, 1893, and the foundation was begun on the 3rd August. The steel frame was completed on the 29th September, and on the 2nd December, steam heat was turned on to the entire building. At the Champlain building, fifteen storeys high, excavation was begun on the 12th September, 1893, and the foundation ironwork on the 10th October. Between the 15th and the 25th October work was stopped pending decision as to the party wall. On the 23rd December the ironwork was completed, and on the 4th January, 1894, the fireproofing of the floors was finished. Both these buildings were ready for tenants in the early spring of 1894.

The Author desires to acknowledge his indebtedness to Mr. D. H. Burnham for much valuable information and kindly criticism, and to Mr. W. L. B. Jenney and Mr. Wm. Holabird for data and drawings relating to the history of skeleton construction.

Aswan Dam, showing masonry and sluices in western channel; engineer: Sir Benjamin Baker; contractor: Sir John Aird & Co.; contractor for iron work for sluices etc: Ransomes & Rapier (from a contemporary photograph, × 37.5%). This, the original Aswan Dam, was a 1950m long granite dam, with 180 regulating gates and sluices. Work commenced in 1898, and was largely completed in 1902, a year ahead of schedule. Its construction is described in papers by Maurice Fitzmaurice, the resident engineer, and Frederick Stokes in the Minutes of the Proceedings of the Institution of Civil Engineers, 1903, volume 152

Sydney Harbour Bridge: design of the structure and foundations

R. FREEMAN, MInstCE

Reprinted from Min. Proc. Instn Civ. Engrs, 1934,
vol. 238, 153-193

By the time the twentieth century had been reached, the public perception of engineering activity had changed, largely because the practice of engineering had itself evolved over the years. In the early and mid Victorian eras individual engineers had been known and recognised by name and some of them became almost legendary in the history of engineering. No doubt they were not entirely alone, but had a number of assistants, resident engineers, clerks and draughtsmen. Even so, their offices remained small, and the younger Brunel, for instance, probably employed between 30 and 40 people even on his greatest works.

Later, as engineering developed and projects became more complicated and demanded a multiplicity of skills, firms became larger, some employing hundreds of employees and a few some thousands. As a result, the engineers became anonymous: the history of engineering ceased to be a history of heroic individuals and became instead a history of firms. That is not to say that there were no longer any engineers equal in ability — even genius — to the famed Victorians. Not at all: if anything there were more. Their activities were no longer performed in small partnerships but in bigger concerns, of which some grew to have hundreds of employees and, eventually, a small number to have thousands.

So, although the Sydney Harbour Bridge is rightly linked to the name of Sir Ralph Freeman, it is nowadays more commonly connected with Freeman Fox & Partners as a firm. As engineering has always been dependent on teamwork more than individual talent, though that has never been lacking, this has been a natural though unromantic development.

Ralph Freeman, who was born in 1880 and died in 1950, was the first of the contributors to this book to have reached the modern era of engineering. While the early engineers had most often started in the profession as apprentices, or pupils, by Freeman's time it was not unusual for young men to come into the profession through higher education, though it would still be many years before virtually all took that route. Freeman was educated at the Central Technical College, Kensington, and on leaving in 1901 he joined the consulting engineers Sir Douglas Fox & Partners. He became senior partner in 1912, and remained in active control of the firm until his death. By then the firm had become Freeman Fox & Partners.

The origins of the firm were deep in the history of civil engineering, for the founder, Sir Charles Fox, who set up his plate as a consulting engineer in 1857, had been present at the Rainhill Trials and had ridden on the footplate of *Novelty* then, one of the competitors comprehensively defeated by George Stephenson's *Rocket*. Fox became a railway and building contractor centred in Birmingham, but his greatest fame and his knighthood came from the part he played in building the Crystal Palace.

Although Joseph Paxton is credited with the architecture of the Crystal Palace, without Fox's contribution as engineering and structural designer the project would never have succeeded as brilliantly as it did.

Within a short time of its foundation the firm was constructing railways in Africa and elsewhere overseas; it has continued in overseas practice ever since, with increasing emphasis on big bridges. Freeman Fox is now the world's leading designer of long-span bridges.

Among Ralph Freeman's first tasks when he joined the firm was to make calculations for the Victoria Falls Bridge over the Zambesi. The bridge had a span of 500 feet and was the longest of its kind in the world when it was completed in 1904. It was fabricated and erected by the Cleveland Bridge and Engineering Co. and the consultants became closely connected with the contractors from then on. Much of the steel for the bridge had come from Dorman Long in Middlesborough and the consultants developed a close relationship with that concern too; it was for Dorman Long that Freeman made the designs for the Sydney Harbour Bridge in the 1920s. It was the Sydney Harbour Bridge which established Freeman Fox among the world's leading bridge designers, and two of the young men who helped Ralph Freeman on that project later became well known in the profession and partners of the firm. They were Oleg Kerensky and Gilbert Roberts. Since then the firm has completed many famous bridges including the suspension bridges over the Forth, the Severn, the Bosporus and the longest in the world over the Humber. In addition, of course, Freeman Fox has been involved in a wide range of engineering projects of which one of the most striking was the Dome of Discovery built for the Festival of Britain in 1951. It was seemly that Freeman Fox should be the consulting engineers for the exhibition associated with the festival since it was intended to celebrate the centenary of the Hyde Park Exhibition of 1881 for which Charles Fox had built the Crystal Palace.

THE contract for the construction of the Sydney Harbour Bridge was let to Messrs. Dorman, Long and Company, Limited, of Middlesbrough, England, by the Government of New South Wales in March, 1924, and the bridge was completed in March, 1932. The following Paper describes the design of the structure and foundations of the harbour span and approaches of the bridge. The Author was consulting engineer to the contractors, and on their behalf prepared the design of the structure of the bridge and foundations, and acted as adviser for its construction and erection. The contractors carried out the construction of the entire bridge with their own organization, only the supply of bolts and rivets, of that part of the rolled steel which could be manufactured in Australia, and of certain special plates and forgings being sub-let. The whole of the work on the site was carried out under the direction of Mr. Lawrence Ennis, C.M.G., O.B.E., M. Inst. C.E., a director of Messrs. Dorman, Long and Company, Limited.[1] The calculations and working drawings for the bridge were got out under the direction of Mr. J. F. Pain, Assoc. M. Inst. C.E.[2]

EVENTS PRECEDING SUBMISSION OF TENDERS.

The importance to the City of Sydney of communication between the north and south shores of the harbour is shown by the numerous proposals that have been made for bridges and tunnels across the

[1] Full details of the manufacture and erection of the main and approach spans are given in the Paper by Messrs. Freeman and Ennis, " Sydney Harbour Bridge : Manufacture of the Structural Steelwork and Erection of the Bridge," p. 194.
[2] These are described in detail in the Paper by Messrs. Pain and Roberts, "Sydney Harbour Bridge : Calculations for the Steel Superstructure," p. 256.

harbour since 1815. The controversy as to the advisability of a bridge or a tunnel was terminated in 1912, when Mr. David Hay, M. Inst. C.E., recommended a bridge crossing at the site adopted.

In 1921 a project for the bridge was prepared by Dr. J. J. C. Bradfield, M. Inst. C.E., chief engineer of the Public Works Department of New South Wales, and bridge firms throughout the world were invited to tender for the construction of a cantilever bridge.[1] This project was abandoned, and early in 1923 further invitations were issued to bridge firms to tender for the design and construction of a bridge in accordance with a new specification which included both an arch and a cantilever bridge. This specification defined all the conditions to be satisfied by the bridge, but it did not include designs for either type of bridge ; firms tendering were therefore obliged either to employ their own organizations to take out the necessary designs and quantities or to engage a consulting engineer to do so.

The Author was retained early in 1922 by the Cleveland Bridge and Engineering Company, Limited, to prepare designs for the bridge. In September, 1923, owing to the sudden death of their Chairman, Mr. C. F. Dixon, a short time before the date for completing the tenders, the directors of the Cleveland Bridge Company decided to abandon their intention to submit a tender. In spite of the great difficulty of transferring the work already done at so late a date Messrs. Dorman, Long and Company decided to take it over, and a tender was submitted by them based on the designs prepared by the Author, who was appointed their consulting engineer, Mr. G. C. Imbault, formerly chief engineer of the Cleveland Bridge Company, who had prepared the erection schemes on which the tender was based, being associated with him.

Messrs. Dorman, Long and Company fortunately had already given the scheme some consideration, and were thoroughly experienced in the production of steel and the manufacture of heavy bridgework. The decision involved the undertaking of a contract of the value of about four million pounds, and the building of what would be by far the heaviest single span yet made in a country on the other side of the world. The opportunity, however, provided a new field for the firm's activities ; their decision was also much influenced by the desire that a great bridge in a British Dominion should not be constructed by a foreign firm, and to demonstrate that it was only for lack of opportunity that British bridge-builders had not constructed any bridge of exceptional span for over a generation. Tenders for the bridge were eventually submitted by six of the leading bridge-building firms of the United Kingdom, America, and Europe in January, 1924, the lowest tender being submitted by Messrs. Dorman, Long and Company, Limited. The contract was awarded to them on

---

[1] Full details of this, and other aspects of the scheme, are given in the Paper by Dr. J. J. C. Bradfield, " The Sydney Harbour Bridge and Approaches," p. 310.

the recommendation of Dr. Bradfield, and the whole of the works were carried out subject to his supervision.

Intention of the Specification and Invitation to Tender.

The specification for the bridge issued by the Government of New South Wales referred to two types of principal span, a 1,600-foot cantilever and a 1,650-foot arch span, but it was interpreted by firms tendering as being intended to leave to them the selection of the type of bridge which would satisfy the requirements of the site. Designs and tenders were submitted for no less than seven different forms of large-span bridge, including two-hinged and three-hinged arch, cantilever-arch, cantilever, cantilever-suspension, suspension and stiffened suspension bridges ; thus comprising every known form of steel structure suitable for a long span.

This variety of proposals arose in consequence of the uncertainty regarding the real intention of the specification, and of the importance which might be attached to conflicting aspects of possible alternatives, and illustrates the difficulties that may arise when tenders for a great engineering project are invited without the inclusion of any design for the work to be carried out. Contractors had either to design completely and submit binding tenders for various alternative types, or to select a type by forming their own judgment of the importance of, (a) a clear headway for navigation throughout the entire span, a condition easily obtained with a cantilever bridge but impossible with an arch ; (b) the improvement of the curvature of the approaches obtained with an arch design as compared with a cantilever ; (c) the advisability of either using steel of a quality that could be made in Australia, or of using steel costing less, but impossible to manufacture in Australia ; (d) the æsthetic value attached to pylons, structurally unnecessary, costing over £700,000. Each firm tendering, therefore, had to make its own investigation of the suitability of each type of bridge, and to submit schemes for all, in the hope that one might be accepted by the Government. On the Author's advice, Messrs. Dorman, Long and Company submitted tenders for three types of bridge with seven alternative schemes, and the cost of their tender alone amounted to over £20,000.

Proposals Submitted by Messrs. Dorman, Long and Company, Limited.

On behalf of Messrs. Dorman, Long and Company consideration was given to every known type of bridge, and the conclusion was reached that any form of suspension-bridge would cost far more than an arch bridge, and would be subject to the disadvantages of relatively large deflection and oscillation under moving loads. These disadvantages would be aggravated in this case by the peculiar distribution of the

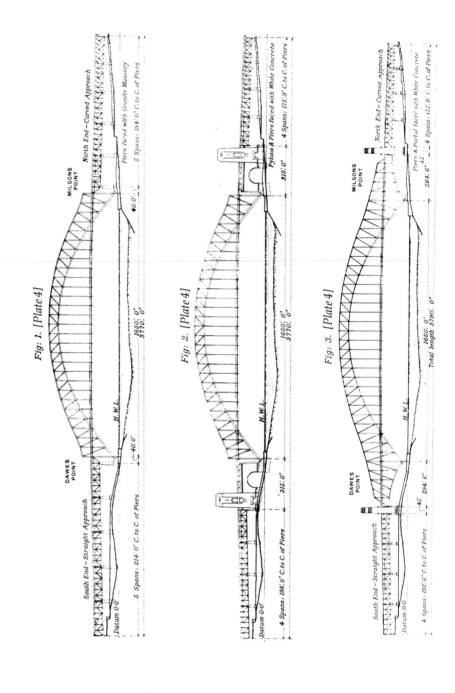

Fig: 1. [Plate 4]

Fig: 2. [Plate 4]

Fig: 3. [Plate 4]

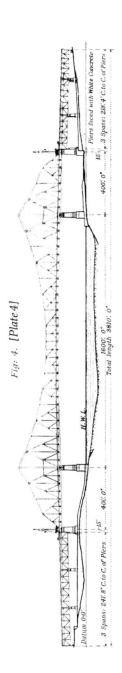

Fig: 4. [Plate 4]

Datum. 0·0

H.W.L.

3 Spans: 241' 8" C. to C. of Piers

400'. 0"

15'

Piers faced with White Concrete

3 Spans: 218'·4" C. to C. of Piers

400'. 0"

1600'. 0"
Total length 3810'. 0"

Scale: 1 Inch = 600 Feet.

Feet 100 0 100 200 300 400 500 600 700 800 Feet.

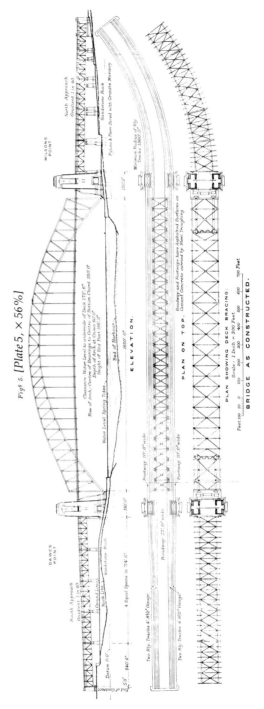

Fig 8 5. [Plate 5, × 56%]

MILSONS POINT

North Approach
Gradient 1 in 40

Sandstone Rock

Pylons & Piers faced with Granite Masonry

Minimum Radius of Rly
Tracks 1360'. 0"

1200'. 0"

Clearance Water Level to underside of Deck 172'. 6"

Rise of Arch, Centre of Bearings to Centre of Bottom Chord 350'. 0"

Depth of Arch at Crown 60'. 0"

Height of End Post 185'. 0"

650'. 0"

Bed of Harbour.

ELEVATION.

Water Level Spring Tides.

PLAN ON TOP.

Roadway and Footways have Asphalted Surfaces on
Cement Concrete carried by Steel Troughing

PLAN SHOWING DECK BRACING.

Scale: 1 Inch = 300 Feet.

Feet 100 50 0 100 200 300 400 500 600 700 Feet.

BRIDGE AS CONSTRUCTED.

DAWES POINT

South Approach
Gradient 1 in 40

Ground Line

Rock Line

Sandstone Rock

350'. 0"

240'. 6"

5'·0"

4 Equal Spans at 704'. 6"

Footway 10'·0" wide

Roadway 57'·0" wide

Footway 10'·0" wide

Two Rly Tracks 4·8½" Gauge

Two Rly Tracks 4·8½" Gauge

End of Contract

DESIGNS SUBMITTED BY MESSRS. DORMAN, LONG & COMPANY, LIMITED.

railway tracks referred to on p. 158. It was therefore considered unnecessary to submit a design and tender for a suspension-bridge. This conclusion was borne out by the tenders submitted by other firms. The lowest tender for a suspension-bridge of 1,600 feet span, devoid of any decorative masonry, amounted to about £5,100,000, whereas the comparable lowest tender for an arch bridge of 1,650 feet span, also omitting all decorative masonry, amounted to £3,500,000, or for a similar span of 1,600 feet to £3,420,000.

Three types of structure were designed to the extent necessary for the accurate calculation of quantities and for the submission of tenders, namely : a two-hinged arch, a two-hinged cantilever-arch, and a cantilever. The tendered costs of the three types of bridges, in each case excluding all decorative features, but including granite piers, were approximately as follows :—

Type.	Span: feet.	Cost.
Two-hinged arch (Fig. 1, Plate 4)	1,650	£3,500,000
ditto	1,600	£3,420,000
Cantilever-arch	1,650	£3,710,000
ditto	1,600	£3,610,000
Cantilever	1,600	£4,550,000

The corresponding tenders including decorative pylons were as follows :—

Arch, 1,650-foot span, with pylons formed in white concrete (Fig. 2, Plate 4) £4,233,000
Arch, 1,650-foot span, with granite pylons (similar to Figs. 5, Plate 4) £4,218,000
Cantilever-arch, 1,650-foot span with pylons in white concrete (Fig. 3, Plate 4) £3,942,000
Cantilever, 1,600-foot span, with piers in white concrete (Fig. 4, Plate 4) £4,310,000

For a span of 1,600 feet instead of 1,650 feet the cost of the arch span is reduced by £80,000, and of the cantilever arch by £100,000. The time for construction stated in the specification, namely 6 years, was considered to be sufficient in all cases.

DESCRIPTION OF ALTERNATIVE TYPES.

The following notes indicate the principal features of the proposed cantilever-arch and cantilever bridges. Loading, stresses, materials, and the method of construction were the same as described later for the arch bridge ; in both cases silicon-steel was adopted for the main trusses and carbon-steel for the deck and laterals ; particulars of these steels are given on p. 170.

Cantilever-Arch Bridge (Fig. 3, Plate 4).—This type of bridge consisted of a two-hinged spandrel-braced steel arch bridge, practically identical with the two-hinged arch actually built, with cantilever shore spans 295 feet long on each side ; the end posts were increased in height to support the cantilevers. The cantilever arms were designed to carry the live and dead loads, and to support the central span during erection as far as the fourth panel; beyond that point independent anchorages would have been required.

The principal dimensions were as follows :—

Distance between trusses	98 feet 6 inches.
Span	1,650 feet.
Cantilevers	295 feet.
Total length of main span and cantilever arms	2,240 feet.
Panels	Thirty-eight, each of approximately 59 feet.
Rise of arch	350 feet.
Depth of arch	60 feet at crown; 227 feet 6 inches at springing.
Curve of chords	Parabolic.

The form of the members was generally the same as that described below for the two-hinged arch. It was not found that the addition of the cantilever ends produced any appreciable saving in the weight of the arch span between its bearings. The approximate weights of steel in the bridge (exclusive of bearings) were as follows :—

Approach spans.		*Carbon Steel.*	*Silicon Steel.*
Trusses		2,850 tons	—
Laterals		1,350 ,,	—
Cross girders		1,750 ,,	—
Deck		3,700 ,,	—
Cantilever arch.			
Trusses		4,300 ,,	26,250 tons
Hangers		—	1,250 ,,
Laterals		3,300 ,,	500 ,,
Cross girders		1,650 ,,	1,350 ,,
Deck		6,350 ,,	—

Cantilever Bridge (Fig. 4, Plate 4).—The principal dimensions proposed for the cantilever bridge were as follows :—

Anchor arms	400 feet
Cantilever arms	600 ,,
Suspended span	400 ,,
Height of main post above bearing.	271·2 ,,
Depth of suspended span	80 ,,
Panel length	50 ,,

In the design prepared the top chord members were to be built up of steel plates with riveted connections, instead of steel eye-bars with pin connections as commonly used in America for these members. In the case of the cantilever bridge the unusual arrangement specified for the four railway-tracks, each truss having a track on each side, required special consideration. Railway-tracks thus placed can produce the full load on one truss while there is no load on the other, and not only cause unequal vertical distortions of the two trusses, but also considerable lateral distortions.

In a normal cantilever bridge structure the principal cause of lateral deflection would be wind-pressure, and the full deflection would rarely occur, wind-pressure rarely, if ever, reaching the specified intensities. The maximum lateral deflection due to wind at the end of the cantilever arm of the proposed Sydney bridge amounted to 11 inches. With the railway-tracks as specified, live load alone would produce comparable lateral distortion. Assuming that lateral bracing would be placed between the lower chords, full live load on one truss only would produce a horizontal deflection of 6 inches at the lower chord-level. If the top chords also carried lateral bracing these would deflect a similar amount, but in the reverse direction, the effect of live load being to extend the top chord and to compress the lower chord of one truss, while the chord of the opposite truss would remain unaltered. Distortions of about two-thirds of these amounts would be caused by every train on the outer railway-track, and would be of frequent occurrence. The lateral deflections would frequently reverse across the diagonally opposite corners of the suspended span ; this would thus be subject to severe racking action, the railway-tracks would be thrown appreciably out of alignment, and there would be a noticeable change of grade. The cantilever and anchor arms of the bridge proposed by the Author had no lateral bracing between the top chords, all the wind-stresses being carried by the lower chord system and sway-bracings. The suspended span was provided with lateral bracings between the top and bottom chords, but had no sway-bracing, the reaction from the top lateral bracing system being carried by the sway-bracing on the end of the cantilever arm.

To diminish, as far as possible, the effect on the railway-tracks of local distortion at the ends of the suspended span, it was proposed to introduce panels into the floor-system, articulated at both ends, between the suspended span and the anchor arms. In submitting a design for the cantilever bridge the Author advised an increase of the spacing between the trusses to 150 feet in order to diminish these distortions, as in a structure with the specified breadth of 100 feet they would have been very serious.

The approximate weights exclusive of bearings were as follows :—

		Carbon Steel.	Silicon Steel.
Approaches.			
Trusses	. . . .	3,400 tons	—
Laterals	. . . .	1,150 ,,	—
Cross girders	. . . .	1,300 ,,	—
Deck	. . . .	3,400 ,,	—
Main spans.			
Trusses	. . . .	8,300 ,,	28,200 tons
Laterals	. . . .	500 ,,	2,250 ,,
Anchorages	. . . .	950 ,,	—
Cross girders	. . . .	1,950 ,,	2,000 ,,
Deck	. . . .	—	—

THE ACCEPTED TENDER.

The tender accepted was that for an arch bridge with concrete

Fig. 6.

COMPLETED BRIDGE.

pylons faced with granite, the amount of the tender being £4,218,000. No separate prices were invited for the supply, manufacture, and erection of steelwork, but the conditions stated that payments would be made in the following proportions at the various stages of the work :—

Non-fabricated steel on delivery . . . . five-sixteenths.
Completely fabricated steel made in Sydney shops,
and delivered at bridge site . . . . five-sixteenths.
Members erected between panel points, and partially
riveted . . . . two-sixteenths.
On complete erection with the exception of painting . three-sixteenths.
On completion of contract . . . . one-sixteenth.

The contract also provided for the deduction of a percentage from each payment to form a retention fund amounting to £250,000, and stipulated that the contractors should be paid an amount representing the value of increases in wages subsequent to the date of the tender. The amount so paid was almost £500,000.

The essential features of the bridge actually constructed (Figs. 5, Plate 4, and *Fig. 6*) differ very little from those proposed in the tender. The following are the principal modifications : the pylons were re-designed by Sir John Burnet and Partners ; the level of the bearings was altered to bring the level required for traffic clearance above the deck within the vertical space between the third and fourth panel points ; the bearings were re-designed ; the angles for the heavy members were increased from 10-inch by 10-inch to 12-inch by 12-inch ; and carbon-steel was used for some bracing members instead of silicon-steel.

SPECIFICATION.

The conditions of contract defined the span of a cantilever bridge as 1,600 feet, and that of an arch bridge as 1,650 feet ; the reason for the longer span in the case of the arch bridge is obscure, as an arch could have been built to comply with the specified clearance-line with a span of 1,600 feet. Responsibility for the design, materials, quantities, construction of the bridge, and for the specification itself were imposed on the contractors by the terms of the contract.[1] The specification stated the span of the bridge, the level and disposition of the railway-tracks and roads to be carried, the loading, and the clearances for navigation. It defined several qualities of steel with the corresponding permissible working-stresses ; the properties and stresses for the two qualities used in the bridge are given later. The drawings supplied were confined to an outline drawing and cross-section of an arch, and detailed drawings of a pylon and of the piers and structural arrangement of the approach-spans. The specifications, however, did not state that these were to be adopted, and it was not found possible to follow any of them. No reference was

[1] " Contract for the Sydney Harbour Bridge," p. 18, para. 20. Sydney, 1923.

made to the bearings, the form of the members of the arch truss, the allocation of compressive stress at the crown between the two chord members, or the disposition of lateral and sway bracing.

The definitions of the construction and workmanship of steelwork were identical with those contained in the specification for the Quebec cantilever bridge.[2]

The specification also required the contractors to prepare and test a number of scale models of the principal members of the bridge made of silicon-steel. A series of models were made and tested to destruction in the contractors' works at Middlesbrough,[3] but the information gained, although of considerable interest, did not justify the alteration in design of any member tested.

DESCRIPTION OF BRIDGE AS CONSTRUCTED.

The following is a short description of the bridge as constructed :—

Arch span	1,650 feet.
South approach-spans . .	One of 238 feet and four of 175 feet.
North approach-spans . .	Five of 170 feet.

(The north approach-spans are on a curve, the radius of the inside railway-track being 1,360 feet.)

Tracks	4 railway-tracks, 4 feet $8\frac{1}{2}$ inches gauge.
	1 roadway of 57 feet.
	2 footways of 10 feet.
Gradient of approaches . .	1 in 40.
Clear headway	170 feet under central 600 feet of arch span.
	160 feet under central 1,200 feet of arch span.
Subsoil	Yellow sandstone rock with horizontal seams of clay and shale.
Pylons	At both ends of the arch spans are concrete pylons faced with granite ; height above water level about 290 feet.

Figs. 5, Plate 4, show the principal features of construction.

PRINCIPAL CHARACTERISTICS OF THE DESIGN OF THE ARCH.

Type of Arch Adopted.—The arch is a two-hinged spandrel-braced arch, similar in many respects to the arch of the Hell Gate railway-bridge near New York, which has a 977·5-foot span, and was built in 1914–16.[1] Although the precedent of Hell Gate has not been followed in many important details, the account of this bridge has

---

[2] " The Quebec Bridge, Report of the Government Board of Engineers," p. 252. Ottawa, 1919.

[3] For the results of these tests see the Paper by Messrs. Pain and Roberts, " Sydney Harbour Bridge, Calculations for the Steel Superstructure."

[1] Trans. Am. Soc. C.E., vol. 82 (1918), p. 852. The Author desires to put on record his indebtedness to the engineers of the Hell Gate bridge, and of the Niagara railway and road bridge, for their valuable Papers, and also to the Canadian Government Board of Engineers for the detailed record of the Quebec Bridge, published by the Department of Railways and Canals of Canada.

been of very great value, and attention is called to some of the more conspicuous differences between the Hell Gate and Sydney Harbour bridges.

When an arch is to be erected in halves, as two cantilevers, one from each end, the form of truss used for the Sydney arch, having its least depth at the crown and its greatest depth at the springings, is obviously well suited to the requirements of erection. The lightest form of truss to meet permanent requirements would probably be that with uniform depth, the two chords separating close to the springings, although it would differ little in this respect from a crescent-shaped arch. The Author has no calculations and estimates of the weights of alternative types which would enable him to give any definite figures, but in his opinion the difference in weight would be small, less than 2 per cent. of the total. Any saving of this order would be far more than offset by the saving in erection costs for the form of truss adopted. The bracing system of the arches is of the simple N-type, a system so suited to the requirements of erection that it has been used on practically every large arch-span bridge.

Number of Hinges.—Some difficult erection-processes could have been avoided by constructing the bridge with three hinges instead of with two. A two-hinged arch is far more rigid under moving loads than a three-hinged arch, and has a superior ability to resist wind-stresses ; but the advantage which most influenced the decision was that it costs less. No calculation has been made of the periods of oscillation of the two alternative types, but the period of a two-hinged arch must be by far the greater. In this case there is a mass of 40,000 tons, with a length of 1,650 feet, having a substantial moment of inertia at the centre ; the three-hinged type contains two masses, each of approximately half the length and half the weight, and the point of articulation between them would transmit vibrations from one half to the other.

The two-hinged arch with continuous upper and lower chords can have two complete and independent systems of transverse or lateral bracing, one in the plane of the lower chords, and one between the upper chords and the end-posts. This allows a more satisfactory distribution of wind-stresses than is possible in a three-hinged arch, and makes possible a reasonably accurate calculation of such stresses ; full advantage can also be taken of the material in the chord members of the structure for resisting them.

If two trusses of the same geometric form as the Sydney arch are compared, one having two hinges and framed at the crown, and the other three hinges with a central pin at a level corresponding to the mean depth of the two-hinged arch, the weight of steel in the two-hinged arch trusses is about 96·5 per cent. of the weight in the three-hinged arch trusses for the same limits of stress. There would be a corresponding reduction in cost, although this would be offset

, by the increased cost of erection. If in the case of the Sydney arch a hinge had been provided at the centre, the independent closure and stressing of the top chords would not have been necessary. This necessitated plant costing approximately £2,000, and the extra field-work cost about £10,000. The saving which might have been effected would have been less than 1 per cent. of the total cost of the trusses.

The three-hinged type avoids indeterminate stresses, and makes the calculations much simpler. There is, however, no reason to doubt the substantial accuracy of the stress-calculations for the two-hinged type, and the cost of making them was a small matter compared with the permanent advantages of the two-hinged type.

Central Panels.—Each truss is symmetrical about the centre-line, and each half was separately erected from its abutments ; the two met at the centre, making an even number of panels with a panel-point at the centre (Figs. 5, Plate 4). This arrangement made the two halves identical for purposes of erection, design, and calculation of stresses, and enabled the final closure to be carried out under the same conditions for the two ends of the bridge, also avoiding the redundant bracing member necessary for geometric symmetry in a structure with an odd number of panels. The official specification showed an odd number of panels and a central panel with a redundant member. An even number of panels was adopted in the Author's design, and has been used in nearly all arch bridges yet built with the exception of the Hell Gate bridge. It is difficult to understand why an even number was not shown in the official specification, and why it was not used on the Hell Gate bridge. The reason given in the latter case was that it was considered æsthetically more attractive.[1] To those who regard the technique of the structure as of consequence, the central panel with a redundant member must be displeasing. An observer seeing the bridge from most view-points would, moreover, find it very difficult to distinguish the location and number of panels at the centre of the trusses. In the opinion of the Author an arch structure of the character of Sydney bridge should on technical grounds have an even number of panels ; this has also a better appearance.

The economic effect of using an odd number of panels is not obvious except on analysis. If the Sydney Harbour bridge had had twenty-seven panels, fourteen erected from one side and thirteen from the other, the anchorages on the former side would have been about 15 per cent. heavier than those on the latter. There would have been corre-sponding increases in stresses arising during erection from direct and wind loading, influencing all members for which the scantlings are determined by erection-stresses, so that members with different sections would have had to be used at the two ends of the arch ; alternatively, material would have been wasted by increasing the

---

[1] *Loc. cit.*, p. 879.

lighter members to the size of the heavier ones. An odd number of panels would have increased the cost by at least £25,000. The design and construction of the anchorages used in the erection would have been complicated, and the process of stressing the central chord-members, and of ensuring the correct stress in the redundant bracing member, would have been very difficult.

Distribution of Total Stresses between Top and Bottom Chords.— The erection of any long-span arch must nearly always be carried out without falsework : if the use of falsework were possible the conditions would rarely justify a long-span bridge. Each half, therefore, generally has to be built out from the abutment to meet the other at the centre, and is supported during this process by temporary anchorages. The primary point of contact of the two parts, if the bracing is of the usual N-type, will be at the lower chord level, and when contact has been sufficiently established and the tension on the anchorages released, the structure becomes a three-hinged arch under the condition of loading then existing. To convert it into a two-hinged arch it is necessary to interconnect the adjacent upper chord members, but it is not essential to subject them to any stress.

In the case of both the Hell Gate and Sydney arches the original point of contact was on the lower chord members. At Hell Gate the top chords were merely joined, having no stress under the condition of loading then existing ; this provided a continuity of structure which converted the arch into a two-hinged arch, and the calculations were made as such for live load, temperature and wind, and all additions of dead load made after the junction.

In the case of the Sydney arch, the Victoria Falls bridge, and the Niagara Falls railway-bridge, the top chords, immediately after they were erected, were subjected to definite compressive stresses reducing the stresses on the bottom chords. The amount of this compressive stress can be arbitrarily adjusted at any figure up to the total thrust carried by the arch, but in these three cases the thrust adopted corresponds to the Clerk Maxwell method of analysis for an indeterminate structure by the method of "least work." This method of design implies that the structure under a condition of no stress has a span equal to the span when under load, so that if the arch were lifted as a whole from its bearings and laid horizontally, the members becoming unstressed, its span would remain unaltered. Any other distribution of the relative total stresses in the top and bottom chord members at closure of the arch will not satisfy this condition. This procedure may also to some extent facilitate the calculation of stresses. These calculations are necessarily progressive, and must be made in stages, the results of each stage forming the starting-point of the next.

In practice the results are commonly expressed as horizontal thrusts due to unit loads at the various panel-points. Provided two arch trusses are designed for a similar stress-distribution at the centre between the top and bottom chords, the calculations for one will appreciably shorten the calculations for the other. This is especially true of the spandrel-braced two-hinged arch, arches of this type having a characteristic similarity of form. The result is that if the closure is made for the " elastic " stresses, the thrusts may be predetermined with fair accuracy by a formula,[1] which might not hold with any other arbitrary distribution of loading between the chords.

This method of calculation produces a distribution of total stress between the top and bottom chords which roughly equalizes the duty of each, so that the sectional areas of the top and bottom chords at the centre of the arch are about the same ; they will therefore both form effective constituent members of the lateral horizontal wind trusses. If either chord were made to carry too large a part of the total stress, the other chord would probably be too light to form an effective member of the corresponding wind truss, and would require an increase of section to deal with this duty. A further advantage is that two chords of approximately equal sectional area, sharing the compression due to the dead load of the structure, form in the central part of the truss a girder having the largest moment of inertia for the material employed ; and are therefore best suited for supporting the local bending stresses due to travelling loads. It would be reasonable to expect that a truss so designed would be less subject to vibration than one in which the chord sections are not so well balanced, and in consequence the relative variations in stress intensity in the lighter chord would be greater.

It follows from this that an arbitrary allocation of stress between the chords, making one chord heavier than the other, would be unsatisfactory, and the Clerk Maxwell method appears to have the most satisfactory general application.

Sway-Bracing.—It is usual in bridge structures to provide cross bracing between opposite vertical or diagonal members of the two trusses, known as sway-bracing, frequently to shorten the lengths of compression members but sometimes not serving this purpose. In the arch of Sydney Harbour bridge there are no sway-bracings. In the Hell Gate arch sway-bracings were used only between five pairs of posts at the ends of the span, none being used between the central fourteen pairs of posts.

Sway-bracings, if used, increase the total weight of the structure by their own weight, and by the extra weight in the trusses required to support them : the latter in a large bridge may be as much as, or more than, the direct weight. Unless the sway-bracings serve a clear and necessary purpose this additional weight will be wasted. Sway-bracings on the Sydney arch, built of proportions sufficiently robust to have any appreciable effect, would have weighed about

---

[1] On p. 259 of the Paper by Messrs. Pain and Roberts the actual thrusts, are compared with those derived from an empirical formula.

600 tons. To have carried these an extra weight of at least 400 tons would have been required in the trusses, and the total extra cost would have been not less than £50,000.

In the case of the Sydney arch sway-bracings, apart from serving no useful purpose, would have been actually objectionable. They would have made the accurate calculation of lateral stresses due to wind almost impossible. Lateral stresses are carried to the bearings by two systems of bracing, one formed between the top chords, and one between the bottom chords. The latter receives the lateral pressures from wind on the deck system also. Without sway-bracings the allocation of wind-pressure between the two systems could be determined, and the wind-stresses could be calculated with a reasonable degree of accuracy. With sway-bracings it would have been virtually impossible to make an accurate allocation, and in consequence the actual stresses in the lateral members might have been very different from those estimated. It would have been necessary to make an arbitrary estimate of the proportions to be assigned to the two systems, resulting probably in the fraction taken by the lower chord system being under-estimated.

It seems probable that in any arch of ordinary dimensions and of moderately large span, if sway-bracings are used and are made of reasonably robust sections, practically all the wind-stresses will be taken by the bottom chord lateral system, and material in the top chord system will not be usefully employed in resisting wind-stresses. The alternative would be to use sway-bracings, and to omit the top chord lateral system. This method would make accurate calculations possible, but would fail to employ the substantial members of the top chord in resisting lateral forces. It would therefore materially increase the weight and cost of the structure, as it is generally recognized (and was also permitted by the Sydney specification) that a member designed for dead load, full live load, and temperature stresses may sustain an additional stress from wind-pressure without addition to its cross-section.

There is a second important reason in the case of the Sydney arch relating to the arrangement of the railway tracks (see p. 158), which made it quite possible for one truss to carry a considerable live load while the other carried none at all. Sway-bracings would have practically prevented distortion of the rectangular transverse frames of the structure, so that when one truss deflected relative to the other due to unequal loading, both would have been distorted out of the vertical plane ; the stresses thus caused would have been so complicated that it would have been practically impossible to calculate them accurately. Without sway-bracings the trusses would remain practically in vertical planes, and although the vertical deflection would subject the members of the transverse bracing system to bending stresses, these stresses could be estimated with a reasonable degree of accuracy.

Inequalities of loading are re-distributed and shared by both trusses in another manner in the case of a two-hinged arch with rigid transverse lateral bracing systems and no sway-bracing. Loading on one truss produces distortions at the panel-points in both vertical and horizontal directions in the plane of the truss. The downward movement of one truss relative to the other is restrained only by the resistance to distortion by bending of the members of the lateral bracing, and of the web members of the trusses. The horizontal movements, or movements parallel to the axis of the bridge, cannot occur without producing resistance in the two lateral systems between the upper and lower chords, provided these systems are formed with redundant transverse members which prevent any change in breadth. This resistance is considerably larger than that caused by the bending of the members. The result of this action is that both trusses, without the assistance of sway-bracing, share in supporting a load, even though it is directly imposed upon one only. The following examples illustrate this :—

(1) If one truss is subject to full live load at the centre of the span, namely, a 1,100-foot train on each of the two tracks, and there is no live load on the other tracks, the total live load is approximately 3,000 tons. The vertical reaction below[1] the loaded truss is 2,700 tons, and that below the unloaded truss is 300 tons ; so that approximately one-tenth of the load is transferred by the lateral bracing to the remote truss.

(2) If the east truss carries full live load throughout the northern half-span, and receives no assistance from the other truss, the downward deflection at the north quarter-point is about 5 inches, and the upward deflection at the south quarter-point is about $3\frac{1}{2}$ inches. If the west truss be similarly loaded at the south end the deflections are $3\frac{1}{2}$ inches upwards at the north end and 5 inches downwards at the south end, the relative deflections of the two trusses at the quarter-points being $8\frac{1}{2}$ inches. The effect of the interconnecting lateral bracing is to reduce this deflection to about $2\frac{1}{2}$ inches.

Support of Cross Girders.—All cross girders are supported from the vertical members of the trusses by hangers and pins, so that the loading applied to the hanger is axial, and bending stresses due to deflection of the cross girder are avoided. This type of connection is not necessary at the top of the hangers, as the arch trusses, when distorted by vertical loading, remain practically in vertical planes. This, of course, would not be the case if sway-bracing were used.

Horizontal Stays Supporting Vertical Posts.—All the vertical posts are built as struts, unsupported from end to end, with the exception of the three posts at each end of each truss. As the cross girders of the deck-system are directly connected to these, it is necessary to maintain the correct spacing between the posts at deck-level under

[1] See pp. 425 and 433.—SEC. INST. C.E.

all conditions of distortion of the arch. They are, therefore, inter-connected by a horizontal member at deck-level attached to the arch truss at panel-point 22. The secondary, or bending, stress in the posts caused by this member is the greatest stress of this character in the structure.

Principal Dimensions.—The maximum length of steel plates and sections which would comply with shipping requirements was about 60 feet. Greater lengths could only have been shipped at a cost disproportionate to the advantage gained by the reduction in weight arising from the use of any practicable panel-length exceed-ing 60 feet. This consideration, therefore, determined the panel-length, and the span was sub-divided into twenty-eight panels of approximately 59 feet.

In view of the method of erection intended, and in order to employ the permanent structure as far as possible for its own erection, a height of about 190 feet at the springings was decided upon. This was also convenient for the reception of the creeper cranes, used for erection, from the temporary steel ramp erected on the deck level of the pylons. The depth of the trusses at the centre was made 60 feet, so that the central vertical members were of a length that could be made in one piece with the maximum available shipping length for raw material. No material saving in weight would have been made by increasing this depth, and from the analogy of other arch bridges of smaller span, and the calculated deflection at the centre and quarter span, it was concluded that sufficient rigidity would be provided by this depth.

The rise adopted for the arch, namely, 350 feet on the centre-line of the lower chords (or 21·25 per cent. of the span) was estimated to be the most economical in the quantity of steel required. The weight of steel would be practically the same with a somewhat larger rise, but the additional rise would add to the difficulty and cost of erection.

The lower chord forms a parabolic curve ; the upper chord is also a parabolic curve throughout the central twenty-two panels, with a depth at quarter span of 86 feet, or $5\frac{1}{4}$ per cent. of the span, but the curvature is reversed over the last three panels at each end to correspond with the depth required at the springings, namely 190 feet, and to provide a conveniently graded track for the erection cranes. The axis of the end top-chord member was practically in line with that of the anchorages during erection, so that there was no pressure on the end-posts from the anchorage stress, and the anchorage link-plates were in line with the top chord.

Railway- and Roadway-Tracks.—The specified arrangement of the railway- and roadway-tracks places the road at the centre of the deck, and the four railway-tracks in two groups of two tracks sym-metrically disposed on both sides of the main trusses. This arrange-ment of the tracks reduces the stresses on the cross girders of a bridge, but unless special precautions are taken to ensure that proper provision is made for its effects, distortions of one truss relative to the other may become serious or even dangerous.

Reference has been made on p. 158 to the possible disturbance of an articulated structure such as a cantilever bridge. A two-hinged arch with complete rigid lateral bracing between the opposite lower and upper chords is particularly well adapted to resist these distortions, as the deflections are small compared with those of other types of bridge, and the lateral interconnection of the trusses enables one to assist the other without disturbing the planes of the trusses, which remain vertical. For this reason, and as the breadth between trusses, namely, 98 feet 6 inches, was sufficient for the lateral stiffness of the main span of 1,650 feet, no alteration of the arrangement of the deck was proposed.

Quality of Steel.—One of the most important decisions before the detailed preparation of a design could proceed was the quality of steel to be used. Three qualities of steel required consideration :—

(a) Carbon-steel :—ordinary mild steel of British Standard type, 27·7 to 32·2 tons per square inch tensile breaking strength.[1]

(b) Silicon-steel :—a mild steel with similar physical characteristics, and a breaking strength of 35·6 to 42·3 tons per square inch.

(c) A nickel or other alloy-steel with appreciably higher tensile strength.

The effect of using these various qualities of steel was studied, and the conclusion was reached that the reduction in the weight of steel in the bridge, if an alloy-steel were used, would not be sufficient to effect the extra cost of the raw material and manufacture.

A high-tensile mild steel, having a tensile strength about 30 per cent. above that of ordinary British Standard mild steel used for structural steelwork, could be obtained without difficulty in the large quantities required, provided the design were made without introducing an undue multiplicity of sections ; it was not considered advisable, however, to attempt the manufacture of a steel with similar characteristics but with higher tensile strength. The cost of the raw material was estimated to be about 25 per cent. above that of mild steel, and the additional difficulties of working would add only a small sum to the costs of manufacture.

It was obvious that these extra costs, amounting to only about 5 per cent. of the total cost per ton, would be more than offset in the arch span by the reduction in weight and erection costs consequent upon using steel with a strength 30 per cent. greater, as the weight of the arch structure itself accounts for a large part of the total

[1] Throughout this Paper all loads and stresses are given in English tons, although the specification expressed them in pounds.

stresses. It was therefore decided to use high-tensile steel for the whole of the trusses, the cross-girder flanges, and the principal lateral bracings.

The steel to be used was left to the decision of the contractors, and complied with the following physical tests and analyses :—

Analyses.	Silicon-steel : per cent.	Carbon-steel : per cent.
Phosphorus (maximum)	0·04	0·04
Sulphur ,, ...	0·05	0·05
Manganese ,, ...	1·00	0·70
Carbon	0·32 to 0·42	minimum possible
Silicon	0·15 to 0·35	0·10

Tests.

	Silicon-steel	Carbon-steel
Yield-point : tons per square inch . . .	20·0	15·6
Tension : ditto	35·6 to 42·3	27·7 to 32·2
Elongation in 8 inches : per cent. . .	$\frac{715}{\text{ultimate stress}}$	$\frac{670}{\text{ultimate stress}}$
Reduction in area	35 per cent.	40 per cent.

Rivet Steel.

Yield point : tons per square inch . . .	12·5	—
Tension : ditto	21·4 to 25·8	—
Elongation.	$\frac{670}{\text{ultimate stress}}$	
Reduction in area	50 per cent.	

As a general rule members of the bridge were made wholly of silicon-steel, or wholly of carbon-steel, but the cross girders were built with webs of carbon-steel and flanges of silicon-steel. Carbon-steel was generally used for those members in which the calculated thickness of silicon-steel would not have provided sufficiently substantial sections.

Although the approach-spans are structures of considerable size, each span weighing about 1,000 tons, it was found that it would not pay to use silicon-steel for the main girders, and carbon-steel was used. A sufficiently extensive demand for steel of higher tensile strength than standard mild steel would enable it to be supplied at a price enabling the cost of ordinary bridges and structural steelwork to be much reduced. To obtain the full benefit of possible economies it would be necessary to reduce the minimum thicknesses commonly specified for structural work, and to find a rivet-steel that would be proportionately stronger, or to modify the somewhat low stresses now allowed in rivets.

Loads.—The definitions of the live loads and other forces on the structure are given in detail in the Paper by Messrs. Pain and Roberts, " Sydney Harbour Bridge, Calculations for the Steel Superstructure."

WORKING STRESSES.

The primary working stresses defined for each of the specified qualities of steel are as follows :—

Steelwork.	Silicon-steel: tons per square inch.	Carbon-steel: tons per square inch.
Riveted Members.		
Tension, net section	10·5	8·0
Compression on gross section,		
L/r less than 50	7·8	6·25
L/r greater than 50	$10 \cdot 0 - \dfrac{1}{22 \cdot 4} \cdot \dfrac{L}{r}$	$8 \cdot 0 - \dfrac{1}{35 \cdot 7} \cdot \dfrac{L}{r}$
Shearing on girder webs	5·8	4·45
Rivets.	Power-driven.	Hand-driven.
Shear	4·9	4·45
Bearing	9·8	8·9

Erection stresses : 20 per cent. above stresses for permanent loads.

Combination of Primary and Secondary stresses : 30 per cent. above primary stresses.

Other Materials.

Granite.	800 pounds per square inch.
Concrete, 1 : 2 : 4	500 do.
Concrete, 1 : 2 : 5	400 do.
Sandstone rock	31 tons per square foot.

The last figure was not considered safe by the Author, and was reduced to 13 tons per square foot.

Specified Intensity of Compressive Stress.—The maximum stress allowed for silicon steel in compression was only 75 per cent. of that permitted in tension. This is slightly less than the ratio defined in the Quebec bridge specification, namely, 78 per cent. ; this specification was influenced by the possibility that the disaster to the first Quebec bridge was due to the failure of one of the principal compression members, and compressive stresses were specified that were beyond doubt. This ratio is not in accordance with accepted British practice for ordinary mild steel (described above as carbon-steel) ; the compressive stress allowed by the British Standard Specification is 6·8 tons per square inch, or 85 per cent. of the tensile stress, and the Author is not aware of any evidence that this is too high. It is certainly exceeded in many old structures.

A higher compressive stress would have been justified also by the precedent of the Hell Gate bridge, where compressive stresses equal to the tensile stresses were permitted on short members where $L/r < 20$, and 94 per cent. of this stress where $L/r = 50$. The steel used for the trusses of this bridge had a breaking strength of 30 to 34 tons per square inch (an average of 32 tons per square inch), and the factor of safety in both tension and compression was 3·0 as compared with British practice of 3·7. The permitted compressive stress for box section members with $L/r = 50$ was practically 10·0 tons per square inch.

The tests on model members of Sydney Harbour bridge made of silicon-steel showed a limit of proportionality for compression members practically the same as for tension members, namely, about 14 tons per square inch. The steel specified had a yield-point of 20 tons per square inch, although it actually reached an average of 22 tons per square inch, and the limit of proportionality shown by diagrams of ordinary tensile tests was also 14 tons per square inch. If the compressive stress for silicon-steel used in Sydney Harbour bridge had been 8·9 tons per square inch, that is 85 per cent. of the tensile stress, the saving in cost would have exceeded £200,000.

Approximate Weights of Structural Steelwork.—These are given for the various members in Table I.

DETAILS OF MAIN SPAN.

Bearings.—The pressure on each hinge-pin under maximum live load amounts to approximately 19,700 tons, acting at practically

TABLE I.

	Silicon steel: tons.	Carbon steel: tons.	Total: tons.
Arch Span.			
Trusses, including lateral gussets and post stiffening girder	23,530	—	23,530
Top laterals	—	920	920
Bottom laterals (all silicon steel except cross members and diagonals 28–26)	780	350	1,130
End post portal (all carbon steel except bottom cross member)	30	260	290
Hangers	1,110	—	1,110
Cross girders (silicon steel flanges and carbon steel webs)	760	2,270	3,030
Deck :			
Footway spans complete	—	670	670
Railway stringers and bracing	—	2,100	2,100
Roadway stringers and parapet girders	—	1,110	1,110
Joists, troughing, handrails, etc.	—	2,220	2,220
Deck laterals and braking girder.	—	1,100	1,100
Bearings (forged and cast steel), total weight including holding-down bolts	—	—	1,190
	26,200	11,000	38,390
Approach Spans and Pylons.			
Pylons	—	1,300	1,300
Trusses and laterals	—	6,200	6,200
Deck complete	—	5,900	5,900
Bearings (cast steel) ; total weight including holding-down bolts	—	—	200
	—	13,400	13,600
Total weight in arch span, approaches, and pylons	26,200	24,400	51,990

45 degrees. It was necessary to design a steel bearing to distribute this pressure over an area of concrete of about 500 square feet, in order to limit the intensity of pressure on the concrete to about 40 tons per square foot, and of sufficient rigidity to avoid variations of pressure. The steel structure required to comply with these conditions was of such mass that ordinary processes of construction could not be used. It was originally proposed to build up a series of steel slabs in successive layers, but the deflections of these would have led to a high intensity of pressure on the concrete under the central part of the loaded area. It was then decided to design the bearing in the form actually constructed (*Figs. 7*), using material of exceptional dimensions, and employing 4-inch diameter turned bolts

Figs. 7.

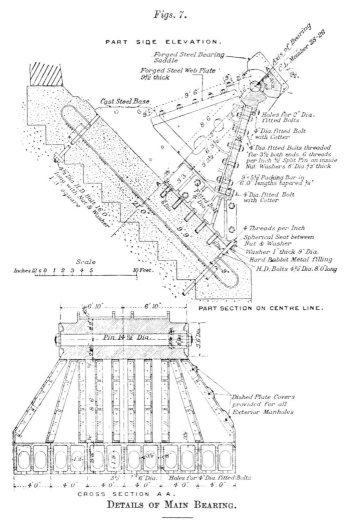

DETAILS OF MAIN BEARING.

for the connections. These bearings were made by the Darlington Forge Company, Ltd.

Workmanship of a high order of accuracy was necessary, and the limits of error allowed in the various parts were as follows :—

Bolts . . . . 1/10,000 inch
Forged saddles, webs, pins, and castings . . . 1/1,000 inch

The pin of the bearing is 14½ inches in diameter, and 13 feet 8 inches in length. Between the pin and the faced end of the lower chord member is the top " saddle " of the bearing, consisting of a steel forging bored to fit the pin, and machined on the upper surface to fit the faced end of the lower chord member. This upper saddle has four projecting ribs machined to fit against the four webs of the chord member. Below the pin is the lower saddle, also of forged steel, with the upper surface bored to receive the pin, and the lower surface machined to fit the two main webs of the bearing. The top and bottom forged saddles are interconnected by recessed circular plates at both ends, secured by nuts to projecting ends of the pin, 8 inches in diameter. The load is thus received above the pin on four surfaces at right angles to its axis, and transferred below it on to two surfaces parallel to the axis, the top and bottom saddles being of sufficient strength to effect this distribution of the loading. The lower saddle is supported by two massive steel webs inclined at 27 degrees to the axis of the structure, each being 9½ inches thick, 9 feet 6 inches deep, 24 feet long at the base, and 14 feet long at the top. These webs were designed as columns and girders capable of spreading the load over two parallel areas 10 feet 6 inches apart without sensible distortion. The inclined webs rest on a series of six box steel castings, 3 feet 3 inches deep, 4 feet wide, and 21 feet long, formed of metal 3½ inches in thickness, designed to receive the pressure from the two web-plates and to distribute it over the concrete. The two inclined webs are secured by ten transverse diaphragms of cast steel, bolted to them by five 4-inch diameter bolts on each side of each diaphragm, the material of these castings being 2 inches thick throughout. They are also secured to the top saddle and to the base-castings by lines of 4-inch diameter bolts passing through corresponding lugs. These connections were designed to carry the stresses produced by thrusts which in the early stages of erection passed outside the base of the lower web-plate, and which tended to bend the web-plates and to put the upper one into tension.

Each bearing was manufactured complete in Darlington, and tested for accuracy before being dismantled for shipment. The steels used for the forgings forming the upper part of the structure were selected by the Darlington Forge Co., and had the following properties :—

Web-plates, B.S. Specification 29 (1909), 30/35 tons per square inch tensile strength, 16 tons per square inch yield-point, 27/22 per cent. elongation.

Saddles, B.S. Specification 29 (1909), 36/40 tons per square inch tensile strength, 20 tons per square inch yield-point, 21/17 per cent. elongation.

Pins, B.S. Specification 29 (1909), 41/45 tons per square inch tensile strength, 22 tons per square inch yield-point, 17 per cent. elongation.

The castings were of steel conforming to B.S. Specification No. 30 (1907), grade " B," but with a tensile strength of 30 tons per square inch and a yield point of 16 tons per square inch.

The design of the bearings provided for the elastic yield of the concrete under pressure corresponding to the elastic yield of the steel structure imposing the pressure.

Form of Chord Members and End-Posts.—The make-up of the members of the arch is summarized in Table II, pp. 176–178. During erection the top chords of the arches had to carry tension, but after erection they were subject only to compression ; the lower chord and end-post were in compression under all conditions of erections and subsequent loading. The members of both chords were similarly designed, and were built up of four webs, with solid flange-plates connected to them by angles on both sides of the webs (*Figs. 8*). The flange-plates are separated into two parts by a longitudinal joint, thus dividing each member into halves for erection. The heaviest members are the lowest chord members resting on the bearings, with cross-sectional areas of 2,700 square inches.

For ten panels of the bridge at each end diminution in sectional area is accomplished partly by reduction in the thickness of the plates and angles, and partly by tapering the members ; the depth of the lowest member, namely 8 feet 3 inches, was gradually reduced to 4 feet. The remaining eight members are all 4 feet deep, and variations in section are obtained by varying the thickness of material. In the top chord variations in section are much less marked, and it was possible to obtain them without varying the depth, which is 3 feet 4 inches throughout.

The end top-chord members are tapered to accommodate the pins connecting the erection anchorage-cables, the depth being increased to 5 feet 5 inches at the shore ends. A similar type of section is used for the end-post, but single angles connect each web to the flange-plates, which are stiffened at intervals by diaphragms. Diaphragms are provided in the chord-members close to the main gusset-plates, and when a member was subdivided for erection, a diaphragm was provided also on both sides of each joint.

The principal characteristic of these members is their great breadth, which is of value in providing resistance to bending where the deck passes through the main trusses, in relation to their depth. At this place the whole of the wind-moment has to be carried by the individual chord members. The relatively small depth also reduces transverse wind-pressure. The depth of the lighter members near the centre of the bridge is no more than is consistent with reasonable vertical

TABLE II.—SUMMARY OF MAKE-UP OF MEMBERS OF ARCH.

Lower Chord.

	Member . .	28–26*	26–24*	24–22*	22–20*	20–18*	18–16*	16–14	14–12	12–10	10–8	8–6	6–4	4–2	2–0
	Gross area : sq. ins.	2693	2270†	2124†	2022	1853†	1678	1584†	1503	1412	1353†	1268	1219	1132	1088
Make-up of Section. All dimensions in inches.	16 Angles	$12\times12 \times1\frac{1}{4}$	$12\times12 \times1\frac{1}{4}$	$12\times12 \times1\frac{1}{4}$	$12\times12 \times1\frac{1}{4}$	$12\times12 \times1\frac{1}{4}$	$12\times12 \times1\frac{1}{4}$	$12\times12 \times1\frac{1}{4}$	$12\times12 \times1\frac{1}{4}$	$12\times12 \times1\frac{1}{4}$	$12\times12 \times1\frac{1}{4}$	$12\times12 \times1\frac{1}{4}$	$12\times12 \times1\frac{1}{4}$	$12\times12 \times1$	$12\times12 \times\frac{7}{8}$
	4 Web plates	99×2	Taper. 99 to $91\frac{1}{2}\times2$	Taper. $91\frac{1}{2}$ to 84×2	84×2	Taper. 84 to 72×2	72×2	Taper. 72 to 60×2	60×2	60×2	Taper. 60 to 48×2	$48\times1\frac{3}{4}$	$48\times1\frac{3}{4}$	$48\times1\frac{3}{4}$	$48\times1\frac{3}{4}$
	4 Side webs	$75\frac{1}{4}\times2\frac{15}{16}$	Taper. $75\frac{1}{4}$ to $67\frac{3}{4}\times1\frac{3}{4}$	Taper. $67\frac{3}{4}$ to $65\frac{5}{16}\times1\frac{1}{2}$	$60\frac{1}{4}\times1\frac{3}{8}$	Taper. $60\frac{1}{4}$ to $48\frac{1}{4}\times1$	$48\frac{1}{4}\times\frac{7}{8}$	Taper. $48\frac{1}{4}$ to $36\frac{1}{4}\times\frac{7}{8}$	$36\frac{1}{4}\times\frac{5}{8}$						
	8 Bars	$11\frac{3}{4}\times1\frac{1}{2}$	$11\frac{3}{4}\times1\frac{1}{2}$	$11\frac{3}{4}\times1\frac{1}{2}$	$11\frac{3}{4}\times1\frac{1}{2}$	$11\frac{3}{4}\times1\frac{1}{2}$	$11\frac{3}{4}\times1\frac{1}{2}$	$11\frac{3}{4}\times1\frac{1}{2}$	$11\frac{3}{4}\times1\frac{1}{2}$	$11\frac{3}{4}\times1\frac{1}{2}$	$11\frac{3}{4}\times1\frac{1}{2}$	$11\frac{3}{4}\times1\frac{1}{2}$	$11\frac{3}{4}\times1\frac{1}{2}$	$11\frac{3}{4}\times1\frac{1}{2}$	$11\frac{3}{4}\times1\frac{1}{2}$
	Flanges, 4 plates	$65\frac{3}{4}\times1\frac{1}{2}$	$65\frac{3}{4}\times1\frac{1}{2}$	$65\frac{3}{4}\times1\frac{1}{2}$	$65\frac{3}{4}\times1\frac{1}{2}$	$65\frac{3}{4}\times1\frac{1}{2}$	$65\frac{3}{4}\times1\frac{3}{16}$	$65\frac{3}{4}\times1\frac{3}{16}$	$65\frac{3}{4}\times1\frac{3}{16}$	$65\frac{3}{4}\times1\frac{3}{16}$	$65\frac{3}{4}\times1\frac{3}{16}$	$65\frac{3}{4}\times1\frac{3}{16}$	$65\frac{3}{4}\times1$	$65\frac{3}{4}\times1$	$65\frac{3}{4}\times1$
	Flanges, 2 bars	$10\times\frac{3}{4}$	$10\times\frac{3}{4}$	$10\times\frac{3}{4}$	$10\times\frac{3}{4}$	$10\times\frac{3}{4}$	$10\times\frac{5}{8}$	$10\times\frac{5}{8}$	$10\times\frac{5}{8}$	$10\times\frac{5}{8}$	$10\times\frac{5}{8}$	$10\times\frac{5}{8}$	$10\times\frac{5}{8}$	$10\times\frac{5}{8}$	$10\times\frac{5}{8}$
	Flanges, 2 bars	$9\times\frac{3}{4}$	$9\times\frac{3}{4}$	$9\times\frac{3}{4}$	$9\times\frac{3}{4}$	$9\times\frac{3}{4}$	$9\times\frac{5}{8}$	$9\times\frac{5}{8}$	$9\times\frac{5}{8}$	$9\times\frac{5}{8}$	$9\times\frac{5}{8}$	$9\times\frac{5}{8}$	$9\times\frac{5}{8}$	$9\times\frac{5}{8}$	$9\times\frac{5}{8}$

* These members are subject to lateral bending due to wind forces.

† Areas given for these taper members are at the point of greatest stress intensity (including bending).

TABLE II. (*continued.*)—SUMMARY OF MAKE-UP OF MEMBERS OF ARCH.

Top Chord.

Member	29-27	27-25	25-23	23-21	21-19	19-17	17-15	15-13	13-11	11-9	9-7	7-5	5-3	3-1
Gross area:* sq. ins.	846†	808	808	714	714	774	851	911	960	1010	1010	1010	1010	1010
Make-up of section. All dimensions in inches. 16 Angles	8×8×7/8	8×8×7/8	8×8×7/8	8×8×7/8	8×8×7/8	8×8×7/8	12×12×7/8	12×12×7/8	12×12×7/8	12×12×7/8	12×12×7/8	12×12×7/8	12×12×7/8	12×12×7/8
4 Web plates	Taper. 65 to 40×1 1/8	40×1 1/8	..	..	..	40×1 1/8	40×1 1/4	40×1 1/4	40×1 1/4	40×1 1/2	40×1 1/2	40×1 1/2	40×1 1/2	40×1 1/2
4 Side webs	:	:	..	..	..	24×5/8								
8 Bars.	7 3/4 × 1 1/8	7 3/4 × 1 1/8	7 3/4 × 1 1/8	7 3/4 × 1 1/8	7 3/4 × 1 1/8	7 3/4 × 1 1/8	11 3/4 × 1 1/8	11 3/4 × 1 1/8	11 3/4 × 1 1/8	11 3/4 × 1 1/8	11 3/4 × 1 1/8	11 3/4 × 1 1/8	11 3/4 × 1 1/8	11 3/4 × 1 1/8
Flanges, 4 plates	62 3/8 × 1 3/16	62 3/8 × 1 3/16	62 3/4 × 1 3/16	62 3/4 × 1 3/16	62 3/4 × 1 3/16	62 3/4 × 1 3/16	65 3/4 × 1 3/16	65 3/4 × 1 3/16	65 3/4 × 1 3/16	65 3/4 × 1 3/16	65 3/4 × 1 3/16	65 3/4 × 1 3/16	65 3/4 × 1 3/16	64 3/4 × 1 1/16
Flanges, 4 bars	10×5/8	10×5/8	10×5/8	10×5/8	10×5/8	10×5/8	10×5/8	10×5/8	10×5/8	10×5/8	10×5/8	10×5/8	10×5/8	10×5/8
Extra web plates used as reinforcement during erection only.	8 Plates 24×3/4; 8 Plates 24×1 1/4; 12 Plates 24×5/8; 4 Plates 24×1/2	8 Plates 24×3/4; 8 Plates 24×1 1/4; 12 Plates 24×5/8	8 Plates 24×3/4; 12 Plates 24×5/8; 4 Plates 24×9/16	8 Plates 24×3/4; 12 Plates 24×5/8; 4 Plates 24×9/16	12 Plates 24×3/8									
Gross area: sq. ins.	504	456	378	378	216									

* The net section cannot be stated exactly. At each connection the net area is calculated for a series of transverse sections through the successive lines of rivets as stress is transferred from the member connected to the covers.

† Area given for this taper member is at the point of greatest stress intensity (including bending).

TABLE II. (*continued.*)—SUMMARY OF MAKE-UP OF MEMBERS OF ARCH.

Diagonals.

Member		29–26	27–24	25–22	23–20	21–18	19–16	17–14	15–12	13–10	11–8	9–6	7–4	5–2	3–0
Gross area * . . . sq. ins.		262	235	208	208	196	188	188	188	181	167	151	167	182	207
Make-up of section. All dimensions in inches.	8 Angles	$8\times8\times\frac{3}{4}$	$8\times8\times\frac{3}{4}$	$8\times8\times\frac{3}{4}$	$8\times8\times\frac{3}{4}$	$8\times8\times\frac{3}{4}$	$8\times8\times\frac{3}{4}$	$8\times8\times\frac{3}{4}$	$8\times8\times\frac{3}{4}$	$8\times8\times\frac{3}{4}$	$8\times8\times\frac{5}{8}$	$8\times8\times\frac{5}{8}$	$8\times8\times\frac{5}{8}$	$8\times8\times\frac{3}{4}$	$8\times8\times\frac{3}{4}$
	4 Web plates	$36\times1\frac{3}{16}$	36×1	$36\times\frac{13}{16}$	$36\times\frac{13}{16}$	$30\times\frac{7}{8}$	$30\times\frac{13}{16}$	$30\times\frac{13}{16}$	$30\times\frac{13}{16}$	$30\times\frac{3}{4}$	$30\times\frac{3}{4}$	$30\times\frac{5}{8}$	$30\times\frac{3}{4}$	$33\times\frac{11}{16}$	$33\times\frac{7}{8}$

* The net section cannot be stated exactly at each connection, the net area is calculated for a series of transverse sections through the successive lines of rivets as stress is transferred from the member connected, to the cover.

Posts.

Member		*29–28†	*27–26	*25–24	*23–22	21–20	19–18	17–16	15–14	13–12	11–10	9–8	7–6	5–4	3–2	1–0
Gross area: sq. ins.		537	338	338	349	360	316	302	266	250	209	191	152	152	152	86
Make-up of section. All dimensions in ins.	8 Angles	$8\times8\times\frac{3}{4}$	$12\times12\times\frac{7}{8}$	$12\times12\times\frac{7}{8}$	$12\times12\times\frac{7}{8}$	$12\times12\times\frac{7}{8}$	$12\times12\times\frac{7}{8}$	$12\times12\times\frac{7}{8}$	$8\times8\times\frac{7}{8}$	$8\times8\times\frac{7}{8}$	$8\times8\times\frac{3}{4}$	$8\times8\times\frac{3}{4}$	$8\times8\times\frac{5}{8}$	$8\times8\times\frac{5}{8}$	$8\times8\times\frac{5}{8}$	$6\times4\times\frac{1}{2}$
	4 Web plates	$54\times1\frac{1}{8}$	44×1	44×1	$44\times\frac{1}{16}$	$44\times1\frac{1}{8}$	$44\times\frac{7}{8}$	$40\times\frac{7}{8}$	40×1	36×1	$36\times\frac{13}{16}$	$33\times\frac{3}{4}$	$30\times\frac{5}{8}$	$30\times\frac{5}{8}$	$30\times\frac{5}{8}$	$24\times\frac{1}{2}$
	Flanges, 4 plates	$61\times\frac{3}{4}$														
	Flanges, 4 bars.	$10\times\frac{1}{2}$														

* Areas and make-ups given for these members apply to portion above deck level.
† This member is subject to lateral bending due to wind forces.

Figs. 8.

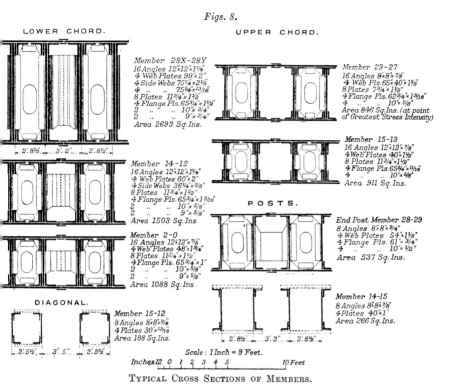

LOWER CHORD.

Member 28X-28Y
16 Angles 12"x12"x1¼"
4 Web Plates 99"x 2"
4 Side Webs 75¼"x2⅛"
4 .. .. 75¼"x13₁₆"
8 Plates 11¾"x1½"
4 Flange Pls.65¾"x1½"
2 .. .. 10"x 3/4"
2 .. .. 9"x 3/4"
Area 2693 Sq.Ins.

Member 14-12
16 Angles 12"x12"x1¼"
4 Web Plates 60"x 2"
4 Side Webs 36¼"x 5/8"
8 Plates 11¾"x1½"
4 Flange Pls.65¾"x13₁₆"
2 .. .. 10"x 5/8"
2 .. .. 9"x 5/8"
Area 1503 Sq.Ins.

Member 2-0
16 Angles 12"x12"x 7/8"
4 Web Plates 48"x1¾"
8 Plates 11¾"x1½"
4 Flange Pls. 65¾"x1"
2 .. .. 10"x 5/8"
2 .. .. 9"x 5/8"
Area 1088 Sq.Ins.

DIAGONAL.

Member 15-12
8 Angles 8"x8"x¾
4 Plates 30"x13₁₆"
Area 188 Sq.Ins.

UPPER CHORD.

Member 29-27
16 Angles 8"x8"x 7/8"
4 Web Pls.65"x40"x1⅛"
8 Plates 7¾"x1½"
4 Flange Pls.62¾"x1³₁₆"
4 .. .. 10"x 5/8"
Area 846 Sq.Ins. (at point
of Greatest Stress Intensity)

Member 15-13
16 Angles 12"x12"x 7/8"
4 Web Plates 40"x1½"
8 Plates 11¾"x1½"
4 Flange Pls.65¾"x1½₁₆"
4 .. .. 10"x 5/8"
Area 911 Sq.Ins.

POSTS.

End Post Member 28-29
8 Angles 8"x8"x¾"
4 Web Plates 54"x1⅛"
4 Flange Pls. 61"x ¾"
4 .. .. 10"x ½"
Area 537 Sq.Ins.

Member 14-15
8 Angles 8"x8"x 7/8"
4 Plates 40"x1"
Area 266 Sq.Ins.

Scale : 1 Inch = 8 Feet.

Inches 12 0 1 2 3 4 5   10 Feet

TYPICAL CROSS SECTIONS OF MEMBERS.

stiffness in relation to the panel-length of the structure, and the practical requirements of manufacture. Subject to these limits the necessary strength can be obtained by increasing the breadth of the member and the number of webs.

Verticals and Diagonals.—All verticals have a primary or dead-load stress which is compressive, although some conditions of live load subject them to tension. These members (*Figs. 8*) are all built up of four channel-shaped sections of plates and angles, laced in pairs with legs turned outwards, and interconnected at both ends and at the centre by substantial tie-plates. All diagonals primarily take tension, but may also sustain compressive stresses, particularly near the centre of the arch. They are built up of four channel-shaped sections, each formed of one plate and two angles, in pairs with legs turned inwards, and laced together with tie-plates at the end and also at the centre in those members subject to compression.

Connections of Members of Arch Trusses.—All principal connections of the members of the arch trusses are of the same form, and depend on four gusset-plates, each 1½ inch thick. The chord-sections are built up of flat bars 1½ inch thick, interposed between each of the four main webs and the flange-angles. At each panel-point the spaces

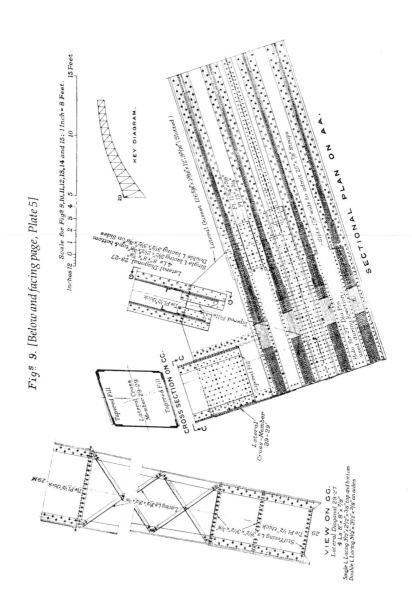

Fig. 9. [Below and facing page, Plate 5]

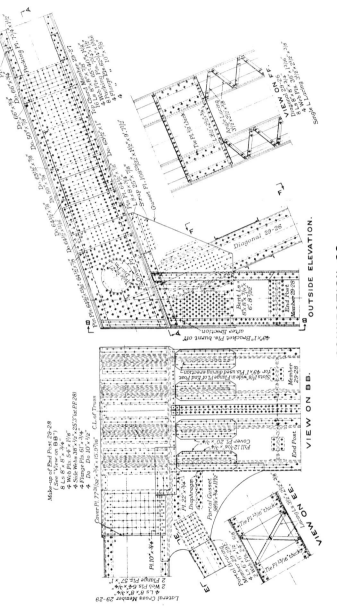

CONNECTION 29.

Fig. 10. [*Plate 5*]

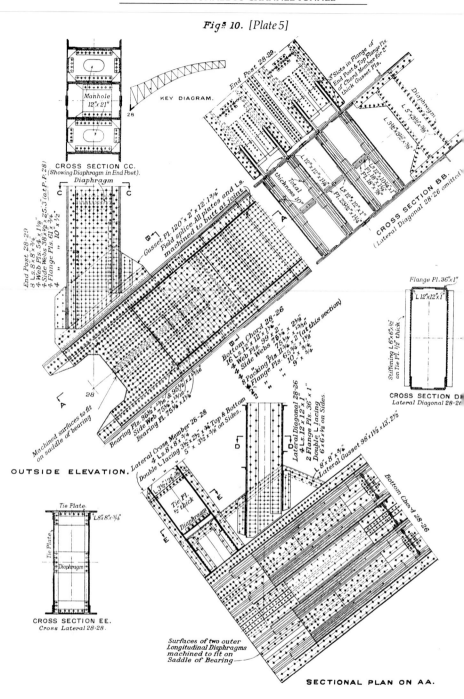

KEY DIAGRAM.

CROSS SECTION CC.
(Showing Diaphragm in End Post).

CROSS SECTION BB.
(Lateral Diagonal 28-26 omitted)

CROSS SECTION DD.
Lateral Diagonal 28-26

OUTSIDE ELEVATION.

CROSS SECTION EE.
Cross Lateral 28-28.

SECTIONAL PLAN ON AA.

Surfaces of two outer
Longitudinal Diaphragms
machined to fit on
Saddle of Bearing

CONNECTION 28.

occupied by these bars are used for the main gusset connections, which pass through slots in the flange-plates of the members, and which connect the posts, diagonals, and hangers. In all connections the compression members are joined by covering material having the full sectional area of the members joined, and secured by rivets sufficient to take the whole compressive stress (p. 183).

Typical details of connections 29, 28, 22, 13, 12, 1, and 0 are illustrated in Figs. 9 to 15, Plate 5. Connections 13 and 12 are typical of all the joints in that part of the arch above the deck (Figs. 12 and 13, Plate 5). A typical connection is shown in *Fig. 16.*

Connection 29 (Fig. 9, Plate 5).—The construction required for the connection of the anchorage-links during erection made the use of the normal arrangement of vertical gussets passing through slots in the lower flange-plate of the chord member practically impossible. As the anchorage-links were inclined to the axis of the bridge, there was a transverse component across the arch structure between panel-points 29, amounting to 580 tons at the south end and 1,120 tons at the north end of the span. To absorb this force uniformly, it was advisable to extend the lateral gusset in the plane of the lower flange across the whole breadth of the member. The vertical gussets were therefore terminated against the lower flange-plate of the chord, so that the chord member with its lower flange-plate intact could be placed complete on top of the gussets, to which it is connected by longitudinal angles. Tension in the plane of the lower flange is sustained by straps passing through slots in the chord flange-plate, and connected to the gussets and the web-plates of the top chord.

The chord members 29–27 increase in depth at joint 29 to accommodate the pins used for the erection-anchorages.[1] The transverse member between the two trusses at panel-point 29 consists of a box, plated on all sides, with its side plates in the planes of the end-post flanges, and the top and bottom plates in the plane of the chord flanges, thus securing symmetry in both planes. The pins to which the anchorage-links were connected were normal to the axis of the cables, and were therefore inclined to the webs of the member. The pressure on these webs was divided into two components, one passing axially along the member, the other, which was transferred through the flanges to the transverse members, at right angles to the axis of the bridge.

Connection 28 (Fig. 10, Plate 5).—This is the end member of the arch structure, and rests on the bearing ; it therefore involves the heaviest steelwork in the bridge. The top saddle of the bearing receives the load from the chord on surfaces at right angles to the axis of the chord and end-post ; the web steel of the lower chord and gusset is supplemented by additional plates to provide the required

[1] A description of this is given in the Paper by Messrs. Freeman and Ennis, "Sydney Harbour Bridge : Manufacture of the Structural Steelwork and Erection of the Bridge."

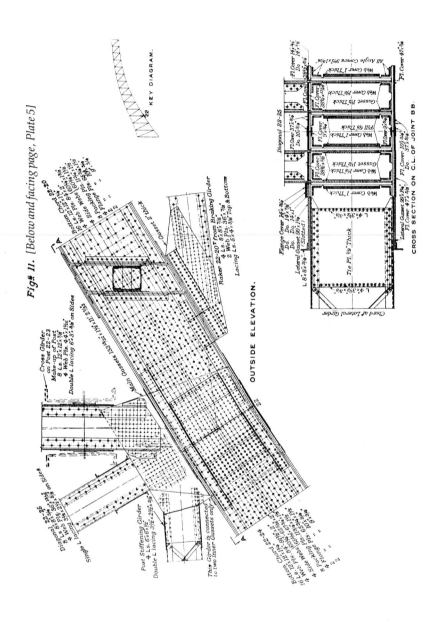

Fig. 11. [Below and facing page, Plate 5]

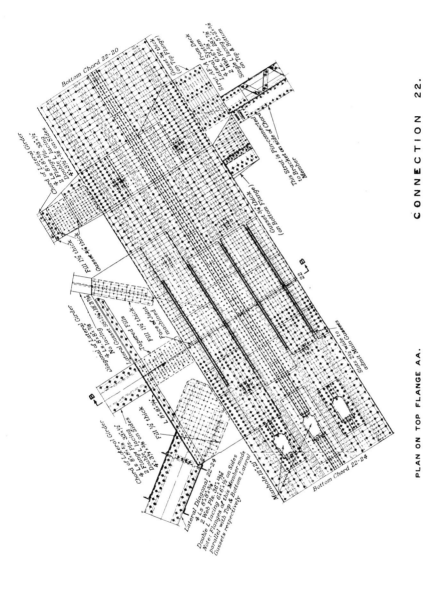

CONNECTION 22.

PLAN ON TOP FLANGE AA.

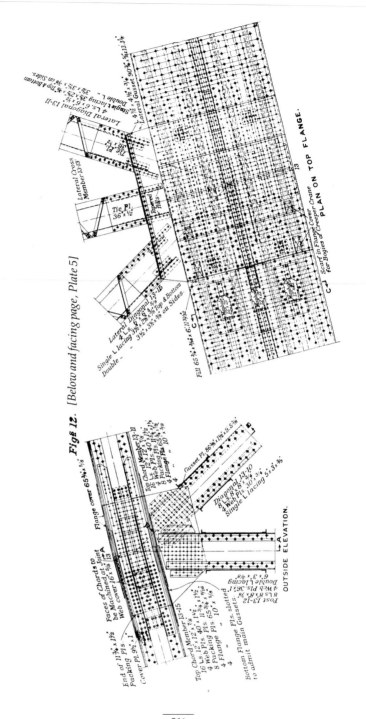

Fig.ª 12. [*Below and facing page, Plate 5*]

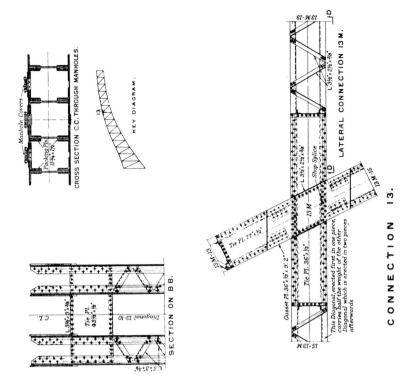

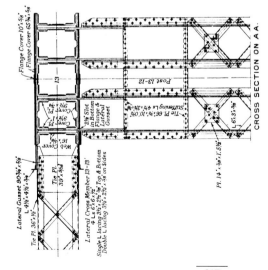

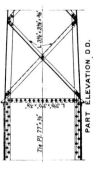

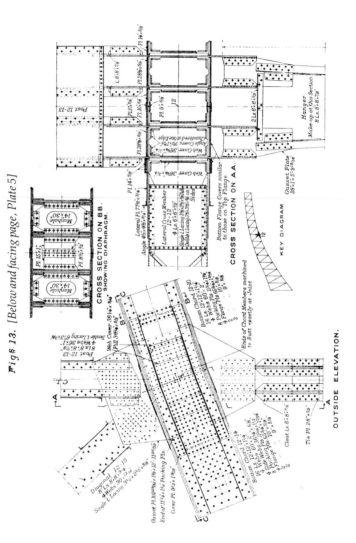

Fig. 13. [*Below and facing page, Plate 5*]

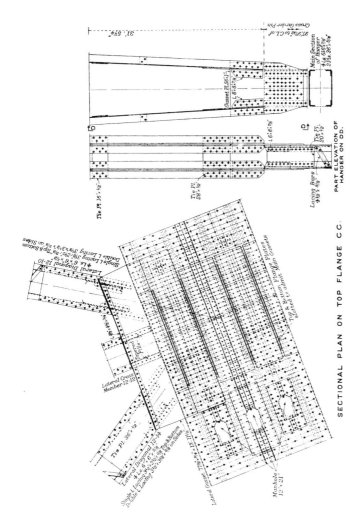

CONNECTION 12.

bearing area, and is interconnected by longitudinal diaphragms formed of $1\frac{1}{4}$-inch plates and 12-inch by 12-inch by 1-inch angles, those in the two outer compartments giving additional bearing area on the saddles. At the base of the lower chord the webs were thickened by the addition of side-plates to $12\frac{1}{2}$ inches, the maximum thickness that could be constructed with the plant provided, and requiring rivets of $1\frac{3}{8}$ inch diameter. The end of the member was shaped and accurately planed on two surfaces, one at right angles to the end-post axis and the other at right angles to the chord axis.

Connection 22 (Fig. 11, Plate 5).—This is similar to connections 13 and 12, but is more complicated on account of the junction of the deck with the lower chord just above this connection. The lateral bracing of the deck is attached to the lower chords by two members, one on each side of the structure, which transfer the reactions from the deck lateral bracing system to the lower chord lateral bracing. These members are connected by pin-joints to the lower chords about 15 feet along the chord between panel-points 22 and 20, to allow deflection of the deck relative to the arch. The two trusses are connected between these points and panel-points 22 by a triangulated framework. Inclined struts are connected underneath the chord members for transferring the braking or longitudinal force from the railway-tracks to the arch trusses. The level required for the deck at this point to allow for the necessary clearance above deck-level and below the main lateral bracings was such that the normal structure of the cross girders and stringers could not be accommodated, and these members had to be made shallower at this connection.

Central Connections (Figs. 14 and 15, Plate 5). The central connections were divided into two separately-completed parts, this construction being adopted to suit the requirements of erection, and the central post members 0–1 were also divided into two parts. In both connections the chord members are terminated by transverse forged-steel saddles, resting against the webs of the members, and provided with horizontal semi-cylindrical recesses. These recesses receive pins forming the actual junctions, and ensure the axiality of the principal stresses at these points. At connection 0 only light covers are used on the top and bottom flanges of the chords, as they are not intended to carry stress. The lateral gussets are interconnected in these planes, and the junction of the two parts of post member 0–1 is continued down to the top flange of the chord.

Allowance is made for secondary stresses in the connection of the vertical gusset-plates above and below the chord. The remaining material subject to bending stresses is so light that no significant stress could be developed. At connection 1 erection requirements necessitated a space between the ends of the opposed chord members at the levels of their top and bottom flanges. After erection this space was filled in with light structural material, and the lateral gussets and chord flange-plates were continued across the gap.

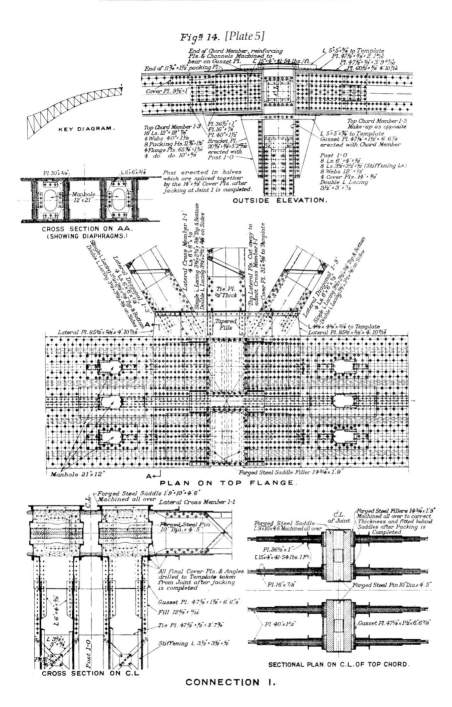

Fig§ 14. [Plate 5]

CONNECTION I.

221

Figs. 15. [Below and facing page, Plate 5]

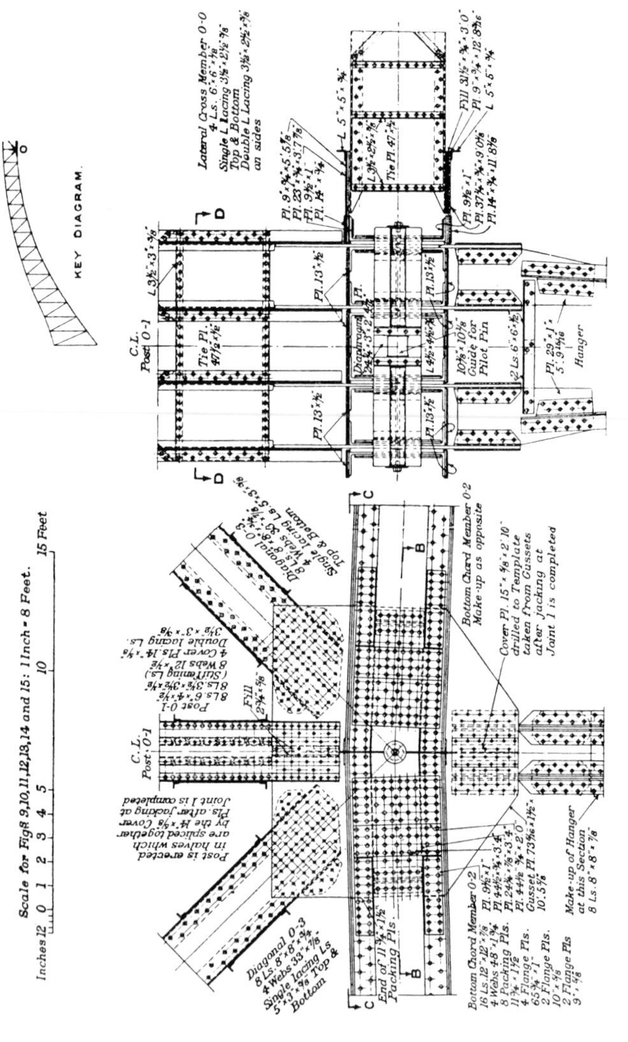

KEY DIAGRAM.

Scale for Figs 9,10,11,12,13,14 and 15: 1 Inch = 8 Feet.

CROSS SECTION ON CENTRE LINE.

OUTSIDE ELEVATION.

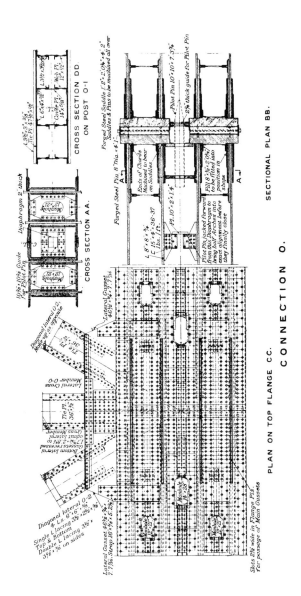

The covering material is designed for secondary stresses arising after the completion of the arch structure.

Riveting of Butt-Joints.—The specification stated that the splices of all butt-joints in compression were to be riveted with sufficient rivets to take the total axial and secondary stresses. The butt-joints were machined to form an accurate metal-to-metal bearing over the entire sectional area of the member; exceptionally massive plant was employed and great care exercised in ensuring the accuracy of the completed work. The workmanship was such that when two faced ends were placed in contact it was impossible to insert a 1/200-inch feeler-gauge at any point. There can thus be no appreciable disturbance in the distribution of stress in the members connected by contact only over the butt-joints, and if precautions are taken to ensure an efficient butt-joint, no useful purpose appears to be served by heavy riveted connections. It is rarely realized how seriously they add to the weight and cost of a bridge structure. If the butt-joint covers of compression members had been replaced by cover-strips proportioned only to hold the abutting edges in place the weight of the main trusses would have been reduced by about 20 per cent., and the cost of the bridge by at least £250,000. This is a very important matter in the design of heavy bridgework and other structural steelwork, deserving more consideration and investigation than it has received.

Lateral Connections.—All lateral connections, except the special links connecting the deck-system to the main trusses, are connected

Fig. 16.

TYPICAL JOINT IN TRUSS MEMBERS AND LATERALS.

to the chord members by top and bottom plates in the planes of the flanges. The flange-plates are cut by slots to accommodate the vertical gusset-plates of the principal connections and hangers. In these cases the lateral gussets are extended beyond the vertical gusset to allow the direct transfer of stress over the chord member, without relying on the heads of rivets passing through the vertical gussets.

Laterals.—The lateral system between the upper chords consists throughout of diagonal crossed members, with direct transverse members between opposite panel-points. These redundant members are necessary to preserve the width of the truss when distortions take place, and enable the truss to resist longitudinal distortion produced by its interaction with the other truss, as explained on p. 167. All these members consist of four corner-angles, with angle-lacing on all sides (*Figs. 17*). The direct transverse members have a clear length between the chords of about 87 feet. These are of the same depth as the chords, namely, 3 feet 5 inches ; they are 3 feet wide and are parallel in both planes. The diagonal members are about 105 feet long between the chords ; one of the members has to be jointed at the centre, so that its weight is carried by the other member, thus increasing the depth at the centre to 6 feet 6 inches. The connections to the chords are made in all cases through gusset-plates in the plane of the top and bottom flange-plates of the chords. The reactions from the girder formed by the system are carried by the transverse bracing between the end-posts, which consists of a portal-frame above deck-level, and three tiers of " K " bracing below it (*Fig. 18*). The top lateral system and portal-bracing was designed to carry wind-stresses concentrated at the top panel-points, while the bracing on the end-posts carries the reaction from wind forces on the deck.

The bracing on the lower chords throughout the central twenty panels is similar to that on the top chords. The ends of this central part of the lower lateral girder terminate at the fourth panel-point from each end, and form a portal-frame over the deck-level, allowing space for the traffic on the deck-surface. The lower end of the fourth panel at panel-point 22 is stiffened by a transverse parallel girder supporting the lower chord members as high as possible below deck-level, and is arranged to take the reaction from the deck lateral system. Below this girder the bracing on the three last panels is of the normal type, but the members have to carry the wind-reaction from the deck-system, and are made with plate flanges. The lateral members in the lower chord system for six panels from the ends of the bridge have the same depth as the chords, this being sufficient for vertical stiffness. The members in the central sixteen panels are similar to those in the top chord system.

Deck-Laterals.—The lateral bracing of the deck is an entirely independent wind girder, 149 feet wide centre to centre of chord members, slung below deck-level (Fig. 5, Plate 4). The chords are directly connected to the ends of the cross girders ; the laterals are

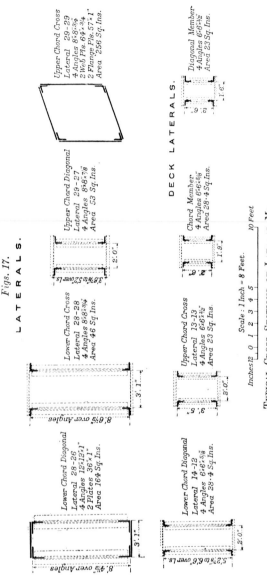

Figs. 17.

LATERALS.

Upper Chord Cross
Lateral 29-29
4 Angles 8×8×¾
2 Web Pls. 64×¾
2 Flange Pls. 57×1"
Area .256 Sq. Ins.

Upper Chord Diagonal
Lateral 29-27
4 Angles 8×8×⅞
Area 53 Sq. Ins.

Lower Chord Cross
Lateral 28-28
4 Angles 8×8×¾
Area 46 Sq. Ins.

Lower Chord Diagonal
Lateral 28-26
4 Angles 12×12×1"
2 Plates 36×1"
Area 164 Sq. Ins.

Upper Chord Cross
Lateral 13-13
4 Angles 6×6×½"
Area 23 Sq. Ins.

Lower Chord Diagonal
Lateral 14-12
4 Angles 6×6×⅝
Area 28.4 Sq. Ins.

DECK LATERALS.

Diagonal Member
4 Angles 6×6×½
Area 23 Sq. Ins.

Chord Member
4 Angles 6×6×⅜
Area 28.4 Sq. Ins.

Inches 12 0 1 2 3 4 5   10 Feet
Scale : 1 Inch = 8 Feet.

TYPICAL CROSS SECTIONS OF LATERAL MEMBERS

crossed diagonal members in panels corresponding to two panels of the bridge. The chords and diagonals are open box sections, 2 feet 6 inches deep by 2 feet 9 inches wide, made up of four angles with flat bar lattice bracing on all sides (*Figs. 17*). At the seventh panel-point from the south end the girder has a point of articulation on the central line of the span, which also forms an expansion-joint. From this point the two parts of the girder are continuous to the ends of the span, and are secured to the arch framework at the end-posts and between the connections 22 and 20, where the plane of the deck system crosses that of the chords.

Deck.—The deck of the bridge is carried by cross girders connected at each end of the bridge by 14-inch diameter pins to the end-posts and the next three posts ; the remaining cross girders are attached by 14-inch diameter pins to hangers suspended below the lower chord (Figs. 19, Plate 4). All are of box type, with flange

Fig. 18.

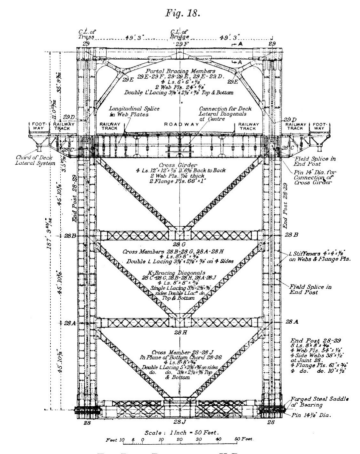

END-POST, PORTAL- AND K-BRACING.

227

Figs. 19. [Plate 4]

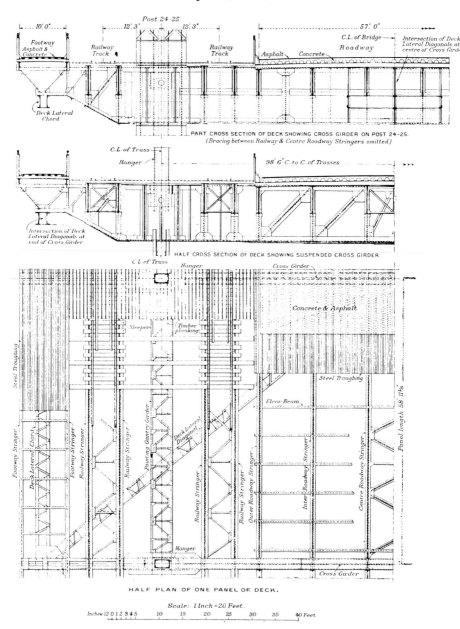

PART CROSS SECTION OF DECK SHOWING CROSS GIRDER ON POST 24-25.
(Bracing between Railway & Centre Roadway Stringers omitted.)

HALF CROSS SECTION OF DECK SHOWING SUSPENDED CROSS GIRDER.

HALF PLAN OF ONE PANEL OF DECK.

Scale: 1 Inch = 20 Feet.

DECK OF MAIN SPAN.

angles turned inwards between the webs to facilitate the erection of the stringers. As the panels of the lateral girder extend over two panels of the bridge, the intersection of the laterals is supported at the centre of alternate cross girders. At both ends of the span the deck has a slope of about 1 in 40, and has a vertical curve in the centre connecting the two slopes. The girders are at right angles to the plane of the deck, but the pins carrying the cross girders are horizontal in each case; this required pin-holes at varying inclinations to the plane of the cross girder.

The railway-tracks are carried on timber sleepers supported by plate-girder stringers. Between panel-points 20 and 18 there is a horizontal girder interconnecting the railway-stringers ; the reactions from this are sustained by the struts transferring the horizontal forces to the lower chords. Between the two lines of railway stringers in the plane of each truss there is a light lattice box-girder, which supports a travelling painting-gantry.

The roadway is carried by plate-girder stringers supporting transverse steel joists, 6 feet apart, bent to the camber of the road. Longitudinal pressed steel troughs, filled in with coke-concrete and

Figs. 20.

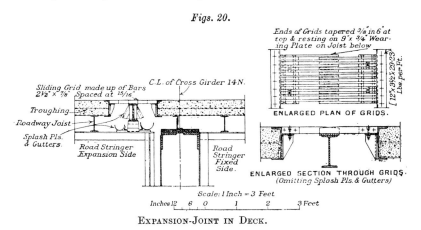

EXPANSION-JOINT IN DECK.

finished with 2 inches of asphalt, were laid on these. The two foot-ways on the outside of the railway-tracks were similarly constructed. The expansion joint in the roadway at north panel-point 14 consists of interlocking grids sliding into one another, which allow for a movement of approximately $5\frac{1}{2}$ inches in each direction from the mean position (*Figs.* 20). The rail expansion-joint consists of rails with long tapered ends, and sliding plates form the necessary joint in the footways. Expansion-joints were also provided at each end of the arch, where the deck system carried by the arch joins the approaches : the total movement for which provision is made is about 4 inches in each direction.

229

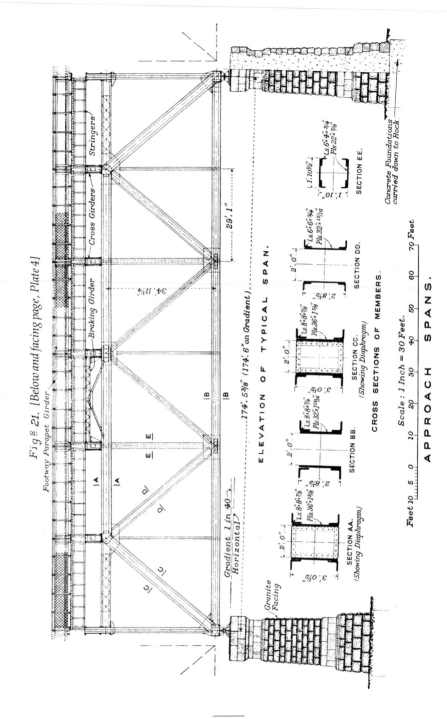

Figs. 21. [Below and facing page, Plate 4]

ELEVATION OF TYPICAL SPAN.

CROSS SECTIONS OF MEMBERS.

APPROACH SPANS.

Scale : 1 Inch = 30 Feet.

SECTION AA.
(Showing Diaphragm)

SECTION BB.

SECTION CC.
(Showing Diaphragm)

SECTION DD.

SECTION EE.

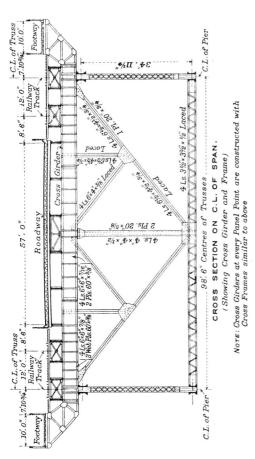

CROSS SECTION ON C.L. OF SPAN.
(Showing Cross Girder and Frame)
NOTE: Cross Girders at every Panel Point are constructed with Cross Frames similar to above

98' 6" Centres of Trusses

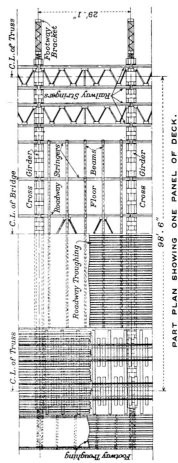

PART PLAN SHOWING ONE PANEL OF DECK.

Figs **22.** *[Below and facing page, Plate 4]*

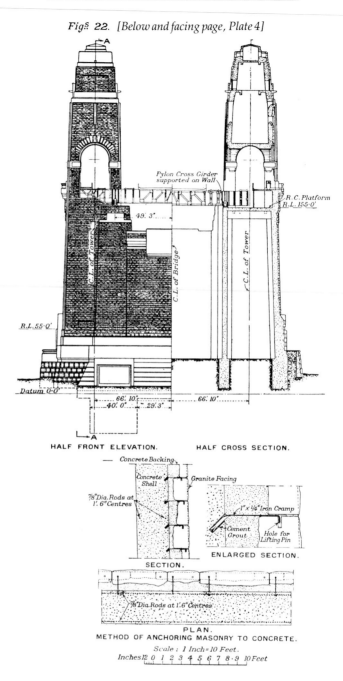

HALF FRONT ELEVATION. HALF CROSS SECTION.

SECTION.

ENLARGED SECTION.

PLAN.
METHOD OF ANCHORING MASONRY TO CONCRETE.

Scale : 1 Inch=10 Feet.

GENERAL   ARRANGEMENT   OF   PYLONS.

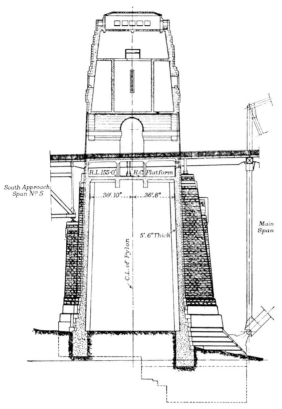

CROSS SECTION ON CENTRE LINE OF TOWER AA.

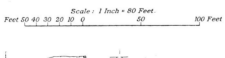

Scale : 1 Inch = 80 Feet.

Feet 50 40 30 20 10 0   50   100 Feet

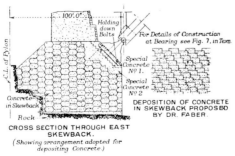

CROSS SECTION THROUGH EAST
SKEWBACK.
(Showing arrangement adopted for
depositing Concrete.)

DEPOSITION OF CONCRETE
IN SKEWBACK PROPOSED
BY DR. FABER.

APPROACH-SPANS.

The approach-spans and piers were the only parts of the structure shown in detail in the specification; four spans were proposed at each end of the bridge. In this design the deck was carried by a continuous cross girder resting on four main girders, the railway-lines being situated so that each track was directly over an outer main girder. The accurate estimation of the stresses in a structure of this form would have been very difficult, and the risk of the structure weakening under the action of live load would have been considerable. The piers for carrying the four main girders were granite-faced and of massive construction.

The Author's design is shown in Figs. 21, Plate 4. The deck of the bridge is carried by two main girders instead of by four, with a braced cross girder having the full depth of the main girders. The use of two main girders necessitates only two relatively small independent piers for each span. The calculation of stresses for a structure having only two main girders can be made with accuracy, and the steelwork is lighter than that required for four main girders. The reduction in the masonry piers greatly reduced the cost, the total estimated saving by the use of this construction instead of that shown in the specification being approximately £150,000. The preparation of the working drawings for the north approach-spans involved some difficult work, as these spans have a gradient of 1 in 40, and are on a curve with a radius of 1,423 feet at the centre of the deck, each line of stringers forming part of a helix with its own special radius, and allowance for superelevation added further complications.

PROVISION FOR INSPECTION AND PAINTING.

The specification required the provision of stairways, ladders, gangways, and travelling gantries to enable the inspection and painting of the bridge to be carried out with as little temporary scaffolding and supports as possible, and with the minimum of risk to the men employed. In each pylon there is a stairway in the central compartment from ground-level to a transverse gangway below deck-level. At each end this gangway leads up to the public footways on the two sides of the deck, and also to further stairways continued to the top of each of the four pylon-towers.

In each of the three compartments of the end-posts of the arch vertical ladders are fixed from bottom to top, and there is also a stairway from deck level up the slope of each of the diagonal members third from the end, and each of the four diagonals at mid-span, with cross gangways on top of the transverse lateral members at the centre and ends of the bridge. Gangways with handrails on both sides were laid along the entire length of the four chord members, the steeply-sloping ends being formed with horizontal treads. The interiors of the closed box sections of the upper and lower chords can be reached through manholes with watertight covers in each of the three compartments of every member. On each of the top chords there are two light electric cranes, each of which can travel over half the length of the chord from the end-post to the centre, and which is capable of supporting a cage alongside the posts, diagonals and hangers, and beneath the underside of the upper and lower chord members.

The most difficult area of a bridge structure to reach with ordinary scaffolding is the underside of the deck ; to deal with this area a system of gantries travelling below the bridge deck has been provided. A gantry, supported on light lattice-girders in the plane of the hangers, serves that part of the deck of the arch span between panel points 22 north and 22 south, where the lower chord intersects the deck level. This gantry extends for the full width of the deck (160 feet), and has a breadth of 20 feet ; it can be moved by power or hand, and enables the whole area of this part of the deck to be reached from below. At the ends of the arch span deck (from panels 22 to the end posts) four small hand-operated travelling gantries are supported below the cantilever ends of the deck, and two other gantries between the trusses.

For the approach-spans a form of travelling gantry was designed which enables the whole of the structure below the deck and between the main girders to be reached. The gantries are hand-operated, and there are two on each of the north and south approaches. Each gantry consists of a transverse bridge about 95 feet long and 4 feet wide, suspended near the two ends on Weston pulley-blocks attached to trolleys running on longitudinal joists supported below the deck, on which the gantry can travel the length of one panel, that is, about 30 feet. At the end of a panel the gantry can be lowered by the pulley-blocks alongside the framed cross girder, and when it has reached a level below the lower member of this it is transferred to trolleys running on a short length of joist attached to the member, and moved to the opposite side of the cross girder ; the blocks are then disconnected and moved to the next panel, and the gantry is again connected to them and raised on the other side of the cross girder.

FOUNDATIONS.

The specification defined the maximum pressure on the sandstone rock as about 31 tons per square foot, and showed the foundations for the main bearings sunk about 5 feet into the rock. The rock is a soft yellow sandstone with horizontal seams of clay and shale. From the records of borings and reports on the general character of the rock the Author concluded that, in view of the responsibility imposed upon the contractors, it was essential when tendering to provide for foundations of far more massive construction ; the contractors' tender therefore allowed for foundations excavated about 25 feet into the rock, imposing a pressure on it of about 13 tons per square foot. The extra cost was about £40,000, and there was a corresponding risk of losing the contract.

Each foundation had to carry a pressure from the main bearing of about 20,000 tons inclined at 45 degrees to the horizontal, and a vertical load from the pylon wall of about 11,000 tons. It was necessary to avoid risk of settlement due to direct pressure on the rock, to longitudinal disturbance due to sliding on clay or shale seams, or to distortion of the concrete by cracking or yielding under pressure ; the nearest practical approximation to uniformity of distribution of the pressure under the base of the steel bearings and on the surface of the rock was therefore used. The Author consulted with Dr. Oscar Faber, M. Inst. C.E., regarding the deposition of the concrete forming the foundations to avoid undefined shrinkage.

The excavations into the rock for the skewback were 40 feet wide and 90 feet long. They were sunk into the rock until the excavation exposed a sufficient area free from horizontal seams or fissures to ensure that there was no risk of longitudinal sliding, the depth being from 30 to 40 feet below the surface of the rock. Borings were also sunk in each excavation to provide that no more weak horizontal seams existed. The ultimate depth and form of the base were settled separately for each skewback according to the actual character of the rock below the excavation.

Dr. Faber advised the placing of concrete in sections as shown in Figs. 22, Plate 4, the intention being that each section should be completed in one operation across the whole breadth, longitudinally interlocking the sections, and thus avoiding any transverse discontinuity. This system was adopted in principle, but the shape of the sections was made hexagonal, as this was considered to ensure equally well the necessary interlocking, and to be easier for use in construction. The concrete was placed in forms having two sides only which formed the two upper inclined edges of each hexagon. This proved quite satisfactory.

This sectional construction was carried up to a level just short of the ends of the holding-down bolts of a bearing. The bolts were then set in position above this concrete, and further concrete to about 6 feet below the base of the bearing placed to secure them in position. The bearing was then set up on the bolts, and the space between the underside of the bearing and the finished concrete below was filled in with high-quality reinforced concrete.[1]

The foundations for the approach-spans were made by excavating to rock, and no particular difficulties were encountered ; the excavations were filled with concrete in the proportions 5 : 2 : 1, brought up to a short distance below ground level.

[1] See the Paper by Messrs. Freeman and Ennis, " Sydney Harbour Bridge : Manufacture of the Structural Steelwork and Erection of the Bridge."

Fig. 23.

END OF ARCH SPAN AND PYLON, DECEMBER, 1931.

PYLONS.

The specification laid down as an essential part of the arch bridge the inclusion of massive decorative pylons at both ends of the bridge, formed of concrete faced with granite. At the time of tendering these pylons involved an outlay estimated at about £750,000 (the actual cost was greater), and it was essential that every effort should be made to ensure the best possible architectural effect.

The importance of designing engineering works so that the appearance is attractive can hardly be over-stated, although it will generally be found that lack of beauty is associated with some technical fault. Although a well-designed engineering work without architectural treatment or decoration should satisfy all æsthetic requirements, there are features sometimes which require the co-operation of the engineer and the architect. In the case of the Sydney Harbour bridge the architectural decoration of the structure was laid down by the Government, and could only be carried out by the addition of features structurally non-essential but of necessity on a vast scale.

The specification contained drawings of pylons, which in the Author's opinion were capable of improvement architecturally ; and on his advice the contractors, when tendering, engaged Sir John Burnet and Partners to prepare the designs for the pylons : Sir John Burnet and Partners accordingly designed the architectural treatment for all the designs submitted by Messrs. Dorman, Long and Company, Limited. The specification further stipulated that the pylons were to be faced with granite obtained from quarries at Moruya, which was about 150 miles south of Sydney.

The external form and architectural treatment are shown in Figs. 22, Plate 4, and in *Fig. 23.* Each pylon embodies two towers above deck level, which are situated on either side of the central road and the inner railway-tracks, the outer railway-tracks and adjacent footway passing through the pylon towers. The lower part of the pylon at deck level has to support the walls of the upper part and the deck of the bridge. This level is about 150 feet above the foundations, and the extension of all the walls to ground-level would have involved a heavy additional outlay. It was therefore decided to form a reinforced concrete platform on which the towers would be built at the level + 155, namely 15 feet below deck level. The cross girders carrying the deck of the bridge where it passes through the pylons are supported on the inner walls. The external walls are faced with granite, rock-faced except at the corners and over those areas which were finished smooth to meet the architectural requirements.

The Author further consulted Dr. Faber upon the design of these external walls to avoid cracking from temperature changes, and from contraction of the concrete ; and it was decided to build the walls in two sections consisting of an inner section of concrete having a thickness of 3 feet 6 inches, and greater according to the situation, and an outer section about 2 feet thick, containing the granite facing and a backing of concrete (Fig. 22, Plate 4). The inner section of concrete was built first to allow of its completion at least six months ahead of the granite facing, although generally a much longer period elapsed. This part of the wall was reinforced in horizontal planes only by $\frac{7}{8}$-inch diameter rods in pairs, one near each face of the wall, forming continuous reinforcement around the entire walls, and placed at vertical intervals of 1 foot 6 inches. The granite facing was originally specified to be laid with stretchers and headers, but to obtain a better bond this system was changed. The granite facing was laid in alternate courses, the lower courses being of stones from 15 inches to 21 inches wide, and the upper courses of stones from 9 inches to 14 inches wide. As each pair of courses of masonry was placed a stepped recess was formed, into which the concrete backing could be placed without difficulty. The granite facing was bonded to the concrete wall with hooked bonding bars, placed in holes drilled in the concrete wall.

APPROXIMATE QUANTITIES AND COST OF COMPLETED BRIDGE.

The figures given in Table III. are approximate only, and totals do not precisely correspond with the quantities and rates stated. The costs do not include additions paid in respect of increase in the rates actually paid to labour employed in New South Wales

TABLE III.

Item.	Quantity.	Description.	Rate.			£
			£	s.	d.	
1	15,100 cubic yards	Earth excavation		9	0	7,000
2	44,500 ,,	Rock excavation		17	3	39,000
3	108,000 ,,	No. 1 concrete	3	19	0	427,000
4	11,000 ,,	No. 2 concrete	3	5	0	36,000
5	700 tons	Reinforcing rods	25	0	0	18,000
6	20,600 cubic yards	Granite masonry	22	10	0	464,000
7	165,000 feet super	Granite 4-cut. work		6	8	55,000
8	24,400 tons	Carbon-steel	53	10	0	1,306,000
9	26,200 ,,	Silicon-steel	61	10	0	1,612,000
10	145 ,,	Cast steel	60	0	0	9,000
11	50 ,,	Cast iron	100	0	0	5,000
12	9 ,,	Bronze	336	0	0	3,000
13	5,025 linear yards	Single-track permanent way	—			104,000
14	2,512 ,,	Footway, 10 feet wide	- -			7,000
15	1,256 ,,	Roadway, 57 feet wide	—			54,000
16	1,190 tons	Bearings of arch	86	0	0	102,000
						£4,248,000

The amount of the tender was £4,218,000.

as compared with those ruling at the date of the tender (the total amount of which was about £500,000), and also the following work not included in the tender :—

A concrete retaining-wall costing . . . . . £34,000.
Additions to permanent-way material, overhead wiring-supports and painting-stages, costing . . . . £20,000.

ORGANIZATION.

The whole of the designs, calculations, and working drawings of the permanent structure and the erection processes were prepared in London, a special department of the contractors' organization being formed for this work under the personal direction of the Author, Mr. J. F. Pain, Assoc. M. Inst. C.E., being his chief assistant. It is difficult to refer to any of the large staff engaged on the designs without doing some injustice to the remainder, but the following were the principal members of the London staff. Principal, Mr. J. F. Pain, Assoc. M. Inst. C.E., Chief Assistant, Mr. G. Roberts, Assoc. M. Inst. C.E. Assistants engaged on designs and calculations, Messrs. K. H. Evans, W. E. Hamilton, O. Kerensky, R. S. Read, H. Shirley Smith, Assoc. MM. Inst. C.E., C. O'Connell. Assistants engaged on the preparation of working drawings, Messrs. J. Beesley, G. G. Forrest, P. Holgate, G. R. Shannon, and E. W. Willett.

Galloway hydroelectric scheme: Tongland Power Station (facing page, top), Tongland Dam, fish pass, flood gates and spillway (facing page, bottom), Carsfad Dam under construction (above); engineers: Sir Alexander Gibb & Partners; contractors: A. M. Carmichael (from J. Instn Civ. Engrs, 1938, volume 8). This was a pioneering hydroelectric scheme for Britain and was completed in 1936. Britain's major hydroelectric development did not follow until after the Second World War

Mulberry Harbour (from a contemporary photograph). This was perhaps the most famous civil engineering contribution to the Allied victory in the Second World War. Technical details are described in a series of papers published by the Institution of Civil Engineers after the war ('The Civil Engineer in War', volume 2, papers by R. W. Hawkey, F. H. Todd, R. Lochner, O. Faber, W. G. Penney, J. H. Jellett, C. R. J. Wood, R. Pavry, A. H. Beckett)

The Skylon

F. J. SAMUELY, BSc(Eng), AMICE, and P. J. A. WARD, AMIEE

Reprinted from Proc. Instn Civ. Engrs, 1952,
vol. 1, 444-466

Although the Dome of Discovery, designed by Freeman Fox & Partners, was the most exciting engineering structure associated with the Festival of Britain in 1951, there can be little doubt that the most popular was the Skylon. The Skylon was an architectural *jeu d'esprit* and it was devised by two brilliant young architects: Phillip Powell and Hidalgo Moya. Its engineer was Felix Samuely but, as Samuely points out in his paper, the Skylon was designed by the architects before he had been appointed. For a structure which was so clearly an engineering one, that was remarkable.

Samuely was born in Vienna in 1902 and he died in 1959. After taking his diploma of engineering at Charlottenburg, he started as an engineer in Vienna and later set up in practice with a partner in Berlin where he specialised in steel and reinforced concrete structures. After a brief period as consultant to the Russian government in Moscow, Samuely came to London in 1933 and began his career in Britain in partnership with C. W. Hamann.

Three of his early works are outstanding: the De La Warr Pavilion in Bexhill, Simpson's in Piccadilly and the block of flats at Palace Gate in London. In addition to the Skylon, Samuely was responsible for two other buildings connected with the Festival of Britain, and his firm also designed the aviary at London Zoo.

The Paper describes the architectural aspects, the design, the fabrication, and the erection of the Vertical Feature—later named " The Skylon "—at the South Bank Exhibition, 1951.

The architectural form of the structure, in relation to the general characteristics of the site, is discussed, and a detailed description of the fabrication of the principal parts, and of the system of erection adopted, is given.

The magnitude, distribution, and nature of application of loading were, naturally, given very careful attention during the preliminary design stages. Since the structure is pre-stressed steelwork, of which very little experience was available, many of the problems encountered had to be solved for the first time, and the results were later checked by wind-tunnel tests on models. Recommendations for wind loading, taken from various sources, are discussed briefly and compared with the results of the wind-tunnel tests.

The stability of the Skylon depends largely upon the pre-stressing of the structure, and this aspect of the design, and the method of pre-stressing, are explained.

A particular feature of the design is the lateral support afforded to the three main struts by the pre-stressed pennant cables passing over their heads ; it is shown that in certain circumstances a mast may be stayed in one plane only, and general equations for stability are evolved.

INTRODUCTION

Two years before the opening of the South Bank Exhibition, 1951, a competition was held for the design of a " Vertical Feature " which was to be 250 feet high and to cost not more than £15,000. This competition was won by Phillip Powell and Hidalgo Moya, two young architects who had previously won the competition for the Pimlico Flat Development Scheme.

Their scheme consisted of a " Feature " that was not resting on the ground, but was completely suspended in the air, held in position by a number of cables. Three supporting struts were arranged to keep the cradle of cables in position, the cables being attached to the centre and bottom of the Feature, as shown in *Fig. 1* (facing p. 452).

It is remarkable that the architects were able to evolve a design of so decidedly an " engineering " nature without the assistance of an engineer. Only after Messrs Powell and Moya had won the competition and had been instructed to proceed with the detailed design of the Vertical Feature, which was later named " The Skylon," did they appoint Mr F. J. Samuely as their Consulting Engineer. Tenders were invited for the structure and the contract was awarded to British Insulated Callender's Construction Co. Ltd, for preparation of shop drawings, fabrication, and erection. Although time was very limited, owing to the fixed opening date of the Exhibition, the Skylon was completed in good time.

Architectural Aspects

The architectural aim was to design a simple dominant vertical feature, soaring upwards in direct contrast to the complex and horizontal character of the exhibition lying at its foot. This feature, a tall thin pointed body, was to be poised 40 feet above the paving—a heavier-than-air structure suspended in a cradle of steel cables supported on three struts. The struts, less than 70 feet high, were not to stand out prominently from the exhibition buildings. The deliberate illusion was thereby to be created of an unusual structure, divorced from the earth, yet with its design based on simple and practical mechanical principles.

Viewed from a distance, or from across the river, the Feature—shining in the sun by day, illuminated from inside by night and reflected in the river—was to give the appearance of a pointer to the exhibition.

At the same time, it was also very important that the feature should be impressive, not only from a distance, but also from close quarters. It was felt that, on this congested site, a vertical feature solidly resting upon the ground would lose its impressiveness when viewed from near by, however important and grandiose it might appear from a distance ; its solid connexion with the ground might also cut up the fine clear area of paving out of which it would rise. But when it was poised above the ground, the paved area was unbroken and exhibition visitors could walk underneath with dramatic views upwards.

The body was covered with horizontal satin-finished aluminium louvres at 3-inch centres and the lighting was effected by a series of tungsten-filament lamps arranged in groups of three in inverted conical reflectors situated in the centre of the feature, the lamps being in watertight holders. The total power of the lamps was 44·5 kilowatts and the intensity of the lighting was graded throughout the height of the feature—being brightest at the top.

244

STRUCTURAL DESIGN

The original design, using aluminium throughout, was abandoned in favour of a steel frame with aluminium cladding, for reasons of economy, and the extra weight of the steelwork was very useful in helping to stabilize the Feature. Another change from the original design was that the lattice struts were replaced by solid construction (part 2 in Fig. 3, Plate 1). This possibly regrettable change was made because the Festival Authorities considered that the lattice struts would bear too great a resemblance to the supports of the neighbouring Dome of Discovery.

The most difficult structural problem was to avoid setting up the high dynamic forces which could be caused by excessive movement of the structure under load. Under normal circumstances, and with ordinary stresses, considerable movement would occur at the top of the Feature, while the bottom would remain almost at rest. The movement at the top would be between 3 feet and 4 feet either way with a wind velocity of 80 miles per hour. This movement would not appear to be considerable from the ground but it would set up large dynamic forces owing to the constant acceleration and deceleration of the mass, and this, in turn, would have set up additional static forces which would have resulted in the need for very large cables (about 5 inches diameter).

To avoid such unsightly and expensive cables, pre-stressing appeared to be the only answer. Pre-stressing did not reduce the original forces in the cables but it was possible to stabilize the Feature in such a way that the movement at the top was reduced to approximately 9 inches and the dynamic forces, being proportional to the square of the amplitude, were reduced to about one-sixteenth of their original value, and so became negligible.

It is appreciated that a certain amount of pre-stressing is inherent in any structure or mast that is stayed by cables but usually the stresses involved are small by comparison with those under load, and such structures are not ordinarily regarded as pre-stressed. Tension may be induced into a cable by increasing its span ; by shortening its length within a span ; or by transverse loading. When loading is uniformly distributed, such as self-weight or wind pressure, its effect on the cable tension is called the " catenary effect," and this commonly plays havoc with all calculations of redundancy in cable-braced structures.

Pre-stressing, therefore, becomes effective only when it is carried out to a degree that far exceeds the normal tensioning of most stays. Investigation showed that if high-tensile-steel cables were pre-stressed to 100 per cent of the full-load value the catenary effect could be neglected for cables having a horizontal projection of up to 400 feet ; if they were pre-stressed to 50 per cent, a horizontal projection of 280 feet, and to 20 per cent, a projection of 170 feet, and so on. Since the horizontal projection of the cables for the Skylon was only 64 feet with a pre-stress of 50 per cent the catenary effect was neglected.

Pre-stressing of a structural system which includes cables is very similar to the pre-stressing of concrete, but in reverse. Concrete cannot take tension, whereas cables, normally, cannot take compression. After being pre-stressed, reinforced concrete is capable of taking a certain amount of tension, and cables of taking compression.

Fig. 2 shows this theory in principle, in one plane. By pre-tensioning the cables shown (a and b) to, say, 5 tons a compressive force of 8 tons is set up in the mast (c). If a horizontal force of 6 tons is now applied at the top of the mast, this force is taken entirely by the two stays. The leeward one (b) would be relieved of its tension and would have a final stress of zero, while the stress in the windward stay (a) would be doubled to 10 tons. The compression in the mast would remain unaltered. These are the same forces that would occur if the system was not pre-stressed, but the deflexion at the top is very much reduced.

For the Skylon, this principle was applied in space instead of in one plane, with three systems of stays arranged at 120 degrees to each other. It can be seen from Fig. 3, Plate 1, that there are two systems, each consisting of three cables. One set runs from the anchorage points (point 5) beyond the struts up to the centre of the Feature (point 9) and one set from the anchorage points (point 5) over the tops of the struts (point 11) down to the bottom of the Feature (point 7) up to the top of the other struts and down to the corresponding anchorage points. Altogether, there are three cables side by side from each anchorage point to the top of the struts—one from the top of each strut to the centre of the Feature, and two from the top of each strut to the bottom of the Feature.

It can be seen that, by tensioning the cables, an initial compressive force is introduced into the lower half of the Feature. There were two possible methods of producing this tension : (1) by using turnbuckles in

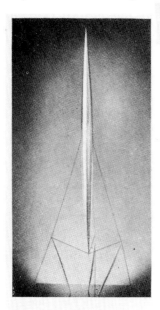

Fig. 1

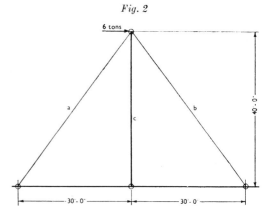

Fig. 2

ORIGINAL MODEL OF SKYLON

DIAGRAM OF FORCES TO ILLUSTRATE THE
PRE-STRESSING OF CABLES

Fig: 3.
[Plate 1, × 45%]

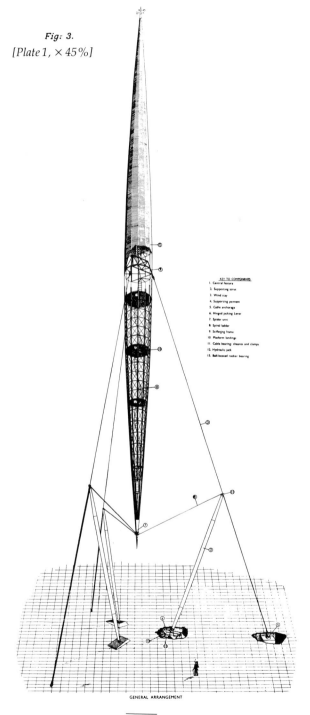

KEY TO COMPONENTS
1. Central feature
2. Supporting struts
3. Wind stay
4. Supporting pennant
5. Cable anchorage
6. Hinged jacking Lever
7. Spider unit
8. Spiral ladder
9. Stiffening frame
10. Platform landings
11. Cable bearing: sheaves and clamps
12. Hydraulic jack
13. Ball-located rocker bearing

GENERAL ARRANGEMENT

the cables ; and (2) by jacking up the struts from the bottom so that they pressed against the cables. The latter method was selected as being the simpler, and because the turnbuckles would have been unsightly. The method of jacking will be described later.

Originally, the top of each strut was to be held by two further stays, in addition to those already described that are connected to the Feature, to hold them in position sideways. During the process of design it was found that the two side cables were, in actual fact, unnecessary because the pre-stressing had the effect of pulling the struts back into their own plane against a laterally applied load. Exact calculation showed that there was a larger factor of safety against buckling than is usual, owing to the pre-stressing. (See Appendix I). This fact might be of value for the design of masts in general, because it shows that, under certain circumstances, masts can be stayed in one plane only, omitting stays in all other directions.

The Skylon was calculated to withstand a wind velocity of 80 miles per hour, which, according to the Meteorological Office of the Air Ministry, is the maximum to be expected in London at a height of 300 feet. For the calculation of the forces in the structure of the Skylon, it was important to assess the distribution of air pressure and suction around the circumference reasonably accurately. Also the fact that the surface was not completely closed in and that the Feature was not cylindrical influenced the wind load. To establish the distribution of wind on the circumference it was decided after long investigation to use the distribution given by Mr Guthlac Wilson (see Appendix II). The curve was modified to give a closer agreement to Flachsbart's publication[1] (see *Figs 4* and *5*).

Wind-tunnel tests showed that it was on the safe side to assume that the Feature was fully closed in. In fact, this appears to be correct for the centre part of the Feature whilst for the ends, which were more open, wind tunnel tests showed that it would have been sufficient to take into account only 85 per cent of the longitudinal section. Furthermore, from the results of previous wind-tunnel tests it had been established that the most dangerous period of oscillation was 0·5 cycle per second, and because of this a factor of 1·8 should be allowed for acceleration and gusts. No additional factor of safety was necessary if the frequency was higher than 2·8 cycles per second. The rate of vibration of the Skylon was calculated to be approximately 1·02 cycles per second. By interpolation it was found that a factor of 1·6 on the load should be used in the final calculation.

Before fabrication was commenced, further wind-tunnel tests were made on a model, designed on this principle, and it was clearly established that, with pre-stressing, a wind velocity of 80 miles per hour with considerable gusts could be resisted without danger. It was also made clear that, without pre-stressing, wind would have caused considerable movement of the Skylon and this would have required special precautions. The wind-

[1] O. Flachsbart, " *Windruckmessunger an einem Gasbehalter. Ergebnisse der Aerodynamischen Versuchsanstalt zu Göttingen* " (" Wind-pressure measurements on a gas-holder. Results of Aerodynamics Research Establishment in Göttingen "), 1927, p. 18.

tunnel tests also confirmed that the theory of omitting the side stays was correct, and no difference in behaviour was apparent after they had been removed.

The Skylon, which is of duodecagonal (twelve-sided) cross-section, is constructed on much the same principle as an airship ; that is to say, it has latticed construction in the surface only, covered by skin. There are twelve latticed girders, one for each surface, running from top to bottom of the Feature, shaped so that the Feature tapers to a point at both ends. It has a diameter of 13 feet at the centre.

The connexion between the foundations and the actual Feature was of considerable importance. The struts produce compression forces and the cables produce appreciable tension, the vertical component of which is 146 tons. This tension is reduced or increased by 54 tons for the worst wind pressure, whilst the compression remains almost constant. The transmission of these forces to the foundations would not normally have presented any difficulties, but owing to the fact that the struts were jacked up from the base to effect the pre-stressing, they had to be hinged at the bottom and provided with jacking members or beams.

The base of one strut is shown in *Fig. 6* and consists of a plate girder, hinged at one end, the strut itself being fixed in the centre by means of another hinge. With this arrangement, the jacks have to sustain only half the load of the struts.

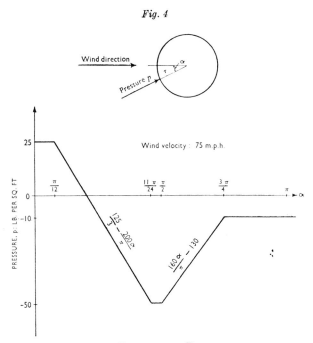

Fig. 4

WIND DISTRIBUTION DIAGRAM
(CIRCUMFERENCE REPRESENTED BY A STRAIGHT LINE)

Although, after jacking, the plate girders were packed in position, the jacks were retained in case the cables slackened and further jacking became necessary. During pre-stressing, the stresses were measured by pressure gauges on the jacks and stress gauges on the cables. The strain gauges on the cables were left in position, and were used to check the constancy of the stresses, but up to the time of writing there has been no appreciable loss of tension.

The foundations are star-shaped as shown in *Figs 7*, with blocks at the end of each arm to provide sufficient weight to counter-balance the vertical component of the tension caused by both pre-stressing and wind load, whilst the arms of the star have mainly to take the horizontal com-

Fig. 5

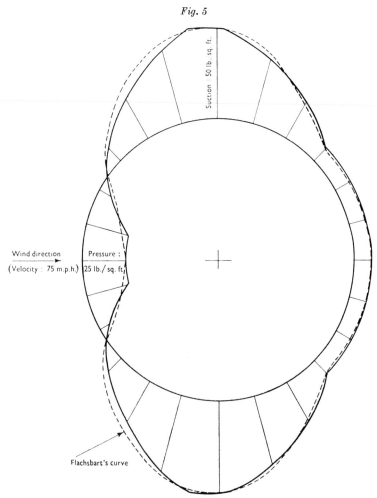

WIND DISTRIBUTION DIAGRAM
(PLOTTED ON CIRCUMFERENCE AS BASE OF ORDINATES)

ponent of the cable tension in compression and are hinged at the ends in order to avoid taking bending stresses.

FABRICATION

Supporting Struts

The 70-foot-long struts supporting the Feature (part 2 on Fig. 3, Plate 1) are triangular in cross-section, the corner members each consisting of 6-inch-by-6-inch-by-$\frac{7}{8}$-inch angle with a 4-inch-by-4-inch-by-$\frac{3}{8}$-inch angle nesting into the root, being spaced and reinforced by $\frac{1}{2}$-inch mild-steel plates welded to form tee-sections. On each face a $\frac{1}{4}$-inch thick mild-steel continuous skin plate is fillet-welded to the main angles.

The first problems of fabrication were those of handling and of preventing possible distortion of the heavy components. Each strut was made in three parts—a parallel-sided centre-section, and two tapered end-sections—and these were built up in jigs which could be rotated through 360 degrees so that all welds could be made in the down-hand position.

At the head of each strut there is an assembly comprising three steel sheaves which form a bearing for the supporting cables (part 11 on Fig. 3, Plate 1) and at the base there is a unit forming part of a pin-bearing on which the strut is supported (part 6, Fig. 3). The three sections of each strut and these head and base bearings had to be joined together in perfect alignment and some difficulty was experienced with this owing to

Fig. 6

BASE OF SUPPORTING STRUT

the awkward size, weight, and section of the parts. Assembly jigs were constructed which positioned the bearings and kept them in alignment during welding and the whole member was lined up and levelled on a concrete road with surveyor's instruments.

The hinged lever at the foot of each strut on which the pin bearing rests is made up of three 12-inch-by-6-inch heavy-section rolled steel joists, placed side by side, with $\frac{1}{2}$-inch-thick web-stiffening plates. The webs were vee-cut and welded to form a slope in the top flanges at one end and, after welding the joists together, a $\frac{5}{8}$-inch-thick plate was welded on to cover the top and bottom faces. To provide greater bearing area at

Figs 7

Scale: 1 inch = 32 feet

DETAILS OF FOUNDATIONS

the hinge, a ½-inch-thick plate was welded on each side of each web of the three R.S.Js and the pin-hole for the hinge was bored after the joists had been assembled, to secure accuracy of position.

The Central Feature

Most of the body was built up of rectangular welded panels, 12 feet long, which, when bolted together, form a series of twelve-sided " rings " each with its own diaphragm bracing. On some of the diaphragm bracings, platforms were sited (part 10, Fig. 3, Plate 1), and a spiral ladder was arranged between these platforms (part 8, Fig. 3) up the centre of the Feature. Each of the panels consists of two side angles, a horizontal angle top and bottom, and an intermediate horizontal member of channel section. They are cross-braced by ⅝-inch-diameter mild-steel rods, tensioned by special hookbolts at their intersections (see *Fig. 8*).

Since the panels were bolted one on top of the other in the structure, with their side angles toe to toe, it was necessary to maintain great accuracy to prevent " growth " during erection. All component members of the panels were completely jigged to ensure a maximum tolerance of 1/64 inch and the panels were welded in assembly jigs capable of lateral adjustment to accommodate the various widths, then removed and checked against a master templet. All mating surfaces were ground off to ensure flush facing, and each " ring " was check-assembled with its diaphragm bracing before being despatched from the works.

One of the most difficult sections to fabricate was that containing the internal stiffening frame at the mid-height of the structure. This framework (see *Figs 9*), distributing loads from the three wind stays (part 3 in Fig. 3, Plate 1), was complicated in that it developed from a triangle at the

Fig. 8

FOUR LATTICED PANELS, ASSEMBLED READY FOR ERECTION

Figs 9

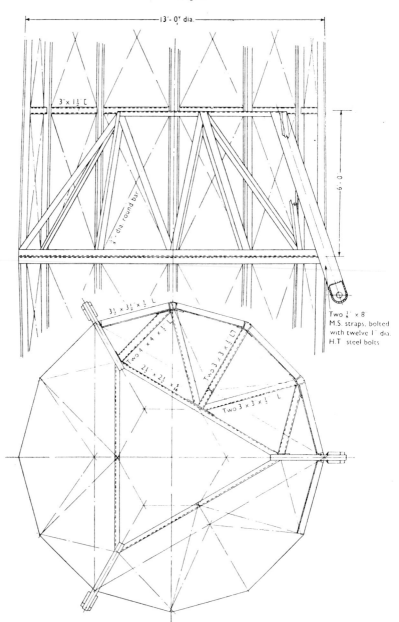

CENTRE STIFFENING RING OF FEATURE

Figs 10

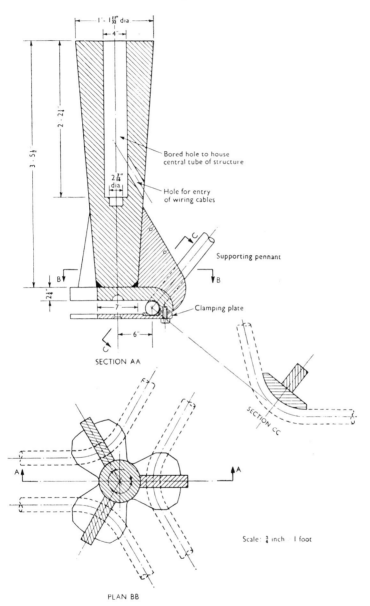

Bored hole to house
central tube of structure

Hole for entry
of wiring cables

Supporting pennant

Clamping plate

SECTION AA

SECTION CC

PLAN BB

Scale : ¾ inch = 1 foot

" SPIDER " UNIT

Fig. 11

" SPIDER " BEING WELDED

top to a twelve-sided figure at its junction with the main members of the structure. It was built up mainly of boxed angles, and heavy reinforcement at connexions was added after welding of the main framework, the whole unit being checked for accuracy from time to time. Each of the three connecting plates for the wind-stay cables was split in thickness, the two halves being bolted together during assembly for welding so that, upon completion of the welding process, the whole frame could be broken down into three separate parts to afford easy erection.

At the base of the Central Feature, supporting cables were passed round the lugs of a special spider unit (see *Figs 10,* and part 7 in Fig. 3, Plate 1), the conical part of which was turned from an 18-inch steel billet and bored centrally to receive the 2-inch-diameter tube which runs right up through the centre of the Feature to carry the lights and spiral ladder. The three legs of the spider were cut by oxy-acetylene flame from a 6-inch-thick plate and the grooves for the cables were formed on a lathe but finished by hand to remove sharp edges. Fins, or stiffening fillets, were cut from $2\frac{1}{2}$-inch-thick steel plate and the whole assembly was welded together using high-tensile electrodes (see *Fig. 11*). The finished unit, weighing 26 cwt, was normalized after welding, and tested to $1\frac{1}{2}$ times its working load in such a manner that all the conditions of actual use were reproduced.

Before joining the spider to the short bottom section of structural steelwork of the Feature, the two parts were pre-heated in a specially

Fig. 12

BOTTOM SECTION OF FEATURE AND "SPIDER," AFTER ASSEMBLY

prepared hearth and, owing to the mass of the sections, sufficient heat was retained to allow them to be transferred to a welding jig where they were aligned, tacked, and finished with a multi-run weld. The two parts after assembly can be seen in *Fig. 12*. To ensure the reliability of the joint, it was subjected to a test shear load of $7\frac{1}{2}$ tons. Before transport to site the whole structure was check-assembled at the fabricators' works.

Cables

The three supporting cables which connect to the bottom of the feature (part 4, Fig. 3, Plate 1) are $7\frac{1}{2}$-inch-circumference steel-wire ropes of multi-strand construction with a breaking load of 193 tons (see *Fig. 13 (a)*), and the three wind-stay cables connecting to the centre of the Feature are $7\frac{1}{8}$-inch-circumference locked-coil ropes, constructed with four layers of shaped wire over a spiral core of round wires and having a breaking load of 276 tons (see *Fig. 13 (b)*). All ropes were constructed from acid steel made by the Siemens-Martin open-hearth process, having an ultimate tensile strength of 110/120 tons per square inch. Ropes were marked to exact length under maximum working design loads and terminated in forged-steel open-type clevis-sockets.

ERECTION

A specially designed square column, 45 feet high and of lattice steel construction, was used as falsework to support the central feature of the

Figs 13

(a)   (b)

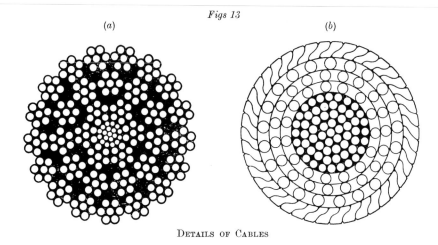

Details of Cables

Skylon during erection.   The column, which was supported at the head
by four ground stays, was raised into position using a 45-foot-high steel
tubular derrick.

The hinged levers at the bases of supporting struts, each weighing
23 cwt, were raised by a winch rope from the head of the falsework and
pulled out by tail ropes to their foundations where, after careful levelling,
they were grouted into position over pre-set holding-down bolts.

After the sheaves were fixed to the head of each strut, the struts were
raised into position by a rig comprising two 30-foot derricks with lifting
tackle fixed at a distance of 20 feet from the head and 6 feet from the
bottom of the strut.   Additional lifting and control tackle was rigged
from the falsework to the head of the strut.   The base was first landed
on its pin bearing and then the strut was raised into position.

To lift the one-piece bottom section of the central feature on to its
supporting falsework, two of the struts were luffed inwards to act as derricks, as shown in *Fig. 14.*   A 45-foot steel tubular derrick was used for
further assembly of the central feature and was lifted through the door
opening in the bottom section, and seated inside on the steelwork ; the
derrick's four head-restraining guys were anchored at ground level.

The individual braced panels of the structure were assembled on the
ground into sections of four panels each (see *Fig. 8*), three such sections
comprising one complete framed " ring " of the structure.   The sections,
ranging in height from 12 feet to 18 feet and in weight from 12 cwt to 15 cwt,
were raised separately using a power winch and single line, the lifts being
controlled by tail ropes to keep the sections clear of the structure.   At
intervals of 24 feet to 30 feet of height, as erection proceeded, the derrick
pole was lifted to a new position and restrained by guys to the steelwork of
the structure.

When the Feature had been erected as far as the centre ring, and the
attachment plates for the cables had been fitted, further erection of the

Fig. 15

TENSIONING FRAME USED AT ANCHORAGE POINTS

Fig. 14

ERECTION OF FIRST SECTION OF FEATURE

Figs 16

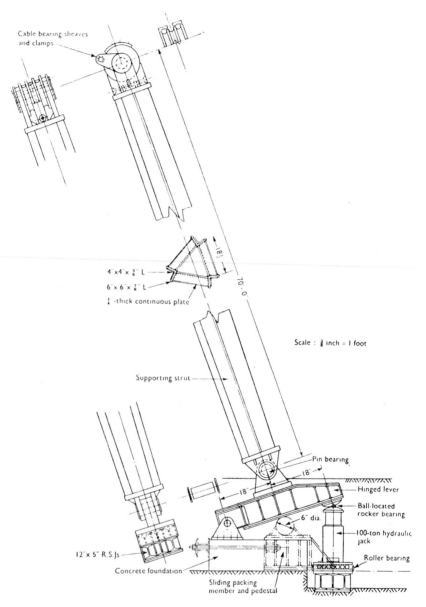

Cable bearing sheaves and clamps

4″ × 4″ × ⅜″ L
6″ × 6″ × ⅞″ L
¼″-thick continuous plate

18″
70·0″

Scale : ⅜ inch = 1 foot

Supporting strut

Pin bearing
18″
18″
Hinged lever
Ball-located rocker bearing
6″ dia.
100-ton hydraulic jack
Roller bearing

12″ × 5″ R.S.Js
Concrete foundation
Sliding packing member and pedestal

DETAILS OF JACKING ARRANGEMENT

central feature was suspended while the main cables (wind stays and supporting pennants) were connected.

The supporting pennants were lifted, one at a time, each rope being slung from a point 6 feet either side of its centre length. It was forced into position around a lug on the spider and held by temporary wedge packers driven between the rope and the head of the erection column. The tails of the rope were then raised to the heads of two adjacent supporting struts where they were passed around outer sheaves and, for the time being, allowed to hang freely.

Wind stays were then lifted, sufficient slack being allowed at the top ends for fixing clevis terminations to connecting plates on the structure. The lower ends were lifted out over the centre sheaves on supporting struts to hang with the tails of supporting ropes ready for anchorage at ground level.

The total force required to land the three ropes at each anchorage was expected to be of the order of 15 tons, and to ensure an easy entry of the single push-fit pin connecting all three clevises to their respective anchor plates a special tensioning frame and rig, shown in *Fig. 15*, was used. It was thought that this operation would be the most difficult part of the erection but, although the actual landing tension was approximately 25 tons, the frame held all nine plate and clevis connecting holes in perfect alignment and no difficulty was experienced in driving home the anchor pins.

When the wind stay and supporting ropes had been completely rigged, the next operation was to induce further tension in them by forcing the three struts upward. By this means, first the supporting ropes were tensioned until they lifted the central feature clear from its falsework

Fig. 17

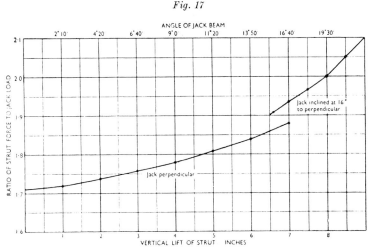

RELATIONSHIP BETWEEN AXIAL FORCE IN SUPPORTING STRUT AND LOAD AND LIFT OF JACK

Fig. 19

THE SKYLON BY NIGHT

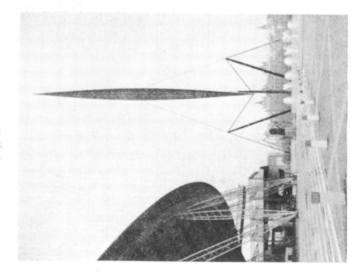

Fig. 18

THE SKYLON BY DAY

Table 1

Member	Load : tons			
	Pre-stress	Dead	Wind	Total
A	55	—	53·2	108·2
B	98·9	17·7	3·9	120·5
C	153·9	17·7	57·1	228·7
P	−154	−26·8	−6·1	−186·9
F	−156	−28	—	−184

and then, of course, further lifting caused the wind stays to tighten.

Jacking arrangements to lever up the supporting struts are shown in *Figs 16*. The jacks and hydraulic pumps had a capacity of 100 tons and the rams had a clear lift of 12 inches. Lifting forces were indicated on pressure gauges calibrated in tons and, when final adjustments were made, the forces were checked on a Macklow-Smith self-contained hydraulic capsule gauge which was inserted beneath each jack in turn.

Jacks were mounted on roller bearings so that they could move freely inwards as the angle of the hinged levers increased. As the jacks were operated, round-sectioned packing members, spanning between supporting pedestals, were moved by screwed tension rods to bear under the hinged levers, so that if a jack failed the load would be held. These packing members also acted as permanent supports with the jacks removed. As a single throw of the jacks was not sufficient to provide the full lift, small pre-cast concrete packing slabs, seated on asphalt, were introduced under the jacks after the first half of the lifting operation had been carried out. These packing slabs were made wedge-shaped, thus inclining the jacks so that the new line of thrust was normal to the slope of the hinged levers.

The curve relating force on the jacks to slope of the hinged levers for the required axial force in supporting struts is shown in *Fig. 17*, and Table 1 shows the total forces in the members.

After pre-stressing, erection of the central feature continued, using the method previously described, until only the topmost section remained to be fitted. To erect this 18-foot-long one-piece section, the derrick-pole was lifted out of the structure and secured to the outside, head guys being taken to ground level. When the section had been lifted and landed, an erectors' cradle was hoisted from the top of the derrick for the purpose of fitting an anemometer and wind-direction vane to the summit of the structure.

To hoist the aluminium cladding, an erectors' cradle was fitted with side frames, each to take several panels or sheets. The cradle was raised into position by a power winch, and panels were fixed by bolts which were placed by erectors operating from the cradle, the nuts being screwed on by men inside the structure using power-operated spanners.

Figs 18 and *19* show the Skylon by day and night.

APPENDIX I

CALCULATION FOR STRUTS, SHOWING THE REASONS FOR OMITTING THE SIDE STAYS

When a column that is hinged top and bottom is loaded, it is common practice to give it direction-fixing both at the top and the bottom; otherwise, the slightest unforeseen movement would result in an ever-increasing overturning moment.

The following calculation will show that a member in tension can restrain another member, in a plane at 90 degrees to it, in such a way that any movement at the top of the second member arising from unforeseen sideway forces, is not increased but actually decreased.

Two different cases have to be investigated :—

1. Where the tensile member itself forms an angle so that it exerts a considerable compression force on the first member (see *Fig. 20*).
2. Where the tensile member is in one line, so that its own stress is independent of that of the column (see *Fig. 21*).

Assume a column of height *h*, held at the top by two guys as shown in *Fig. 22*, and assume that the two guys are pre-stressed so that a compression force is produced in the column.

<table>
<tr><td align="center">*Fig. 20*</td><td align="center">*Fig. 21*</td></tr>
</table>

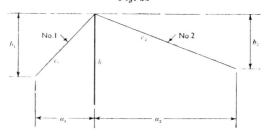

Fig. 22

The forces in the tensile system are in a certain geometrical proportion, following the equilibrium of the forces. If the forces in the inclined guys are T_1 and T_2. and V in the column, then :

$$T_1 = V \frac{c_1 a_2}{b_1 a_2 + a_1 b_2} \qquad \cdots \qquad \text{(1)}$$

$$T_2 = V \frac{c_2 a_1}{b_1 a_2 + a_1 b_2}$$

If there is an additional external load P on the column, the column load is $V + P$. Assuming that the top of the column moves sideways by an amount ϵ then member No. 1 in *Fig. 22* will be lengthened from c_1 to $\sqrt{c_1{}^2 + \epsilon^2}$ or $c_1\sqrt{1 + \dfrac{\epsilon^2}{c_1{}^2}}$.

Since $\dfrac{\epsilon}{c_1}$ is small, then :

$$c_1\sqrt{1 + \frac{\epsilon^2}{c_1{}^2}} c_1 = \left(1 + \frac{\epsilon^2}{2c_1{}^2}\right) \text{ (the first approximation).}$$

The new value of T_1 then becomes T_1' where

$$T_1' = T_1 + \frac{\epsilon^2}{2c_1} \cdot \frac{EA_1}{c_1} = T_1 + \frac{\epsilon^2 EA_1}{2c_1} \left.\right\} \quad \ldots \ldots \quad (2)$$

Similarly
$$T_2' = T_2 + \frac{\epsilon^2 EA_2}{2c_2{}^2}$$

The tension in member No. 1 (*Fig. 22*) will tend to turn the column back. The vertical component $T_1' \dfrac{b_1}{c_1}$ will actually work at a slight angle, on the line A_1R (see *Fig. 23*) and its horizontal component at R will be :

$$T_1' \frac{b_1}{c_1} \frac{\epsilon}{b_1} = T_1' \frac{\epsilon}{c_1}$$

Fig. 23

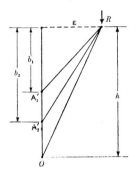

and allowing for the same effect from member No. 2 (*Fig. 22*), the actual overturning moment will be :

$$M = P\epsilon + \left(T_1' \frac{b_1}{c_1} + T_2' \frac{c_2}{c_2}\right)\epsilon - \left(T_1' + \frac{T_2'}{c_2}\right)\epsilon h \quad \ldots \quad (3)$$

$$= \epsilon\left[P + T_1' \frac{b_1}{c_1} + T_2' \frac{b_2}{c_2} - \left(\frac{T_1'h}{c_1} + \frac{T_2'h}{c_2}\right)\right]$$

or, expressing T_1' and T_2' in terms of V :

$$M = \epsilon\left[P + V + \frac{\epsilon^2 EA}{2c_2{}^3}(b_2 + b_1 - 2L) - \frac{h(a_1 + a_2)}{b_1 a_2 + a_1 b_2} V\right]$$

or, neglecting terms in $\dfrac{\epsilon^2}{c^3}$:

$$M = \epsilon\left[P + V - \frac{h(a_1 + a_2)}{b_1 a_2 + a_1 b_2} V\right] \quad \ldots \ldots \quad (4)$$

This can be expressed in a different way.

If $V > \dfrac{P}{\dfrac{h(a_1 + a_2)}{b_1 a_2 + a_1 b_2} - 1} = \dfrac{P(b_1 a_2 + a_1 b_2)}{a_1(h - b_2) + a_2(h - b_1)} \quad \ldots \quad (5)$

the structure will be stable and, after any unforeseen movement, will return to its original position.

It should be noted that, if $a_1(h - b_2) + a_2(h - b_1)$ is positive, it is possible to find a pre-stressing force V which renders the system stable. Geometrically, this condition means that, for the Skylon, the line connecting the anchorage points of cables must intersect at a point higher than its base.

Alternatively, if the external load P disappears, any pre-stressing force V will be sufficient, provided the above condition is fulfilled.

265

Fig. 24

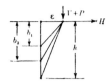

Effect of Side Thrust

If, owing to wind or other causes, a side thrust H occurs (see *Fig. 24*), in addition to the above-mentioned pre-stressing and the external force P, the overturning moment would be :

$$M = \epsilon\left[P + V\left(1 - \frac{h(a_1 + a_2)}{b_1 a_2 + a_1 b_2}\right)\right] + Hh \quad \ldots \quad (6)$$

In this case the sign of M depends upon the magnitude of ϵ. On the other hand, the deflexion ϵ is no longer accidental, but can be calculated from the load H. Assuming ϵ to be known, the forces T_1 and T_2 can be considered to be the sum of those forces produced by pre-stressing and shown in formulae (2) and those produced by H. The part of the force produced by H may be calculated by the following formulae.

$$\left(\frac{T_1}{c_1} + \frac{T_2}{c_2}\right) \cdot \epsilon \cdot \frac{(h - b_1)a_2 + (h - b_2)a_1}{a_1 + a_2} = Hh$$

$$\frac{T_1}{c_1}a_1 = \frac{T_2}{c_2}a_2$$

$$\left.\begin{array}{l} T_1 = \dfrac{Hha_2 c_1}{\epsilon[(h - b_1)a_2 + (h - b_2)a_1]} \\[2ex] T_2 = \dfrac{Hha_1 c_2}{\epsilon[(h - b_1)a_2 + (h - b_2)a_1]} \end{array}\right\} \text{caused by } H \quad \ldots \quad (7)$$

The total extension of the guys must be equal to the geometrical extension.

The total extension is, of course, $\dfrac{T_1 c_1}{AE} + \dfrac{T_2 c_2}{AE}$ where T_1 and T_2 are the additional forces caused by pre-stressing and H.

The geometrical extension is :

$$\sqrt{c_1{}^2 + \epsilon^2} + \sqrt{c_2{}^2 + \epsilon^2} - c_1 - c_2 \quad \ldots \quad (8)$$

But $\dfrac{\epsilon}{c_1}$ and $\dfrac{\epsilon}{c_2}$ are very small, and the first approximation is :

$$c_1\sqrt{1 + \frac{\epsilon^2}{c_1{}^2}} + c_2\sqrt{1 - \frac{\epsilon^2}{c_2{}^2}} - c_1 - c_2$$

The total extension, therefore, becomes :

$$\frac{T_1 c_1 + T_2 c_2}{AE} = \frac{\epsilon^2}{2c_1} + \frac{\epsilon^2}{2c_2} = \frac{\epsilon^2}{2c_1 c_2}(c_1 + c_2)$$

Replacing the total extension by formulae (7) and (1) :

$$\frac{Hh}{\epsilon[(h - b_1)a_2 + (h - b_2)a_1]}(a_2 c_1{}^2 + a_1 c_2{}^2) - \frac{V}{b_1 a_2 + a_1 b_2}(a_2 c_1{}^2 + a_1 c_2{}^2)$$

$$= \epsilon^2 \frac{EA}{2}\left(\frac{c_1 + c_2}{c_1 c_2}\right) \quad \ldots \quad (9)$$

This equation is of third degree for ϵ. It can be solved numerically and ϵ be substituted in equation (4).

In many cases V is large enough for the term in ϵ^2 to be neglected. (This means that a cable that is pre-stressed to an appreciable amount is not subjected to additional stresses by comparatively small horizontal forces, and this is confirmed by calculated examples). In this case :

$$\frac{Hh}{\epsilon[(h - b_1)a_2 + (h - b_2)a_1]} = \frac{V}{b_1a_2 + a_1b_2}$$

$$\epsilon = \frac{Hh(b_1a_2 + a_1b_2)}{V[(h - b_1)a_2 + (h - b_2)a_1]} \qquad \cdots \cdots \quad (10)$$

Substituting in (7), as was to be expected, the old values for T_1 and T_2 are derived.

Again the pre-stressing force can be chosen to keep ϵ within certain limits. (For the Skylon $\epsilon = 5$ inches).

This case is of no practical importance for the struts of the Skylon, because the straight cable can be completely unstressed under full wind force, and therefore it does not help in keeping the head of the strut in position. It is given here, however, for general interest.

Figs 25   Fig. 26

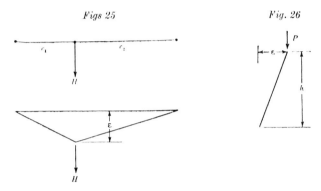

Assuming a tensile force T_0 in the straight cable (neglecting the effect of its own weight) and a sideways force H (see Figs 25), then :

$$T\epsilon = \frac{Hc_1c_2}{c_1 + c_2}$$

$$\frac{(T - T_0)(c_1 + c_2)}{EA} = \sqrt{c_1^2 + \epsilon^2} + \sqrt{c_2^2 + \epsilon^2} - c_1 - c_2$$

$$= \frac{\epsilon_2}{2c_1c_2}(c_1 + c_2) \quad \cdots \cdots \quad (11)$$

(see equation (8))

which reduces to :

$$T - T_0 = \frac{EA\epsilon^2}{2c_1c_2}$$

Combining this with equation (11) gives :

$$\left(\frac{Hc_1c_2}{\epsilon(c_1 + c_2)} - T_0\right) = \frac{EA\epsilon^2}{2c_1c_2} \quad \cdots \cdots \quad (12)$$

which again is an equation of third degree for ϵ from which T can be found. The rectifying force in this case is

$$T\epsilon\left(\frac{1}{c_1} + \frac{1}{c_2}\right) = \frac{T\epsilon(c_1 + c_2)}{c_1c_2}$$

If a force P acts on a member of height h (see Fig. 26), then :

total moment $M = P\epsilon - T\epsilon h \dfrac{c_1 + c_2}{c_1c_2}$.

This is negative when $T > \dfrac{Pc_1c_2}{h(c_1 + c_2)}$, which indicates stability.

APPENDIX II

DETERMINATION OF WIND FORCES

The following were available, to be used as bases for determining the wind load :—

A. Code of Practice, Chapter V (Loading).

B. Calculations, based on published information about the pressure distribution, due to wind, on circular objects.

C. Experiments made in a wind tunnel on a section closely resembling that of the Skylon.

A. Code of Practice

For southern and eastern England, in open country, at a height of about 40 feet the following velocity is suggested : $V = 65$ miles per hour.

At a height of approximately 200 feet this corresponds to a velocity of 123·5 miles per hour or 181 feet per second.

Allowing a reduction factor of 0·7 because the cross-section is only approximately circular, the corresponding wind pressure would be :

$$p = 0·7 \times 25·4 = 17·8 \text{ lb. per square foot.}$$

B. Published Information

(a) Dryden and Hill, " Wind Pressures on Circular Chimneys and Cylinders." U.S. Bureau of Standard Research, Report 221.

(b) Distribution of Forces in accordance with Flachsbart.

(c) Flachsbart's distribution as simplified by Guthlac Wilson in " The Encasing Structures for the Hot Water Accumulator for the Pimlico District Heating Scheme." (Structural Engineer, vol. xxviii, p. 85 (April 1950).)

A new approximation curve was adopted, following Guthlac Wilson's for the windward side, but approximating more to the Flachsbart curve for the leeward side.

Fig. 4 shows the approximate pressure, based on a total pressure of 25 lb. per square foot (see A), plotted against an angle increasing from 0 to π.

Fig. 5 shows the same pressure distribution plotted against a circle and compared with Flachsbart's curve (broken lines).

Total pressure per foot of height, $p' = 2 \int_0^\pi pr \cos \alpha \, . \, d\alpha$

Pressure on projected area $= \dfrac{p'}{2r} = \int_0^\pi p \cos \alpha \, . \, d\alpha$

$$= 25 \int_0^{\frac{\pi}{12}} \cos \alpha \, . \, d\alpha + \frac{125}{3} \int_0^{\frac{1\pi}{24}} \cos \alpha \, . \, d\alpha - \frac{200}{\pi} \int_{\frac{\pi}{12}}^{\frac{11\pi}{24}} \alpha \cos \alpha \, . \, d\alpha$$

$$- 50 \int_{\frac{11\pi}{24}}^{\frac{\pi}{2}} \cos \alpha \, . \, d\alpha + \frac{160}{\pi} \int_{\frac{\pi}{2}}^{\frac{3\pi}{4}} \alpha \cos \alpha \, . \, d\alpha - 130 \int_{\frac{\pi}{2}}^{\frac{3\pi}{4}} \cos \alpha \, . \, d\alpha$$

$$- 10 \int_{\frac{3\pi}{4}}^{\pi} \cos \alpha \, . \, d\alpha$$

$$= 17·12 \text{ lb. per square foot.}$$

C. Experiments in Wind Tunnel

In view of the fact that the cross-section of the Skylon is not circular but duo-decagonal, and that the surface is not completely closed in, tests were carried out by Professor N. A. V. Piercy at Queen Mary College, London, on a " closed " model approximating to the centre part of the Skylon, and on an " open model " approximating to the ends.

According to the report issued by Professor Piercy, for a wind of 75 miles per hour the closed model showed a pressure of 17·5 lb. per square foot and the open model, 14·5 lb. per square foot.

The Meteorological Office gave a wind velocity of 80 miles per hour as being the maximum to be expected at a height approximating to the top of the Skylon (in London) and, correcting the figures in the proportion of 75 to 80, the forces were :

$$14·5 \; \frac{80^2}{75^2} = 16·5 \text{ lb. per square foot}$$

and

$$17·5 \; \frac{80^2}{75^2} = 19·8 \text{ lb. per square foot.}$$

Since the major part of the Skylon is " closed ", a figure between 16·5 and 19·8 was taken as being adequate. To be on the safe side, the figure was taken as 19·4 lb. per square foot.

Summary

	lb. per square foot
Pressure, according to Code of Practice	17·8
Pressure according to calculations	17·12
Pressure in accordance with wind tunnel test	16·5 to 19·8
Pressure selected for actual design	19·4

Shock and Resonance Factor

Previous tests carried out by Professor Piercy at the Queen Mary College showed that, with frequencies above 2·8 cycles per second there was no need to introduce a shock factor, whilst with a frequency of 0·5 cycle per second a factor of 1·8 should be introduced.

Calculation showed that the frequency of full vibration of the Skylon was 1·02 vibration per second, which by interpolation, gave a factor of 1·6.

The actual pressure used for the design, is, therefore :—

$$19·4 \times 1·6 = 31 \text{ lb. per square foot (calculated on the projected area)}$$

North Sea oil development: Cormorant A platform (from a contemporary photograph). The development of oil recovery in the North Sea in the 1970s provided the opportunity for large-scale construction in both steel and concrete. The photograph shows the Cormorant A platform leaving its Ardoyne Point construction site, in Scotland, for Norway where its deck was installed. The platform in the background is Brent C. Both platforms were constructed by McAlpines' Ardoyne Point yard for Shell. This yard was the next most prolific to Norwegian contractors

Dubai Dry Dock: design and construction

G. H. COCHRANE, MA, FICE,
D. J. L. CHETWIN, BE, FICE, and
W. HOGBIN, MA, MICE, MASCE

Reprinted from Proc. Instn Civ. Engrs, 1979,
vol. 66, 93-114

As has been noted earlier, twentieth century engineering is no longer the domain of talented individuals but relies instead on closely integrated teams of highly qualified engineers working together and sharing their experience. This is true whether the engineers were consultants or contractors. Individuals were replaced by firms and eventually, in some cases, by giant corporations.

These trends were plain to be seen in the period between the two World Wars, and they have been accelerated since then. Nowadays, projects are occasionally so vast that even giant corporations are unable to cope with them unaided, and joint ventures are needed in which two, or even more, of these giants pool their resources in order to bring the work to completion.

One project requiring such a joint venture was the Dubai Dry Dock, which was opened in February 1979 after more than five years of concentrated engineering endeavour. The cost of these works was £232 million, and they required a work-force of over 6700, of whom 250 were specialists and supervisors from Britain and other parts of Europe. By far the most of the remainder came from India and Pakistan.

Because of its position at the east end of the Gulf, Dubai provided a uniquely suitably site for oil tanker repair facilities. Facilities for dry docking, repairing and servicing these tankers, which had become very large by the early 1970s, sited at Dubai would allow the least deviation from their trade route and hence the least possible delay.

In 1971 Sir William Halcrow & Partners, one of the biggest and most respected of Britain's consulting engineering concerns, was commissioned to investigate the feasibility of constructing such a facility at Dubai. After further studies a world-wide design and build competition was held, which was won by the Costain International-Taylor Woodrow International joint venture, and work was started at the beginning of 1973. Since Halcrows were retained to design and supervise the construction of the work, the project was in the hands of three of the leading engineering concerns in Britain.

Halcrows were by far the oldest of the three, and had grown from the classic modest beginning to a consultancy with offices scattered throughout the world and almost as many partners and senior members of the firm as Brunel had employees in his entire office, and these were supported by a considerable army of qualified engineers and other staff. Taylor Woodrow had begun as a small building firm in the 1930s in the north of England, but by the 1970s had become an international giant with activities and interests ranging from house-building, through nuclear power stations to opencast coal-winning in the USA. In a word, everything related to the construction industry was grist to the Taylor Woodrow mill. Costain's story was similar. All three companies had begun in a relatively small way and had grown to eminence through the excellence of their engineering.

At Dubai the contractors were expected to produce all the civil, mechanical and electrical designs for the work as well as to construct it. The contractors and the consulting engineers worked in close harmony, sharing experience and perhaps going some way towards dispelling the supposedly traditional antipathy between contractors' men and consultants, and final approval was given by the consultants. Among the subcontractors were some famous British names including those of Redpath Brown Dorman Long and Sir William Arrols.

In a way the very size of this project and the joint organisation of the resources needed to carry it through had brought the engineering process full circle. Just as the early engineers had been responsible for civil, mechanical and architectural work — and indeed some of the earliest had called themselves architects as often as they had called themselves engineers — here was a giant joint venture doing the same thing. But the circumstances were very different, and the engineers were bathed in anonymity.

The preceding paper describes the background to the Dubai Dry Dock project, the scope of the work and the form of contract, and discusses some detailed aspects of the design. This Paper highlights some of the interesting aspects of the Contractor's civil engineering work, including the principal design decisions and design procedures, the organization required to effect the works and the methods by which the various elements of the dry docks were constructed. The requirements for the design and provision of buildings, services and specialized equipment are not discussed.

Design

The contract arrangements for the Dubai Dry Dock project required the Contractor to initiate and propose civil, mechanical, electrical and architectural designs to achieve broad objectives set by the Engineer. After agreement in principle by the Engineer, these proposals were then developed in detail by the Contractor's design team, working closely with the Engineer's team. It was thus possible for the designers to take construction requirements fully into account at all stages of the design process, from the major decisions on form of construction down to minor aspects of detailing.

Principal design decisions

2. The short construction period available for the project meant that major civil engineering decisions had to be based on relatively extensive geotechnical information of a general nature, but sparse local detail. Contingency plans therefore had to be made to allow for inaccuracy or local variations in the assumptions for sensitive geotechnical parameters.

3. After examination of a number of alternative schemes the following decisions were taken, which then controlled the subsequent designs.

    (a) The docks would be built out from the shoreline, rather than within existing or made ground.

    (b) The docks would be grouped together in such a way that the pump-houses and the heavy lift cranes could each serve two adjacent docks.

    (c) The dock floors would be of a pressure-relieved type if possible, with continuous pumping from an underfloor drainage layer. Should the ground conditions later prove unsuitable for pressure-relieved floors an anchored floor would be substituted, but the floor thickness and hence dredging level would remain unchanged.

    (d) The dock walls would be formed from concrete caisson units. These units would be built on shore, launched by shiplift and founded on legs within trenches drilled below the general floor dredging level.

Dubai Dry Dock (from a contemporary photograph)

4. In the event, the ground conditions were found to be similar to the initial predictions and these initial decisions were justified.

Site investigation

5. A preliminary site investigation showed the geological conditions to be reasonably uniform over the site area.   Recent deposits of sand, shells and corals, which are locally cemented, overlie a miliolite 'sandstone' consisting mainly of calcareous materials.   The sandstone extends from approximately 11 m below datum (mean low water level) and contains zones of very poorly cemented calcareous sands.   Between the −32 m and −40 m levels bands of sand, sandstone and conglomerate are encountered, underlain by a substantial thickness of dolomitic limestone.   The foundation level of the main dock structures is at −14·8 m.

6. After construction had started a second-stage investigation was undertaken to confirm the critical design parameters, particularly

   (*a*) the rate of seepage into the underfloor drains with a pressure-relieved type of dock floor, and whether or not this rate of seepage would increase or decrease with continuous pumping;

   (*b*) the ultimate strength and elastic constants for the foundation material beneath the dock walls and floors.

7. Nineteen additional boreholes were sunk, but it was considered that boreholes alone could not provide sufficiently reliable information to answer either of these questions, and the second-stage work therefore included the excavation of a 12 m dia. shaft within the existing beach down to the proposed dock foundation stratum at 13 m below beach level.   The surrounding groundwater levels were monitored as excavation and pumping progressed, the procedure thus being equivalent to a large-scale well-pumping test.   Two 750 mm square in situ plate loading tests were conducted at the base of the excavation and block samples cut from the rock surface were subjected to triaxial compression tests in the laboratory.   At the end of the second-stage site investigation it was concluded that the total inflow into the underfloor drainage system of the three docks would be 0·5–1·5 m^3/s and would probably reduce with time.   The average bulk elastic modulus of the subgrade could be taken as 800 MN/m^2 for design purposes, and the allowable surface bearing pressure as 1·2 MN/m^2.

Dock walls and finger pier

8. The design of the dock walls was crucial to both the cost and construction time for the project, and many variations of structure were considered before the basic caisson shapes were defined.   The principal decisions to be made were as follows.

   (*a*) Should each dock wall be formed by a single caisson element extending from side to side or by two parallel rows of elements ?

   (*b*) Should the elements be made able to float when launched or require support by detachable buoyancy tanks ?

   (*c*) Should the caisson units be sand-filled or only water-filled ?   If sand-filled, should they be continuously drained by connection to the underfloor drainage system (greatly reducing the outward wall pressures) or should the internal water level be allowed either to vary or to stabilize at some equilibrium level ?

   (*d*) If the caissons were to be sand-filled, should the deck loadings be carried by the contained fill or wholly by the concrete structure ?

9. The wall element finally selected was a reinforced concrete self-buoyant caisson of I form in plan, extending the full width of the dock piers and filled with sand (Fig. 1). The dockside crane, bollard block and hauling-in trolley loadings are carried directly on the caisson walls, while the pavement loadings are carried on the sand fill. It is assumed that the standing water level within each caisson can vary by the full height of the caisson walls.

10. The foundation arrangements for the caissons were designed to minimize diver work and sea-bed preparation. The main weight of each caisson, with its fill and surcharge loadings, is carried directly to the foundation stratum through a sand–cement grout layer. Before injection of this grout the caissons were supported by downstand beams at the ends, which rested in two accurately cut trenches formed in the dredged sea bed. The height of the downstand beams was chosen to cover the full vertical tolerance in dredging while maintaining a minimum 150 mm thickness of grout beneath the caisson floor.

11. The standard shape of caisson for the dock walls having been established, and the casting and launching arrangements sized accordingly, variations on the

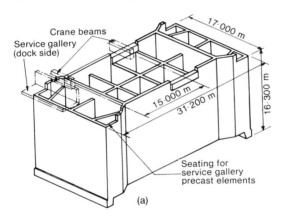

(a)

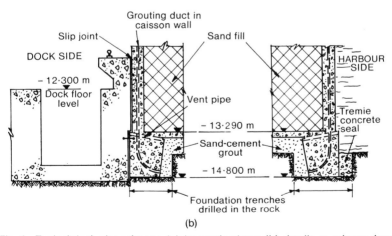

(b)

Fig. 1. Typical dock pier caisson : (a) isometric view ; (b) details at caisson down-stand beams

standard caisson were used for other parts of the works. Reduced-length caissons were used in the dock headwalls; full length caissons were used end to end as retaining walls extending the lines of the outer dock piers; the finger pier was formed from full length caissons placed both transversely and longitudinally; and modified caissons were used to form the dock lead-in and tank cleaning berth dolphins. The standard foundation procedure, using downstand beams, applied to all caissons.

12. The analysis and design of the caisson walls proved to be a very substantial task. The walls running perpendicularly to the dock pier centre-lines act as shear walls resisting the full differential water pressures between docks, while carrying heavy vertical loadings from the cranes and also an allowance for differential water and soil pressures from cell to cell. Various flotation and filling conditions had to be considered. Every effort was made to standardize the caisson walls, but the weight of reinforcement—and hence the potential for cost savings—was so large that refinements had to be made to the standard design for each of the many differing wall situations. Each wall was analysed in turn as a two-dimensional problem, using a dynamic relaxation computer program and Nielsen's equations for assessing the required reinforcement for in-plane shear. In retrospect it might have been better to have undertaken a three-dimensional analysis.

13. The decision to slipform the caisson walls, though vital to the economical execution of the project as a whole, imposed severe restrictions on the designers: wall thicknesses had to be kept constant for the full wall height and between one caisson type and another; no reinforcement could run diagonally up the walls; horizontal bars were generally limited to 4 m lengths; and great care in detailing was needed to avoid excessive congestion of reinforcement at laps and corners.

14. During flotation the floors of the caissons had the function of withstanding the external pressure and holding the plan shape of the caissons. Once the caissons were in position, however, the floors were considered to act only as a series of independent strip footings for the walls. Vertical frictional forces between the sand fill and the walls are sufficient to stabilize the walls against external overturning forces.

15. A particular problem in the caisson design was the set of assumptions to be made for the sand infill. This fill was well graded granular material selected from the reclamation area, tipped by lorry into the flooded caisson cells. Caisson design could be based on a series of conservative assumptions, but an accurate assessment of the settlement characteristics of the fill remained a problem which could only be resolved by site testing. Cone penetration tests were therefore conducted within the filled caissons which showed that the sand fill was assuming a very loose condition and excessive settlement of the surfacing could possibly occur under vibration or shock loading. A compaction method then had to be devised which would not overload the caisson walls in the final condition or during the compaction process.

16. An elaborate compaction test programme was conducted on site, using a 610 mm dia. × 12 m long vibrating steel tube 'poker' working within a caisson fitted with soil pressure cells, piezometers and inclinometer tubes attached to the walls. It was found that controlled insertion and withdrawal of the poker at the centre of the caisson cell could produce an average settlement of the sand surface of up to 900 mm. Local excess pressures on the caisson walls during vibration were much lower than expected, generally matching the excess piezometric head measurements. It appeared that there was no appreciable transfer of load from the vibrator to the walls by intergranular contact. The forces on

the walls during fill compaction could therefore be kept to acceptable values by limiting the piezometric pressure rise, which in turn could be related to a limiting insertion rate for the vibrator. All caisson cells were then vibrated in a carefully controlled manner and satisfactory densities were achieved.

Dock floors

17.   The floors of the three docks are of the pressure-relieved type, and are designed to carry vessels placed in any position within the docks. In each case the main structural member is a reinforced concrete slab of 1·5 m uniform thickness. A permeable gravel drainage blanket immediately beneath the floor and a system of open jointed drains conducts seepage water to automatically controlled pumps located in the two pump-houses. The arrangement is shown in Fig. 2.

18.   The requirement that vessels should be able to dock stern first or bow first and at any location within the floor area in each dock necessitated a uniformly level floor surface. The time taken to drain the last 2 m depth of water from so large a flat surface was expected to have a major influence on the total dock dewatering time, and large drainage channels were therefore provided around the perimeter of each dock. Analysis of the drain behaviour proved to be extremely difficult, and a one-tenth scale model test was therefore undertaken to verify the calculated values and optimize the hydraulic arrangements of the culverts and pump-house entry sumps. The model showed that the side drains are ineffective until the depth of water over the floor has fallen to approximately 0·5 m. Below that depth the side drains have a substantial influence and are sufficient to keep one main dewatering pump supplied until the average water depth over the whole dock floor falls below 150 mm.

19.   The underfloor drains are wholly disconnected from the surface drainage system, except that the underfloor pumps and stripping pumps can be interchanged within the pump-houses. The 1 m dia. pipes of the underfloor system act as storage reservoirs controlling the frequency of operation of the pumps. Pressure relief valves are provided within the dock floor as a precaution against pump operational failure.

20.   The main reinforcement in the slab was placed transversely to the dock centre-line and the slab was analysed as a two-dimensional problem of a continuous flexible strip supported by a deep elastic medium. The computer program used allowed soil stiffness to be varied between layers and a no-tension condition to be applied to any layer. Keel and bilge loads were treated as strip loads and the worst possible combinations of load locations checked. An axisymmetric analysis, rotating the two-dimensional mathematical model about a vertical axis, was used for the 'end of strip load' and concentrated load situations.

21.   The effective stiffness to be taken in the analysis for the reinforced concrete slab required considerable thought. The design was eventually based on the assumption that the slab was fully cracked for both hogging and sagging moments and differing stiffnesses were assumed for the hogging and sagging zones according to the reinforcement proposed, with a modular ratio of 15. Reinforcement quantities in the floor slab varied from 45 kg/m^3 at the edges to 140 kg/m^3 under the 800 t/m loading in Dock 2.

22.   As soon as the dock floor foundation rock was exposed the geotechnical parameters assumed for the floor analysis were verified by plate bearing tests. Some very weak material was revealed, mainly occurring as thin layers or lenses at or just below formation level. Where the material was close to the surface it was removed and replaced by concrete. In other cases the floor slab reinforcement was increased locally, or the gravel drainage blanket was replaced

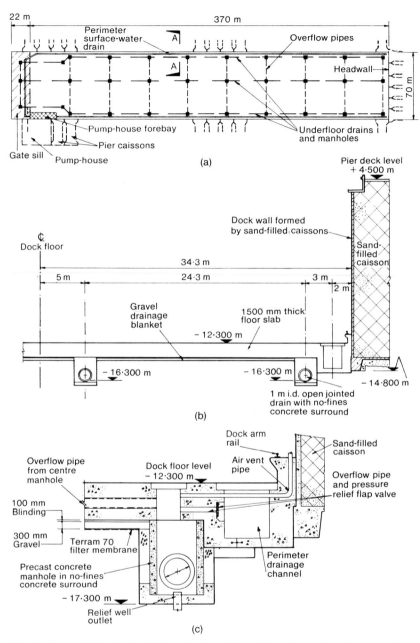

Fig. 2. Floor details for Dock 1 : (a) plan; (b) section AA; (c) section at under-floor drainage manhole

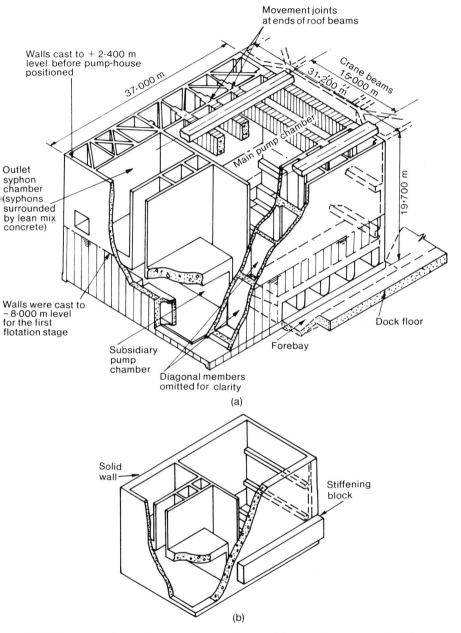

Fig. 3. Isometric views of a pump-house caisson: (a) general arrangement; (b) as analysed by computer

by no-fines concrete to compensate for reduced stiffness in the subgrade.

Dewatering pump-houses

23. The configuration of the docks and dewatering pump-houses allows each pump-house to serve two docks with minimum lengths of entry culverting. Initially an attempt was made to contain each of the two dewatering pump-houses within a group of modified caisson units, but limitations of weight on the shiplift caused this proposal to be abandoned and the pump-houses were designed so that the floors and lower walls could be cast within a dewatered excavation to the minimum height necessary for flotation. The walls and internal members were finished progressively while the pump-house was afloat. The outer walls and the floors therefore had to withstand a series of temporary loading conditions which were not directly related to the working conditions when in place.

24. Figure 3 shows the general structural arrangement of the pump-house and the idealized form used in the initial calculations by the STARDYNE computer program. The analysis was repeated later with the side walls modelled in more detail. Difficulty was again met in assessing the relative stiffnesses of the reinforced concrete members, and also in relating the calculated principal stresses to reinforcement placed only horizontally or vertically.

25. The seaward compartment of each pump-house contains the underfloor drainage and dock stripping pumps with their associated intake chamber. These pumps are of 1 m^3/s nominal capacity. A valving arrangement allows any one or more of the four pumps in each pump-house to be used on each duty.

26. The dock flooding culverts, incorporated in the double-skin side walls of the pump-houses, gave particular difficulty in design, due to the small amount of space available in which to form two right-angled bends. Model tests were undertaken at the British Hydromechanics Research Association and a compromise arrangement was worked out, using a plug type vertical action valve with guide vanes.

Dock gates and sills

27. The 100 m width of Dock 2 presented a formidable problem for any form of dock gate which was designed to act as a horizontal girder between the dock walls. The form investigated was a propped-cantilever gate supported wholly by the gate sill and for which the weight per metre would be virtually independent of dock width. Inclined-face, vertical-face and combination shapes were considered in detail and the 'Promod' design shown in Fig. 4 was finally adopted. The gates in the other two docks are similar.

28. When fully open the gates and their propping members lie flat within a recess below sill level. The gates are closed by means of electrically linked winches which haul on the ends of the gate top girder. Fixed buoyancy chambers reduce the operating load to 5% of the gate weight. As the gate rises under the winches, the upper ends of the gate props roll up the back of the gate until they engage against thrust blocks.

29. The gates are built up from a series of modules, fabricated in the UK and bolted together on site. Buoyancy modules weighing 35 t and intermediate plates weighing 10 t alternate along the gate length. The layout of the hinges for both the gate sections and the props is such that in the gate-closed position all the hydraulic pressure forces are carried by thrust pads remote from the hinges themselves. The hinges thus carry only the gate and prop self-weight forces.

30. Temperature movements presented a particular problem in the gate design, the worst condition occurring during construction when the gates are

fully exposed to the sun. The centre of each gate is fixed and the calculated movement at each end of the largest gate is then ± 38 mm.

31. The gate sill cross-section is also shown in Fig. 4. To allow for differential thermal and other movements of the sills relative to the dock floors and walls the sills have been made independently stable. The horizontal component of the water pressure on the gate face is resisted by a combination of friction on the sill base and passive pressure on the sill heel. Seepage beneath the sill is reduced by a 10 m deep cut-off wall, formed by grouting contiguous 300 mm wide precast concrete plate units into a drilled slot. Lateral movement of the

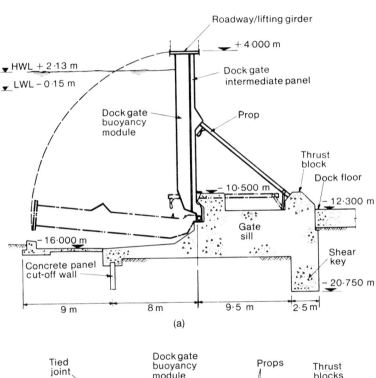

(a)

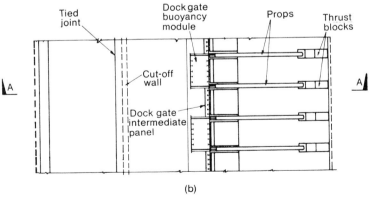

(b)

Fig. 4. Dock gate and sill arrangement: (a) sectional elevation on AA; (b) plan (top girder omitted for clarity)

sill relative to the surrounding structures under normal gate loading was calculated to be 1–2 mm.

Dockside crane tracks

32.   The 120 t cranes have 16 wheel bogies at each corner applying a maximum vertical loading of 49 t per wheel.   This load has to be distributed by the crane beam to seating pads on the caisson walls.   To avoid the severe wear that could occur at joints in the track it was decided that the whole track and its supporting crane beam should be continuous from end to end.

33.   The caisson walls supporting the crane beams are unable to resist large horizontal forces in a direction parallel to the beams.   The beam seating detail was therefore designed to allow $\pm 2{\cdot}5$ mm longitudinal movement of the beam relative to the walls, and the initial casting shrinkage was kept within this figure by forming a maximum length of 15 m of the beam at any one time and leaving 1 m gaps between bays.   The gaps were concreted after 7 days' delay to make up 70 m lengths.   These 70 m lengths were linked together after the beam had been surrounded by fill, and then only at one of two specified times of year when the average beam temperature would be close to the middle of its annual range. Special arrangements were made in the caissons at the seaward ends of the piers to anchor the crane beams and prevent movement.   At the landward end the beam movement is restrained by passive soil pressures on the supporting piles and soil friction on the beam sides.

Service gallery and service trenches

34.   The provision along the dock walls of a gallery, tunnel or trenches to carry the mechanical and electrical services was given careful consideration at the initial design stage.   Three factors had a major influence on the decision: the number of pipes and cables which might eventually be required; the locations of the crane beams and the hauling-in trolley tracks; and the difficulty of forming any structure within the caisson units below high tide level.

35.   A compromise solution was finally adopted, with a service gallery sufficient to carry some of the smaller services and all the outlet points for the larger services.   The main service trenches are located within the caisson fill. The hauling-in trolley tracks run above the service gallery and all service entries to the gallery therefore have to pass beneath these tracks.

36.   The galleries are formed from L shaped precast concrete units bolted to the caisson outer walls.   The rear wall of the gallery acts as a retaining wall for the caisson fill, and is tied back to the caisson transverse walls.

37.   The anticipated 34 m freeboard of an unladen million ton tanker produces a very steep vertical angle for the hauling-in trolley lines and hence severe loadings on the trolley wheels and track.   In the course of examining the problem a new form of trolley was developed, running on a cruciform-section concrete track.   The 24 wheels (twelve with horizontal axles and twelve with vertical axles) are rubber-tyred and allow a tolerance in track surface of 9 mm offset from a 5 m long straight edge.   The trolley acts as a travelling fairlead, controlled by signals from a cabin placed at the head of the dock.   Automatic cut-out mechanisms protect the winches against accidental overload.

Construction

38.   The construction of the Dubai Dry Dock facility was undertaken concurrently with the detailed design of the works.   Site operations commenced on the first day that the design and construct contract became effective and the

entire £232 million project was substantially complete five years later.

39.   This achievement was greatly facilitated by the initial planning and conceptual design being undertaken by an integrated team of senior site staff and designers, which advanced definition of the form of construction and thereby accelerated release of detailed design criteria.   Other benefits were that communication links were established early, difficult construction details were minimized and both the designers and construction management firmly believed that the agreed concepts could be put into practice.

40.   As construction work developed the senior site staff went to Dubai as managers responsible to the Project Manager for sections of the works.

41.   For management and planning purposes the project was subdivided into the following sections:

(a) breakwaters, dredging, tank cleaning berth and dolphins;
(b) Hatta Quarry road;
(c) caisson casting yard;
(d) caisson launching, positioning, filling and grouting;
(e) dock floors, pier surface works, pump-houses and dock gates;
(f) concrete and blockwork buildings;
(g) steel-framed buildings and civil works on shore;
(h) mechanical and electrical services and permanent plant.

In addition there were five service sections:

(a) administration, accounting, storekeeping;
(b) plant repair and maintenance;
(c) quantity surveying;
(d) productivity services;
(e) labour.

These latter sections reported to the Contracts Manager.

42.   The production sections were responsible for their own detailed planning based on the overall contract programme and were largely autonomous while maintaining close links with the service sections.   The philosophy of autonomy assisted in dealing with the size and complexity of the project and provided the necessary flexibility to cope with difficulties and inevitable changes in design, specification and programme as they arose.

43.   It is the Authors' experience on overseas contracts that self-reliance is fundamental to success and to this end the site was equipped with

(a) a plant workshop with spares holding valued at over £1 million;
(b) a pipe fabrication and coating facility which produced 40 km of pipework, ranging in diameter from 75 mm to 750 mm;
(c) grit blasting and galvanizing plants;
(d) a temporary works steel fabrication yard in which more than 2000 t of structural steel and formwork was produced;
(e) a workshop which produced approximately 250 t of ventilation ductwork;
(f) a carpenters' shop capable of producing everything from formwork to office furniture;
(g) an offset printing press;
(h) two mini-computers for payroll, costing, invoicing and accounts.

44.   The scale of the project is illustrated by figures for the workforce, materials and plant.   At peak the following numbers of personnel were on site:

255 expatriate staff employed from the UK;

475 other staff recruited outside Dubai;
5950 operatives, of whom half were Pakistanis and half were Indians; the vast majority were accommodated in a specially constructed labour camp.

Approximate total bulk materials quantities utilized were

85 000 t of reinforcing steel;
330 000 t of cement;
850 000 m³ of concrete;
4 000 000 t of rock in the breakwaters;
5 000 000 m³ of dredging and reclamation.

More than 1500 items of construction plant were required, having a total rating of 75 000 hp and a value exceeding £36 million at current prices.

Breakwaters

45. Breakwaters of length 4 km and maximum height 17 m were constructed, incorporating 3 200 000 t of rock as hearting (rock size 0–2 t) and 750 000 t of rock as secondary armour (rock size 2–5 t); 18 000 Stabits, the majority of which weighed 15 t, provided the primary protection. The main breakwater was built from the seaward end by formation of an island and then working towards the shore, thus giving the earliest possible protection to the caisson launching and positioning operation from the prevailing winds (Fig. 5).

46. The quarry was 32 km from the site and rock was transported and placed at an average rate of 70 000 t/week. Half the rock was hauled in dump trucks which tipped into a 450 m³ capacity bottom dump barge which placed the breakwater core below water level. The remainder was loaded into 10 t capacity

Fig. 5. Breakwater island after a storm (November 1974)

rock trays, hauled in pairs on flatbed trucks and transferred by portal cranes onto flat barges. The barges were towed to a Manitowoc 4600 crawler crane sitting on the previously formed breakwater and tipped to a pattern calculated relative to the boom angle and angle of slew of the crane about the centre-line of the breakwater to complete the required breakwater profile. Maximum slope of the dumped hearting material averaged 1 : 2·5 and the tray placing technique achieved the steepest required slopes of 1 : 1·25 with little difficulty.

47. Stabit placing was carried out at the same time as rock placing to protect the breakwater until it could be finally completed from the seaward end by concreting of the wave wall and placing of the final Stabits on the crest. Despite several storms during the construction period there was little significant damage to the breakwater.

Dredging and reclamation

48. Five million cubic metres of underwater excavation was carried out by cutter suction dredgers, reducing the sea bed to the level required for the harbour and preparing the dry dock foundation. The dredging and reclamation quantities were designed to leave a surplus for the dredger-placed cofferdam. The material dredged varied in both depth and hardness and whereas the overall weekly output was 45 000 m³, the maximum in any one week was 92 000 m³.

49. Dredging to the tolerance of 500 mm generally specified presented little difficulty, and the reclamation produced a material which consolidated well above water level. Subsequent experience proved that it could also be readily compacted to provide a foundation for buildings and pavements.

50. After dewatering the dock area and removal of some 600 mm of loose material the dredging contractor had a unique opportunity to inspect the results of his work. The tolerance required in this area was 400 mm with the overriding condition that the rock foundation should not be disturbed. By extremely careful control and multiple cutter passes these stringent requirements were consistently achieved.

Hatta Quarry road

51. More than a million tonnes of coarse aggregate were required for the reinforced concrete works. A suitable material was found near the village of Hatta, 110 km from the coast, and 80 km of new road had to be constructed through varied terrain. From the initial requirement of a quarry haul road this new road was upgraded to form a major part of the Dubai–Oman highway and was constructed as a 9 m carriageway with 1·5 m hard shoulders.

52. Cost was minimized by using materials occurring naturally at various places along its route. This necessitated constant laboratory research and several design and specification changes but the final 1975 cost of the road of £145 000/mile reflects the achievement in moulding the design to suit local topography and materials.

53. Design was based on Road Note 29 using 4·65 million standard axles on the loaded lane and 1·2 million on the unloaded lane. Surfacing comprised 75 mm of bitumen bound gravel with a 50 mm bitumen macadam wearing course. Wadi crossings were generally constructed in reinforced concrete.

Caissons

54. Of the 162 cellular caissons required to form the dock walls, the 133 for the berths and dolphins were 31 m long × 17 m wide × 17 m high and weighed 3250 t each when cast, and the remaining 29 were only 20·8 m long and weighed 750 t less.

Fig. 6. Aerial view of the caisson casting yard (August 1975)

55. *Manufacture.* The caissons were slipformed utilizing two mobile gantries, each covering five casting beds, and the yard produced an average of 1·7 caissons per week with a maximum of 3 per week. The arrangement of the caisson casting yard is shown in Fig. 6. The gantries were rail mounted and at the start of a production cycle lowered the 1 m high slipform shutters onto a prepared concreted base slab in which the vertical starter bars and first 1 m of horizontal wall reinforcement had been fixed. All the wall reinforcement was loaded in strict order onto racks at two levels on the climbing platform, the upper level to facilitate splicing of vertical bars and the lower to facilitate fixing of horizontal reinforcement and placing of concrete.

56. Slipforming normally commenced on the night shift and progressed continuously at rates of 100–450 mm/h. Initial concern as to the practicability of maintaining a 24 h slipforming operation throughout the hot summer months

Fig. 7. Caisson being towed from launching platform for placing (September 1975)

proved unfounded and, except when slipforming at low speed, the high temperatures and humidity proved to be advantageous.

57. After completion of slipforming, and curing, the mobile soffit shutters were removed and five sets of bogies, which incorporated hydraulic lifting jacks, were run underneath the caisson on rails for transverse transfer. The caisson was then jacked clear of the casting bed and pushed to the centre of the yard where it was lowered onto longitudinal transfer bogies. Movement of the caisson down the centre of the yard to the launching platform was effected by two hydraulic jacks pushing off horizontal fixed racks.

58. *Launching.* After fixing of access platforms, draught markers and towing lines, each caisson was pushed onto the 4000 t capacity Syncrolift and lowered into the sea until 7 m was immersed. To ensure stable flotation off the platform, 1000 t of sand ballast was then systematically added by a conveyor system. Immersion then continued until the caisson floated clear of the platform and bogies at a draught of 10·5 m. In this condition the caissons were stable and could be manoeuvred to the adjacent fitting-out berth to be fitted with temporary platforms carrying mooring winches, pumps and the flooding manifold necessary for final location and sinking (Fig. 7).

59. *Placing.* The method adopted to found the caisson on the bedrock was to cut two parallel trenches into which the downstand beams of the caisson could be set and then to grout the void below the base slab prior to sand filling. To form these trenches a self-elevating platform was built carrying a 2500 mm dia. reverse circulation multicone drill working over one side. The method proved extremely successful and an accurate level foundation was formed in the miliolite with a minimum of diver attendance. The speed of the drilling generated valuable unallocated time on the equipment which was utilized by drilling

Fig. 8. Drilled trench in the rock—for drainage
(December 1976)

the dock underfloor drainage trenches prior to dewatering. This proved to be a major advantage when the docks were dewatered (Fig. 8). After trench drilling, the foundations for the caisson were cleared by grab and airlift of any loose material left after dredging, and inspected for high spots prior to the landing of each caisson.

60. Caissons were manoeuvred by two 600 hp tugs into approximate position and held between anchors on the sea bed and the caisson which had already been fixed in position in the pier. Accurate positioning against the adjacent caisson was assisted by instrument stations on shore.

61. Sinking was normally carried out on a rising tide by ballasting with water through a filling manifold, maintaining level trim at all times. Location tolerances were generally within ± 50 mm, which was considerably more precise than had been anticipated. Only on very few occasions had refloating to be resorted to for achievement of accurate positioning.

62. *Grouting and filling*. With the caisson in position and full of water the gaps between caissons were sealed to base slab level with tremie concrete. Each vertical joint between the caissons at their edges was formed using two nylon bolsters fixed to one caisson and inflated with grout to form shutters; the space between was later filled with grout. This use of bolsters accommodated variations in the joints and satisfactorily retained the sand–cement grout; this would have been difficult with more conventional formwork.

63. The outer trench was sealed by grouting with a sand–cement grout from floating plant. The void between the caisson base and the rock was finally grouted using a 3:1 sand–cement grout mix with Colplus admixture pumped through preformed intrusion holes within the caisson walls. Starting at one

Fig. 9. One of the pump-house caissons being berthed in preparation for the second stage of construction (September 1975)

edge the grout was allowed to flow progressively under the caisson until it reached the vent holes along the opposite edge. The grouting crew, assisted by diver inspection of vent holes, were able to identify the behaviour of the grout. Dewatering of the docks, as well as drilling through some base slabs, established that intimate contact had been achieved.

64. Once the caissons were fully supported they were filled with dredged material by side tipping trucks discharging into the cells from steel bridges, care being taken at all times to limit the differential head across any internal crosswall to 2 m.

65. *Pump-houses.* The two main dock dewatering pump-houses were also constructed as caissons but their plan dimensions and flotation weights prohibited their construction within the caisson casting yard. Both pump-houses were constructed together to a height of approximately 5·8 m within a dewatered excavation behind the reclamation bund. When these base sections were complete the bund was breached and the caissons floated (Fig. 9) into water of sufficient depth to enable construction to proceed afloat to a stage at which the caissons could be finally placed in a similar manner to the slipformed caissons.

66. Care had to be taken in setting out to use lines related to the estimated final position rather than levels which varied according to the trim. The sequence of construction was chosen to maintain the flotation trim of the pump-house and also to minimize shrinkage problems from the restrained internal slabs. The difficulty of construction as a floating element was more than offset by the ability to place the pump-house utilizing similar techniques to those developed for the other caissons and by minimizing underwater work.

67. External work was completed after dewatering, in conjunction with the forebays, gate buttresses, gate sills and roundhead works.

Dock floors and sills

68. *Initial dewatering.* For the formation of the cofferdam, a windrow of specially selected granular material was first dumped along the inner toe line of

Fig. 10. View showing Pier A caissons being placed and Pier B connected to the cofferdam, the large dock being dewatered for the first time (December 1976)

the bund; the dredger discharge pipe was then moved across the end of the docks until the bund was complete. A cut-off wall of Larssen 4B sheet piles was driven through the centre of this bund and linked with straight web sheet pile cells built out from three of the four dock piers (Fig. 10).

69. Two stages of dewatering were carried out, the first to dewater Docks 2 and 3 together and the second to dewater Dock 1. All vertical joints between caissons had been progressively tested by pumping down waist gaps prior to sand filling so that the main imponderable factors remaining prior to the dewatering of the docks were the effectiveness of the caisson base grout seal, inflow through the rock itself and leakage through the cofferdam. Inflows through the rock were found to be significantly less than anticipated and the caisson base seal proved extremely effective.

70. The bottom dumped granular windrow placed on the inner toe of the cofferdam to assist drawdown of water levels within the bund proved unsatisfactory, and additional drainage of the bund had to be provided; apart from this, dewatering of the cofferdam proved largely uneventful, with cell movements much as predicted.

71. *Dock floors.* After dewatering, the soft material overlying the rock was removed by rubber-tyred front end loaders and trucks hauling out over the inner face of the cofferdam bund. The rock foundation was then carefully cleaned in preparation for the drainage blanket and its underlying fabric filter membrane. Selection of the drainage media involved a compromise between permeability and strength, and choice was further limited by local availability. Open jointed precast drain pipes were supported by no-fines concrete in the underfloor drainage trenches. Polythene sheet was laid over the drainage blanket to prevent contamination from fines from the blinding concrete underlying the main floor slab.

72. The 1·5 m thick floor was concreted in bays 100 m long and 6 m wide, using truck mixers at dock floor level fed from a tremie pipe by a shuttle service of trucks running between the batchers and dockhead hoppers. After construction of the central pilot bays, by crane and skip, the trucks discharged directly into the pours using extending tail chutes. Compaction and finishing were carried by a special rail-mounted unit with centrally controlled poker vibrators suspended from a beam which could be mechanically raised and lowered to cover the full depth of the pour, followed by a conventional concrete paving finisher.

73. Curing was effected by spraying with an aluminium impregnated plastic membrane, covering with polythene sheeting and tenting to protect the surface from the sun and wind. Adjacent bays were not concreted for at least three days to allow for initial shrinkage. Each 900 m^3 pour took 10–15 h to complete.

74. *Gate sills.* In general, construction of the gate sills followed conventional methods; steel formwork was used (Fig. 11). Sealing face units were accurately precast and grouted in position after alignment on set screws. Tolerances of ± 5 mm overall and, locally, of $\pm 1·5$ mm in 3 m were required in this critical location and were satisfactorily achieved.

75. A cut-off wall extending 10 m below the sill apron was constructed, by first drilling a row of 600 mm dia. contiguous holes. Verticality and intersection with previous holes was achieved by use of a dummy steel guide placed in the adjacent drilled hole with the intersecting portion preformed to enable the drill bit to run down it. Precast panels were set into this predrilled trench and subsequently grouted to provide an impermeable wall within the rock. Where water flows prevented normal grouting procedures the trench around the panels

Fig. 11. Gate sill construction showing gate locating bearings being installed (October 1977)

was filled with single sized aggregate and capped off with concrete, leaving provision for pressure grouting when the completed concrete cap was capable of resisting the necessary pressure. This method proved entirely satisfactory in overcoming all difficulties encountered.

Dock gates

76. The dock gate steelwork was fabricated in the UK in modular form and delivered to site requiring only external painting prior to erection. Pivot bearings were accurately positioned on the gate sill. The buoyancy modules were then erected and connected to their respective props by temporary erection bolts (Fig. 12). Intermediate plates with vertical seals attached were installed and clipped to the bouyancy modules. When the steelwork temperature was predictably steady the joints were connected in a specified sequence and assembly was completed.

77. After flooding of the space between the cofferdam and the gates, and checking for effective sealing and adequacy of structural assembly under full water load, the docks were filled with water. A sequence of raising and lowering the gates using both the primary electric and the standby diesel motor powering

Fig. 12. Erection of 100 m dock gate ; buoyancy modules and intermediate plates are in the foreground (November 1977)

Fig. 13. Precast service gallery elements fixed on to caissons as the first stage of the Pier C surface works (May 1975)

of the winches was completed before the cofferdam was removed. Measurements of dock sill movements were made to ensure that these remained within precalculated limits. Excessive movements would have required partial re-dewatering of the cofferdam to relieve load on the props and insertion of compensatory packing. However, sill movements proved to be less than 2 mm, whereas 8 mm were allowed; no adjustments were necessary.

Dock wall and berth superstructure

78. As soon as the caissons had been completely filled and the fill consolidated utilizing the vibrating probe developed on site, construction of the superstructure to the piers was progressed. Throughout the works precasting was utilized wherever convenient in order to increase the number of available working areas and avoid expensive soffit formwork and falsework. The precast service gallery units (Fig. 13) were a typical example and were bolted to the outer caisson walls and later integrated into the main structure by buttresses and a hauling-in beam, both cast in situ; for the latter a purpose-built mobile shutter was used.

79. A complex arrangement of capstan blocks, bollards, lighting tower foundations, crane beams and service trenches were constructed, followed by the infill paving and covers to the trenches. This complexity, exacerbated by the comparatively small difference between the paving level and the top of the caissons, made machine paving impossible.

Conclusion

80. The successful completion of the Dubai Dry Dock represents a significant achievement for British engineering and demonstrates the capability of British contracting. Step-by-step approval of the Contractor's design by the Engineer was time-consuming but this disadvantage should be carefully weighed against the greater depth of understanding of the controlling factors by both parties, which resulted in an unusual capability for resolution of difficulties encountered during the execution of the Contract.

Acknowledgements

81. In addition to the acknowledgements given in the preceding paper the Authors would like to acknowledge the efforts of the many other organizations and companies who were directly involved in the provision of equipment and services. Senior Contractor's staff involved were Mr H. D. Newell, Director, Costain International; Mr J. M. Thomas, Director, Taylor Woodrow International (to August 1978); Mr M. V. Angwin, Joint London Manager, and Director, Taylor Woodrow International; and Mr L. F. C. Tarrant, Joint London Manager, and Director, Costain International.

RETROSPECT

This book has touched on only a fraction of the thousands of papers which have been presented to the Institution of Civil Engineers in the past 150 years, and has barely scratched the surface of the work which British civil engineers have carried out in Britain during that time, let alone overseas.

Nothing has been said of the Severn Tunnel, for instance — the longest underwater tunnel of its day. Nor has anything been said of such achievements as the Forth Railway Bridge, nor of the motorway system, nor of the Manchester Ship Canal, nor of Dinorwig or the other hydroelectric schemes, nor of the Thames Flood Barrier, nor of the nuclear power programme, nor of London's Underground system, nor of the Jodrell Bank telescope, nor of a myriad of other projects all of which are worthy of attention and admiration.

The biggest gap of all lies in the omission of Britain's railway system. It is hard to say when that began, but the opening of the Liverpool and Manchester Railway in 1830 seems as good a starting point as any. That was just before the first volume of *Proceedings* was published, and at a time when the earliest authors were launched into their careers. The railway system has continued to develop — sometimes growing fast and sometimes shrinking to a leaner network — during the whole period. It is now engaged in an electrification programme which will bring it up to date, and looking forward to crossing the Channel in an Anglo-French adventure which has been talked about during the whole of these 150 years and which now promises to be one of the most striking engineering achievements of the day.

The railway system was of central importance to British civil engineering and, although it was preceded by the canals, the trunk roads and harbours of such men as Brindley, Smeaton, Jessop and Telford, it is no exaggeration to say that the railways made the profession. They created a demand for engineering skills which the profession learned to meet and, as projects multiplied and public concern at construction and design methods became aroused, a demand grew for a science of engineering to replace the mainly empirical methods which had been in use.

Robert Louis Stevenson, the novelist, who came of a family of engineers and who might have been one himself had he not had other talents, wrote that 'the duty of the engineer is twofold — to design the work and to see that the work is done'. The papers reprinted here and the many more which have not been reprinted show how well that has been achieved.